Cattle, economics and development

Cattle, economics and development

R. CROTTY

COMMONWEALTH AGRICULTURAL BUREAUX

Commonwealth Agricultural Bureaux
Farnham Royal
Slough SL2 3BN
England
Tel. Farnham Common 2281
Telex 847964

ISBN 0 85198 452 5

Printed by Unwin Brothers
The Gresham Press
Old Woking
Surrey

Preface

This book has been occasioned by two sets of experiences: farming in Ireland and working as a consultant in countries that are variously classified as less developed, LDCs, or Third World countries.

Ireland, though now a member of the European Economic Community, has had a profound historical experience that is common and exclusive to LDCs. Capitalism, spreading from its European heartland at the end of the 15th century, eventually enveloped the earth. The indigenous cultures in those parts of the non-European world that were occupied by hunter-gatherers were effectively exterminated, leaving in America north of the Rio Grande, in Oceania and, to a less extent, in Southern Africa a *tabula rasa* where transplanted capitalism flourished better than in its native Europe. Japan held capitalism at bay for centuries and eventually accepted it on Japanese terms. The vast, ancient bulk of China was only ever partially assimilated into the capitalist system. Capitalist colonialists elsewhere superimposed capitalist technology and institutions on, and dominated, indigenous cultures that were either riverine crop-growing or tribal pastoral.

Ireland, by reason of its offshore location, lay outside the mainsteam of European affairs. Taking no part in the evolution of capitalism in Europe, Ireland retained an ancient, tribal pastoralism that was overwhelmed in the first wave of European capitalist expansion in the 16th century. The indigenous culture, though at one stage threatened with extinction like the hunter-gatherers of North America and elsewhere, was suffered to survive. The resulting interaction between alien capitalism and indigenous tribalism has been more intense and more protracted in Ireland than in other capitalist colonies located further from the European heartland of capitalism and colonised later. The elements were so alien that they precluded assimilation but have instead given rise, as R. H. Tawney observed, to a wound that has festered for centuries.

Conflict between the alien, superimposed capitalist culture and the indigenous cultures intensifies with the advance of capitalism and the closer integration of the cultures that that advance implies. Conflict is manifested essentially by the inability of substantial and growing sections of the colonised societies to get a livelihood. Every other person born and surviving childhood in Ireland during the century-and-a-half since the establishment of factory capitalism in England has starved to death or emigrated; and competition for jobs between Catholics and Protestants is murderous in an island where fewer people now get a livelihood than at any time in the past 250 years. This phenomenon is paralleled throughout the Third World by the explosive growth of the landless, jobless class, which hardly existed a century ago but is now the largest and by far the most rapidly growing social class in virtually every former capitalist colony.

The manner of exploiting pastoral resources lies close to the heart of the process through which the imposition of capitalist technology and institutions on indigenous, non-capitalist cultures results in the condition of underdevelopment and the denial of a livelihood to large sections of society. I participated in that process for almost 20 years, when farming in Ireland was my sole livelihood, before leaving active farming to study and to write about the subject. I have since observed a similar process operating in a dozen other countries that are former capitalist colonies and are now LDCs, during a decade of consulting work, much of which related to cattle projects. This book, in seeking to understand the principles of pastoral resource exploitation, seeks also to understand something of why capitalism's former colonies remain poor and fail to provide a livelihood for a large and increasing proportion of their populations.

Exceptional experiences enable unexceptional persons to acquire new insights. They also, however, normally preclude access to the resources necessary for systematic research into, and for the orderly presentation of, these insights. The time spent researching and writing this book was, therefore, restricted to what I could afford from my own resources. This lack of funds compounds inadequacies of erudition and style that might have been attenuated to a degree under financially less pressing circumstances.

A visiting fellowship at the Institute of Development Studies at the University of Sussex, that was subsequently extended by an honorary research fellowship, provided an opportunity to write this book. Association with the IDS, as well as securing office accommodation and secretarial services, gave access to its incomparable library, planned and developed as a national centre of documentation in Third World development. It also secured access to the facilities of the University of Sussex library, a most congenial academic library in which to work.

I am indebted to colleagues at IDS for helpful advice and much-needed criticism. I am especially indebted to Michael Lipton, who read the whole of an early draft and commented most perceptively and constructively on it. Henry Lucas helped to make good some of the weaknesses in my mathematics and demonstrated, with impressive programming skill and not a little computer time, that it is mathematically (at least) possible to optimise returns from pastoral resources. Robert Chambers and Michael Howes (research fellows at IDS) and Diana Hunt, Semei Nyanzi, Miguel Teubel and John Whylmshurst (visiting fellows at IDS) commented usefully on drafts of individual chapters. My compatriot, Sean Morrow, also at Sussex University, steered me clear of some of the pitfalls of African historiography. All of these helped to reduce errors; none is responsible for the errors that remain. That responsibility is mine alone.

Christine Annells, Joan Gibson and Sue Simmonds, of the IDS's secretarial staff kindly found time from regular duties to type successive drafts. I am especially indebted to Sasha Dryden who, with great meticulousness, patience and skill, produced a final draft as error-free as a human enterprise can be. Much of the benefit I derived from the IDS's library was due to the patience and diligence of its staff in making its wide-ranging and specialised materials available to me.

I am grateful to Messrs Guthrie for permitting me to observe at Labu Estate and at Chemara Research Station, Malaysia, their most valuable research and development work in growing and handling high-yielding, high quality grass in the tropics and for permission to quote from their findings.

Anthony Coughlan of Trinity College, Dublin, has been throughout the time worked on this book a constant source of encouragement and inspiration.

Sarah Cooper, at the Commonwealth Agricultural Bureaux, has been a most competent and patient sub-editor and I gratefully acknowledge my indebtedness to her.

My principal indebtedness is to my beloved wife and to my children on whom fell the cost of my engaging for a prolonged period in the financially rewardless work of reading, thinking and writing about the world's cattle. I am also indebted to my son, Ray, for preparing the diagrams.

Contents

Tables

Figures

Introduction

Background The domestication and exploitation of grazing animals made possible human progress beyond the stage of primitive hunter-gatherer. Pastoral man, with his flocks and herds, has spread from his earliest known habitation, in northern Iraq 12 000 years ago (Sills 1968 s.v. "Domestication: Animal Domestication"), to every latitude, from the sheep pastures of the cone of South America to the reindeer lands of Lapland, and westwards from the buffalo cultivated paddy fields of China to the cattle feedlots of California. Two thirds of the world's agriculturally useful land is pastureland, exploited by the domesticated ruminants that convert rough herbage into useful products; the other third is cropland (FAO 1977a p. 45). A millenium ago the cropped areas were far less, absolutely and in relation to the grazed area.

It is possible only to speculate on the number whose livelihoods depend directly on grazing livestock. Of the seven to eight hundred million persons economically active in agriculture (FAO 1977a, p. 61), probably two thirds, and possibly three quarters, are wholly or partly dependent on grazing livestock for meat, milk, draft services, dung or cash. Far more people, in far more extensive areas of the world depend on exploiting pastoral resources than on any other agricultural enterprise, including rice or wheat growing.

This most ancient and ubiquitous activity (Mellaart 1970, p. 249), that occupies two thirds of the world's agricultural area and that engages the "tender, loving care" of hundreds of millions of owners and their families, for billions of cattle, buffalo, sheep, goats and camels, is failing to make the contribution to human well being that it might. The gap between the attainable and the attained, with existing pastoral resources and knowledge, is wider than in any other major enterprise. For example, annual output per head of cattle is 14 lb of beef and 10 gal of milk in the countries with the poorest one third of the world's population; it is 140 lb of beef and 140 gal of milk in the countries with the wealthiest one third. The shortfall in respect to cropland is much less: yields of cereals and pulses in the poorest countries are two thirds those of the wealthiest (Table 2.1). Production of beef per head of population in the countries with the poorer half of the world's population, already low, is declining (FAO 1977a pp. 68, 223).

Occasional, dramatic breaks-down in poorly endowed, sensitive regions, like recent devastating droughts and famine in the Sahel, are the tip of an iceberg representing not merely an inadequate contribution by, but increasing pressure on, pastoral resources. Various examples will be considered in following chapters.

Widespread failure to exploit pastoral resources is not due to neglect. Public concern was never so general or articulate, as is evident from field visits and from the literature. There is hardly a country without an official plan or programme to develop its pastoral resources. A high proportion of all World Bank lending for agriculture is related to livestock projects (IBRD 1974a p. 80). The misdirection, rather than the adequacy, of concern and resources appears to be the problem.

Methods of livestock exploitation, some almost as old and ubiquitous as man himself, have evolved through the ages to suit environments as different as the paddy fields of equatorial Malaysia and the mountainous highlands of Scotland. The institutions and customs governing the exploitation of pastoral resources of necessity evolved in varied and complex ways, delicately tuned to the varying needs of the societies served, as these societies eked a normally precarious existence from a multiplicity of environments. Relations between man and his domesticated grazing livestock are now subject to change that, by comparison with earlier, imperceptibly slow evolution, is explosive. To quote a single illustrative fact: the human population depending on the world's pastoral resources has increased by as much in the past 25 years as it did during all the millenia previously during which man exploited those resources. Livestock diseases that regularly decimated flocks and herds have been virtually eradicated. Immemorial laws and customs pertaining to pastoral resource exploitation in large areas of the world are being rapidly replaced by others introduced from the West. If, when subjected to these and other changes, a pastoral economy collapses, as in the case of the Sahelian droughts and famines, efforts are made to shore up the tottering structure. Other, less acute but in sum vastly greater, problems pertaining to livestock, such as India's surplus "sacred cows", are treated similarly in an ad hoc, pragmatic way. There has been missing so far an awareness, first, of the profoundness and complexity of the change occurring. Because there has not been an adequate awareness of change, neither has there been an awareness of the need for a formal understanding of the nature of man's complex relations with his grazing livestock that are now subjected to such drastic change.

Pragmatism is the hallmark of the owner's behaviour towards his livestock. What works is right; innovation may be beneficial but the risks are great and to be minimised by cautious, experimental change. Pragmatism, while an entirely appropriate approach in a stable situation, is inadequate in circumstances characterised by major, rapid change, where decisions affect not only the decision-maker, his immediate associates, and their flocks and herds, but whole countries and even continents. The cost of error is so great and the link between the making and the consequences of decisions so tenuous that pragmatism ceases to be an adequate guide. It needs to be supplemented by a knowledge of the principles of man's exploitation of pastoral resources.

Scope

This book aims to identify and to explain the principles of pastoral resource exploitation. The intended readership, following from the nature of the subject, is broad. It spans many interests and disciplines in many countries; it embraces students, policy-makers and administrators. The book is directed to those concerned with grazing livestock, with agriculture and with rural development, as agronomists or anthropologists, as geographers or economists, as sociologists or veterinarians.

The inquiry has three principal strands: livestock husbandry, cultural-institutional arrangements, and economics. Owners imbibe a knowledge, that is mainly informal, of the physiologically and genetically determined needs and capabilities of their animals. This knowledge, best termed "stockmanship", that, for example, enables an owner to distinguish as individuals every one of 100 apparently identical cattle or sheep, is exercised within a particular cultural-institutional context that is the product of climate, topography, history and interaction with neighbouring societies. The cultural-institutional content determines matters like the conditions of access to grazing land, the nature of property rights in livestock, the value of livestock products, and the cost of inputs to the livestock enterprise. Owners are perceived to exercise stockmanship within a given cultural-institutional framework in order to maximise the benefits they derive from livestock. The considerations that influence them in maximising the benefits derived from livestock are the proper subject of livestock economics.

The thrust of the work is speculative. Rather than to establish new, or to recall old, facts, the work is concerned, from consideration of the existing mass of facts, to discover and to elucidate the laws governing society's relations to pastoral resources and the exploitation of those resources. Knowledge and understanding of these, as of all laws of natural and social science, are the condition for control and fruitful exploitation of resources. Perception of these laws must inevitably be imperfect, a more or less crude approximation of the truth; but it can be the basis of further inquiry that sharpens the perception and moves closer towards the truth.

Pastoralists themselves, as noted, operate on the implicit assumption that what worked or failed in the past will also work or fail in future. Public policy on pastoral resource exploitation is not formulated or administered in a vacuum; it too is based on hypotheses that are usually implicit. Readers can judge if the crude perception of the laws governing society's relations to pastoral resources and the exploitation of those resources achieved here is more or less realistic or useful than the generally implicit assumptions on which public policy on pastoral resource use is based.

This book, in seeking to understand and to expound the principles of pastoral resource use, is concerned with the relationship between society and pastoral resources, and with how the one has acted on, and has reacted from, the other. The grazing animal, in the process, has been placed much closer than is customary to the centre of the stage of human activity. Experts in various aspects of these activities may consider that the position allocated here to the grazing animal is too close to the centre of affairs; if so, it is pleaded in extenuation that in the past a graver error has been committed in failing adequately to recognise the role of the domesticated grazing animal as an explanatory factor in man's fortunes.

This book, as noted, has three principal strands: husbandry, sociological-institutional, and economic. Few readers are likely to be familiar with two of these disciplines; hardly any will be familiar with all three. The relationships treated of are complex, as is understandable with an enterprise so ancient, so ubiquitous and so integrated with social activities and wellbeing. If the relationships were less complex, there would have been less misunderstanding, less misuse of resources and opportunities, and less need for a work of this nature. The aim being to identify and to elucidate the principles of pastoralism, the book simplifies and aggregates as much as possible. One result is that the book deals only with cattle and buffaloes, and excludes from explicit consideration the other domesticated, grazing species — sheep, goats, camels, reindeer — which is justified on two grounds. First on the ground that, according to the common if crude approximation of one bovine equalling 10 sheep in terms of grazing needs and of output, cattle and buffalo together represent overwhelmingly the larger share of the domesticated grazing species. Second, the difference between exploiting one grazing species and another, or between exploiting one species and several, is one of degree and not of principle as is, say, the difference between exploiting grazing ruminants and nongrazing, nonruminant pigs or poultry. To treat of the other species would have increased the complexity of the book disproportionately to the insights that might be gained.

Arrangement

Chapter 2 presents basic facts about world pastoral resources and their distribution, and considers some associated variables. The presentation is principally for reference, to give readers some concept of the relative orders of magnitude involved in subsequent discussion. It is temptingly easy, with modern computing facilities, to identify statistically significant correlations between the variables; but these correlations are more likely to mislead than to enlighten.

The following two chapters are historical. Chapter 3 presents the main outlines of what is conceived to have been the evolution of socio-cultural institutions governing pastoral resource exploitation in a particular society: that of West Europe and North America. These institutional arrangements are used as a benchmark in subsequently considering pastoral resource exploitation by other societies that, though differing greatly from, are in process of adopting the technology and institutions of, West European and North American society. Chapter 4's perspective is nearer, and relates to the development of demand for livestock products in modern time.

A mathematical model of the decision-making process by cattle owners is presented in Chapter 5. This format is unavoidable if the many variables and the complex relationships between them that are pertinent to cattle owners' decision making are to be kept in mind and analysed. Noneconomist and innumerate readers should not be daunted by the symbolism; the underlying reasoning and mathematics are straight-forward; and even if all details of the argument are not followed in this or subsequent chapters, the drift and purpose of it should be clear. A list of the symbols used and where they first appear is given in Appendix C.

The model suggests a typology of six primary cattle keeping situations, coinciding roughly with broad, geographical regions in the world. The model is used to facilitate examination of each of these situations in turn, in Chapters 6 to 11. An attempt is made for each of the six primary cattle/buffalo keeping situations (a) to explain its distinctive characteristics; (b) to evaluate present policies, programmes and projects pertaining to cattle; (c) to identify changes that will result in consumers having more cattle products to consume, and in producers getting more benefit from producing them.

Chapter 12 is concerned to draw together the more general conclusions arising from the analysis of earlier chapters. It is particularly concerned to identify at a global level the causes of the disappointing progress in mobilising the world's cattle potential, and, at a similar level, to identify major changes in policy, programmes and projects conducive to that end.

Statistical Review

Values of 10 variables pertaining to 186 countries have been assembled in Appendix A. These are considered to be the variables that are most generally available and are most relevant to the cattle economies of the 186 countries and of the world. Price and cost data would be at least as relevant as the quantity data but price data, other than GNP data, are not generally and readily available.

The 1860 observations in Appendix A are of limited use other than as source material. They allow conditions in individual countries to be examined and they make possible comparisons between individual countries. The array of data does not, however, afford a perspective of cattle economies; the mass of detail conceals perspectives that might contribute to an understanding of cattle economics. It is necessary, in order to get a perspective, to aggregate the data. The greater the aggregation, the clearer the perspective becomes, of course; but, because of suppression of detail, the relevance of the resulting data to specific situations diminishes. Aggregating the values of the variables over the 186 countries reduces the observations to 10, which clearly are easier to comprehend than the 1860 original. Various secondary data can be derived from the original, which can contribute to a perspective. The aggregated data show, for example, that worldwide there are 2.53 ha of grassland per head of cattle. This statistic has a limited value as a benchmark to assess whether, by global standards, stocking rates are high or low; it is, however, of little use in determining whether a specific stocking rate is undesirably high or low. The global figure of 2.53 ha per head makes it clear that, by world standards, Gabon's stocking rate of 1020 ha per animal is very light while South Korea's rate of 0.01 ha per head is very heavy. The comparisons are far too crude, however, to permit even the most tentative conclusions as to appropriate stocking rates in Gabon or South Korea.

The data for the 186 countries have been aggregated into groups in Table 2.1. The groups are:

1. Continents;
2. Market directed economies and centrally planned economies;
3. Major regions later considered in the text;
4. Thirds of the world's population according to average GNP per caput.

These groupings do facilitate the recognition of distinctive characteristics of broad groups of countries, first by comparison with global data and then by comparison with data for other major groupings. Many comparisons of this sort between regional groupings are made in the following chapters. Consideration is given here to distinctive characteristics, as revealed by the data, of countries categorised in Table 2.2 according to their GNP per caput.

The wealthiest third of the world has 25 times the GNP of the poorest third. Of the other attributes considered here, the greatest discrepancies between the endowments of the richest and the poorest are in respect to milk and total meat production (and, of course, "meat equivalent" production). The wealthiest third produces 21 times as much milk and 14 times as much meat as the poorest third. The other discrepancies in endowment are much less.

Possibly in no other material respect are the world's poorest one-third as well endowed, relative to the wealthiest one-third, as in respect to cattle stocks: per head of population, the wealthiest one-third has only half as many more cattle as the poorest third. But the cattle of the poor are unproductive. To facilitate comparison, eight tons of milk may be taken as equivalent to one ton of beef. The cattle of the wealthy, on this basis, produce in total almost 18 times as much milk and beef as the cattle of the poor; per head, the cattle of the wealthy produce just 12 times as much as the cattle of the poor.

Table 2.1   The world's cattle economy: some statistics.

	Population (× 10³)	GNP (US $ × 10⁶)	Arable (× 10³ ha)	Pasture (× 10³ ha)	Cattle (× 10³)	Beef/Veal (× 10³ tons)	All Meat (× 10³ tons)	Milk (× 10³ tons)	Cereals & pulses (× 10³ tons)
Africa	391 684	114 300	211 283	787 201	148 129	2277	4710	10 122	72 657
Asia	2 170 566	897 920	476 738	532 584	352 506	3263	23 834	24 601	535 527
Europe	718 577	1 991 779	375 244	463 557	239 902	16 274	46 849	252 696	433 059
N. & Cent. America	331 715	1 504 150	272 971	352 732	189 950	12 658	27 852	66 019	256 866
S. America	202 623	169 730	89 380	383 891	207 299	5953	9175	20 885	61 910
Oceania	20 301	71 120	47 155	466 052	40 833	1716	3208	12 589	17 808
Market	2 579 101	3 772 450	1 050 132	2 383 811	960 236	31 869	75 809	249 705	838 336
Planned	1 259 315	982 969	422 846	602 536	218 924	10 294	39 871	137 590	539 499
S.E. Asia (a)	248 386	49 000	51 970	14 390	16 613	363	1823	277	66 486
India	581 911	71 590	164 980	13 130	237 900	71	813	24 300	117 485
Poorest third	1 271 033	162 630	402 384	519 618	368 314	2246	6050	16 505	253 195
Middle third	1 293 155	459 410	307 774	776 326	256 046	5976	24 552	23 365	355 414
Wealthiest third	1 271 278	4 126 959	762 613	1 690 073	554 259	33 919	85 025	347 042	769 218
World (b)	3 835 466	4 748 999	1 472 771	2 986 017	1 178 619	42 141	115 628	386 912	1 377 827
World (c)					1 309 471	43 246		410 355	

See FAO 1975a, IBRD 1975b.
Notes. (a) See Chapter 10.
(b) Excludes buffaloes, buffalo meat and milk.   (c) Includes buffaloes, buffalo meat and milk.

Table 2.2   Attributes of third of world's population with highest GNP per caput as proportion of those of world's population with lowest GNP per caput.

	Wealthiest third as proportion of poorest third
GNP	25.38
Cropland	1.90
Pastureland	3.25
Cattle numbers	1.50
Beef and veal production	5.61
Total meat production	14.05
Milk production	21.03
Cereals and pulse production	3.04
Meat equivalentª production	17.94

Source: Appendix A.
Note a: The dry matter content of milk is approximately 11–12%. Eight tons of milk are taken as equivalent to one ton of beef to facilitate comparisons. "Meat equivalent" production is, therefore, beef production in tons plus one-eighth of the tons of milk production.

Where the poor are quantitatively least weak — in cattle numbers — they are qualitatively most weak — in cattle productivity. Even in respect to their pastureland the productivity of the poor is higher relative to that of the wealthy, whose pasture are only 5.52 times as productive as the pastures of the poor. Both in respect to pasture productivity and cattle productivity, the poor fare far worse than in respect to cropland productivity. Output of cereals and pulses per acre of cropland in rich countries is only 1.6 times as great as in poor countries. If the poor could reduce the disparity in the productivity of their cattle to the same as that of their cropland, they would increase the production from their cattle seven and a half times.

Eight secondary variables were derived from the primary data for each country:

1. GNP per caput (GNP/caput)
2. Beef production per acre of grassland (beef/acre)
3. Beef production per head of cattle (beef/head)
4. Milk production per head of cattle (milk/head)
5. Milk production per acre of grassland (milk/acre)
6. Beef as a proportion of total meat produced (beefmeat)
7. Grain production per caput (grain/caput)
8. Grazing land per caput (grazing/caput)

Large numbers of statistically significant correlations exist between the secondary variables. The statistically significant correlations are given only for the global data, with 186 observations, in Table 2.3.

Table 2.3   Statistically significant correlation coefficients: cattle data for 186 countries.

	Value of r	Significant at level		
		0.1%	1%	5%
GNP/caput and milk/acre	0.2265	+		
,, milk/head	0.5223	+		
,, beefmeat	−0.1590		+	
,, grain/caput	0.2390			
Beef/acre and milk/acre	0.7082	+		
,, milk/head	0.2856	+		
,, grain/caput	0.1590		+	
Milk/acre and milk/head	0.4347	+		
,, grain/caput	0.2207	+		
Beef/head and milk/head	0.1669			+
Milk/head and grain/caput	0.3247	+		
Beefmeat and grain/caput	0.1547			+

Source: See text.

The statistics presented here are, for the most part, descriptive. They describe the situation as it is; they afford little light as to why it is so. They show, for example, that the productivity of cattle in rich countries is 12 times as great as in poor countries; but they do not explain why. Are countries rich because their cattle are productive? Or are their cattle productive because countries are rich? Whether productive cattle are a condition or an attribute of wealth is not merely academic. If the former, increasing cattle productivity even at disproportionate cost might be warranted to stimulate overall development. If the latter is the case, increasing cattle productivity, like prematurely acquiring spacious motor cars or any other attribute of the wealthy, might well postpone, or even prevent, development. The best way to make cattle productive in that case would be to focus resources on achieving economic development, relying on cattle to become productive in the process.

Statistical analysis, combined with a knowledge of the structure of cattle production and of the socio-cultural-institutional context in which production occurs, has much to offer. It is used in the following chapters to identify broad quantitative differences and to suggest and test some explanatory hypotheses.

Historical Aspects: The Wider Perspective

Primary Exploitation of Land

One third of the world's land area is exploited by agriculturists. The remainder is either waste, or yields a precarious living to a sparse population of hunters (FAO 1974, p. 3). The world's cropped area, approximating now to one tenth of the land area, is very many times greater than it was 2000 years ago. Crop growing was then, with one important exception, concentrated into a few closely circumscribed areas, mainly tropical or semitropical river valleys. The principal ones were Egypt's Nile, Mesopotamia's Tigris-Euphrates, India's Indus-Ganges, the Irriwaddy and Mekong of South East Asia, the Yangtze and Yellow rivers of China. Japan had several smaller river based crop growing societies. The Aztecs and Incas of Mezzo-America relied on irrigation to cultivate their high valleys. All these locations, within 40° latitude of the equator, combined a warm sun, abundant moisture and alluvium from higher reaches to nourish the land. Java, another major ancient centre of crop growing, was exceptional in that, though its equatorial location ensured abundant heat and moisture, its terraced mountainside fields relied on their own rich volcanic ash soils instead of alluvium for fertility.

Man in these favoured locations, combining heat, moisture and fertile soil, could extract from the soil enough crop products for his subsistence and reproduction. Beyond these narrow confines, with the technology of the time, man generally could not extract, by his efforts, sufficient for maintenance and reproduction. He relied instead on various forms of livestock to gear down the natural growth, that his own stomach could not digest into useful products. The livestock included herbivores and carnivores that preyed on the herbivores. Most men, outside the crop growing enclaves, depended on domesticated herbivores, though there were extensive areas of the world where these did not exist. There were no domesticated grazing animals in the western hemisphere of America, north or south,[1] in Australia and New Zealand, or in the tropical forests of Africa and Asia.

The crop growing areas referred to, though accounting for only a tiny proportion of the earth's surface two millenia ago, probably accounted for most of the world's population. Most of the remainder were pastoralists, the hunters, though exploiting extensive areas, being relatively few.

An intensive land use forces out an extensive one. Pastoralists force out hunters, and crop growers force out pastoralists. Two considerations suggest this generalisation. First, a society exploiting land intensively is more numerous, and weight of numbers tends to enable the former to overcome and replace the latter. Second, a densely settled people is likely, from greater division of labour, to be more efficient than a less densely settled one. The combination of numbers and efficiency won possession of appropriate locations for the crop growers, but could not always secure for them the fruits of their labour. The primordial conflict between crop growers seeking to extend their cropped area and pastoralists seeking to win back lost ground and to plunder the wealth of crop growing societies has been a main, recurring theme of history. The Great Wall of China, stretching 4000 miles from the Yellow River into the Asian

---

1. The alcunae of the South American Altiplano were an exception of limited social significance.

heartland, was the culmination of efforts by the Chinese to extend their crop cultivation and to defend their culture against Mongolian pastoralists (Lattimore 1951, pp. 440–3). Indian history is largely the story of successive invasions by the pastoralists of South West Asia (Dodwell 1934 Chs. 1, 5), while much of Mesopotamia's history is concerned with the struggle between pastoral tribes from the region and inner Asia and the region's urban centred crop growers (e.g. Oppenheim 1964 especially p. 36).

Some crop growing societies were unthreatened by pastoralists. The Libyan desert on one side and the Arabian on the other was a superb natural defence that allowed Egyptian civilization to develop earlier than others. Tropical jungles insulated crop growers of South East Asia, while Japan's insular location was a far better defence than China's Great Wall. The failure of migrants to take cattle, sheep and horses across the Bering Strait meant that Mezzo-American crop growers had only to contend with the much less developed hunters who occupied most of the hemisphere, until the Spaniards fell on them as wolves on lambs.

The arena of conflict is suggested by genetic differences between ethnic groups. Species of the order *mammalia*, including man, require milk in infancy. They normally display, thereafter, an intolerance of milk by clinically well defined symptoms of digestive disorder. Some human ethnic groups have acquired the exceptional genetic characteristic of lactose tolerance that allows them, beyond infancy, to consume milk and milk products without ill effects. These are the ethnic groups that have been heavily dependent on pastoral resources and include, mainly, the indigenous inhabitants of northern Eurasia, and the Masai, Fulani and other pastoral inhabitants of the African savannahs. These ethnic groups, presumably through natural selection, have acquired a genetic tolerance of lactose that enables them better to subsist upon the domesticated grazing animals on which they have been exceptionally dependent. Ethnic groups that have been less dependent on pastoral resources have a low incidence of aberration from the normal mammalian characteristic of adult lactose intolerance. These groups include the crop growers of East and South East Asia, the Bantus and other nonpastoral African races, and the indigenous populations of Oceania and the Americas. Typically, less than 10% of individuals from these ethnic groups are lactose tolerant; and, typically, less than 10% of individuals from lactose tolerant ethnic groups are lactose intolerant.

There are, in addition to these distinctive groupings, ethnic groups in which the incidence of lactose tolerance is less pronounced and, typically, lies midway, around 50%. These ethnic groups inhabit the Mediterranean littoral, the Middle East, and Northern India as far as Bengal. The principal social, commercial and military intercourse occurred between pastoralists and crop growers in this region, and apparently has resulted in a diffusion of the genetic characteristic of lactose tolerance acquired by pastoralists.[2]

It may be surmised that the principle of more intensive ousting less intensive land use obtained within, as well as between, cultures. There were, particularly for pastoralists, pressures to supplement pastoral production with hunting and crop growing, giving rise to "mixed crop and pasture farming" long before the term was formulated. This varied exploitation of land resources, that might have required the same individual to be hunter, pastoralist and crop grower, does not invalidate the distinction between these primary activities. Though the individual may have combined all three roles, normally one role supplied much the largest share of his group's needs justifying accordingly the designation of hunter (rarely), pastoralist (commonly), or crop grower (less commonly in a mixed economy).

The allocation of land between pastoralism and cropping is a matter of continuing

---

2. For an excellent review article on this important issue see Simoons 1978.

concern meriting further consideration.[3] The manner of allocation is illustrated here for a predominantly pastoral society, like Africa. *Mutatis mutandi*, similar principles obtain when, like India, crop growing is the predominant activity.

A pastoral society is assumed to occupy an area of land (see Fig. 3.1). An individual, if left to operate all the land, when under pasture would produce an amount equal to OG. As successive individuals work the grassland, their individual, or marginal,

Fig. 3.1   Returns to labour: on pasture and cropland

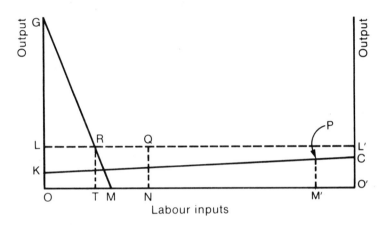

contributions to output decline, as indicated by GM. Labour inputs to the grassland beyond OM have no effect on output. If the land is used for crop growing, a single individual working it will have an output O'C (right hand side), that declines more slowly, as indicated by CK, as more labour is applied to the cropped land.

OL is assumed to be the level of nutrition necessary for people to maintain and reproduce themselves. If the land is used exclusively for grazing, total output will be OGM, assumed equal to OLQN, capable of supporting ON people, of whom MN produce nothing if all the land is under pasture. OL is assumed greater than O'C,[4] indicating that even a single crop grower could not get a subsistence from the land. However, if there are MN persons maintained by the pastoral product, but without a productive outlet for their work on the grassland, they could be employed productively cultivating part of the land. Their output would be O'CPM' (where O'M'=MN), which is less than the full subsistence needs of the labour (M'O'×O'L') but is greater than the zero output that would result from leaving the land entirely under grass.

It is common for traditional and family agriculturists, who are predominantly pastoralists, to use some of their land and surplus labour in this way. It makes it possible for more people to subsist on an area than if either pastoralism or crop growing were exclusively practised.[5]

---

3. The principles of resource allocation between different activities are treated in most economic textbooks (e.g. Boulding 1955 Ch. 9).
4. The analysis is more complex, but not materially different, if O'C is greater than O'L', provided that it is less than OG.
5. Population is maximised when (a) all produce is used for subsistence, and (b) the marginal products of grassland and of cropland, with respect to labour, are equal. See Boulding 1955, pp. 585–93 for explanation of "marginal product".

Mediterranean Crop Production

Crop growing on the Mediterranean littoral was a remarkable exception to the location in antiquity of crop growing societies in tropical or semitropical riverine valleys. The northern shore of the Mediterranean, especially, had not the continuous warmth of the tropics or semitropics, rainfall was sparse, and alluvium was not carried down by rivers to fertilise the cropped land. No natural barrier, like the Libyan desert or a tropical rain forest, protected the crop growers on the northern Mediterranean shores against raiding pastoralists. The situation was distinctly marginal for crop growing. It did, however, have potential that a people of genius were able to exploit.

Mediterranean crop growers, by taking to the inland sea, were able to exploit an element beyond the control of pastoralists. The beginnings of Greek civilization are thought to have been laid in the islands of the Aegean, where the crop growers were secure against pastoralist attack.[6] Settlements of a sea going people, close to the mainland coast, while supporting one another militarily against the pastoralists, could also support one another economically by trade, those with good harvests trading their surplus for the reserves of wealth of those with poor harvests. Adaptable people from these Mediterranean settlements could also trade their olives and wines for the grain grown on the better favoured soils of Mesopotamia and Egypt.

The crop growers of the Mediterranean, though marginal, survived and established themselves by combining the roles of citizen, cultivator and soldier. The citizen, with his fellows, defended today, against the barbarian pastoralists, the fields that he cultivated yesterday. Defence was not static; war was carried, at a profit, to the barbarian. Barbarian captives, forced to work as slaves beside the citizen-cultivators, produced a surplus that set the citizen increasingly freer to specialise as a citizen-soldier, slave owner.

Fig. 3.2   Returns to labour: on non-riverine and riverine land

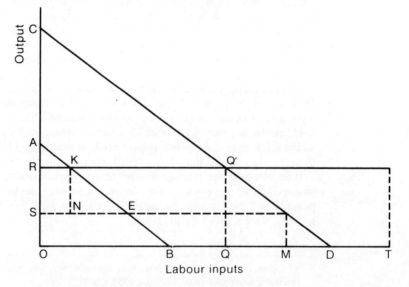

6. The oldest surviving Mycenaean art shows urban based, crop growing Greeks, who spun and wove cloth, in battle with skin clad, presumably pastoral, "barbarians". Almost all ancient Greek settlements were on, or close to, the shore of the Mediterranean sea that permitted widespread commercial intercourse from the start (Stubbings 1975).

In Fig. 3.2 AB represents the output from increasing quantities of labour applied to cropped land on the north shore of the Mediterranean (CD represents the output of labour applied to a similar area of more favoured land in the Nile Valley). OR is the income labour required for its maintenance and reproduction (hereinafter "full maintenance"). OS is a maintenance income, or the income that enables a worker to maintain himself, without providing for children. A population RK on the Mediterranean shore can reproduce itself under the postulated conditions. It may, however, be too small to defend itself against pastoralists and be therefore incapable of surviving. (At the limit, an individual crop grower, though able to get a full maintenance, would be easily destroyed by pastoralists). Crop growers must be able to get a full maintenance in sufficient numbers to make survival in the face of hostile pastoralists possible.

If the RK crop growers, in war against pastoralists, capture and put to work NE slaves, the slaves yield a surplus over their maintenance of NKE to add to the RAK surplus over full maintenance produced by the citizens. NKE allows the RK citizens to spend less time as cultivators and more time as soldiers, extending the area of land under control, and capturing more slaves to operate the new land and to replace the existing slave stock that, because it receives per person less than full maintenance requirements, OR, fails to reproduce itself. The situation simultaneously made possible and necessary continued expansion by the crop growing society. Slaves set the citizen-soldiers free to conquer more land and to enslave its inhabitants, some to cultivate the conquered land and others to maintain the slave stock.[7]

The conditions of production, arising from the marginality of the Mediterranean littoral for crop growing in antiquity, determined the political and cultural quality of the society that it supported. The RK citizen-cultivator-soldiers of a Greek city state produced each, at least, OR, their full subsistence needs. Additionally, they generated a surplus, NKE, from the labour of the slaves whom they captured, owned and supervised. Every citizen from his own resources thus provided for his full maintenance and, from the surplus produced by his own and his slaves' labour, contributed to public services, like the defence of the city against barbarian pastoralists without and slave insurrection within.

Fellahin labouring on a coextensive but more favoured area of Nile valley land could produce OCD, sufficient for the full maintenance of OT persons. Population in excess of OQ could not get from their own labour a full maintenance; that in excess of OM could not get sufficient for maintenance without reproduction; while that in excess of OD depended absolutely on transfers from the RCQ' surplus. The wealth of riverine societies, that enabled them to support an absolutely surplus population, DT, implied that the marginal product of labour was less than full subsistence needs and may have been zero.[8] It placed citizens in a position of absolute dependence on a State that was normally despotic.[9] It also implied that if the "free born" population exceeded OM, slavery was unprofitable. Any population in excess of OM could not maintain itself; it would be more profitable to set it "free" to starve. Similar

---

7. For the importance of slavery in classical Greece and Rome see especially Finley 1960 and 1975.
8. The situation has not apparently changed in modern China. "In this valley alone they laboured for nearly seventy thousand man days to complete the 25 walls, and if you take into account the length of the working day here, which in summer goes from four thirty in the morning till after dark, then that would mean nearly a million man hours. And what did all that backbreaking toil achieve? They reclaimed little more than three acres of agricultural land" (Pettifer 1978).
9. The relationship between riverine crop growing and despotism is well treated by Wittfogel (1959). The difference between production conditions in Ptolemaic Egypt and the rest of the Hellenic world is made explicit by Rostovtzeff (1953 pp. 272–80).

considerations obtain in the case of tribal pastoral society; the individual's productivity is insufficient for maintenance (Fig. 3.1) and he is dependent on transfers from society.

Political relationships between the individual and society, based as these were on very dissimilar material conditions of production, differed greatly in Mediterranean polities from those in riverine or pastoral societies. The relationships in Mediterranean polities, reflecting the two way flow of benefits between citizen and society, partook more of the character of the "social contract" as envisaged by such later writers as Locke and Rousseau. A contractual type relationship was expressed most clearly by the preoccupation of Mediterranean societies with law, as the determinant of the citizen's relationships with his fellows and with society, and as the citizen's protection against arbitrary political power.[10]

Law created property or *dominium*, which in ancient Mediterranean society meant especially property in slaves, society's economic basis. Only the legal assurance of having the benefits of the slave's labour could induce the citizen to capture, control, direct and maintain slaves.[11] The riverine states did organise masses of labour for social hydraulic investment, or to build the Great Wall of China, or the pyramids of Egypt and of other riverine cultures; but only the citizen, working beside, or closely supervising, slaves could extract from labour, on the less favoured fields of the Mediterranean littoral, a surplus over their maintenance. The slave-based economy was jeopardised when the chain of command was extended; *latifundia Italiam perdidere*.

Conditions of crop production on the Mediterranean littoral necessitated a rule of law that simultaneously set some free and enslaved others, as they never were in riverine societies. The rule of law gave to some property, and this property was the power to dispose of other persons. Slave based freedom evoked a creativity in art and science that continues a most glorious part of the human heritage.

The dynamics of slavery

Ancient Mediterranean crop growing had a distinctive dynamic. Expansion was of the essence. Expansion was essential to maintain the existing slave stock and to capture more slaves to operate conquered land (Jones 1956). Expansion, by increasing the area occupied, shortened the periphery to be defended relative to the area defended. Also, by increasing the population, it permitted more specialisation and hence greater efficiency. The military strength, administrative competence, industrial considerations obtain in the case of tribal pastoral society; the individual's productivity is insufficient for maintenance (Fig. 3.1) and he is dependent on transfers from society.

Expansion brought disadvantages also. Political balance between citizen and State became increasingly difficult to maintain as the State outgrew its original small-city form. Growth of administrative skills was insufficient to offset the more rapid increase in the complexity of administration as the State expanded, and the real burden of administration increased. The most serious consequence of expansion was the effect on agriculture (Jones 1974 pp. 132–5).

Concentration of wealth was a corollary of specialisation. The citizen-soldier cultivator became first a citizen-soldier and then a citizen *simpliciter*, slaves cultivating the land and mercenaries defending the *limes*. The chained slave gangs that, according to the Younger Pliny, cultivated half of the African empire in six great latifundia were a far cry from the one or two slaves working alongside the owner on the smallholdings of classical Greece (Haywood 1959 p. 89). Productivity per member of

10. A succinct treatment of a complex subject is given by Atkinson (1965). See also Rheinstein (1954).
11. "Of property, the first and most necessary kind, the best and most manageable, is man' (Finley 1960 p. 54 quoting pseudo-Aristotle.).

the chain gang on the African latifundia must have been far below that on the Greek smallholding, where the labour, being either family labour or closely supervised by the farmer and his family, was flexible and adaptable.

The African latifundia owner could better finance the equipping of his labour than the Greek smallholder, but he had little incentive to do so. Whips, chains and crude hoes and spades are the only equipment that can be productively used by gang labour; other equipment is likely to be damaged while adding little, if anything, to output. It would normally have been less costly for the latifundia owner to increase output by buying more slaves than by supplying the slaves he had with destructible equipment. Little progress was made by ancient Mediterranean crop producers in increasing output per person (Jones 1974 p. 138, Finley 1975 p. 109).

Graeco-Roman expansion was bounded on the west by the Atlantic, on the south by the Sahara, and on the east by Mesopotamia and Persia. Expansion of necessity was northwards. As the empire spread northwards to secure the captives essential to maintain its labour force, labour productivity on the more northerly lands declined. A crop growing technology that, on the Mediterranean littoral, yielded enough for a cultivator's maintenance but not enough for maintenance and reproduction, yielded less and less as the margin of cultivation was pushed towards the colder, wetter northern lands. A point had to be reached where crop cultivation could no longer produce even a maintenance for the slave or *colonus*. Whether that point lay on the northern limits of the Empire — Hadrian's Wall, the Rhine and the Danube — or somewhat south or north of those limits, is secondary to the fact that the Empire ceased to expand beyond these defensive lines. Further conquest of land and people could no longer yield a surplus for the Mediterranean core, and, without a flow of surplus from the expanding periphery, the core's resources diminished. Expansion, that had perhaps proceeded for a millenium, ceased in the second century AD. The third was a century of recurrent crisis — currency debasement, mutiny among the unpaid legions, manpower shortages and barbarian eruptions. There was a partial recovery in the fourth century that was marked by widespread, detailed regulation of economic activity and by the tying of people to their trades and locations in an attempt to cope with chronic shortages; but collapse was complete in the West in the fifth century (Oertel 1961, Mattingley 1961, Jones 1966 pp. 362–70, Rostovtzeff 1957 vol. 1, pp. 502–41).[12]

Capitalist Crop Production

Descriptions by Julius Caesar of the food and attire of West Europeans and Britons of 2000 years ago were of pastoral people, who were also probably dependent on hunting. "The Germans are not agriculturists, and live principally on milk, cheese and meat." In Britain "most of the tribes in the interior do not grow corn but live on milk and meat, and wear skins" (Caesar 1951 pp. 36, 136). The England conquered by the Normans and described in the Doomsday Book, a little over 1000 years later, was a predominantly crop growing one (e.g. Finberg 1972). This transition from a pastoral to a crop growing society, that appears to have been unique prior to modern times, is clearly relevant to a study of man's relations with his domesticated ruminants. Questions arise as to how the transition occurred, and why it occurred when and where it did.

---

12. Compare the depletion of the slave stock and the subsequent collapse of the Roman Empire in the West with the chronic tendency for cattle stocks to decline in South America and South East Asia, analysed in Chapters 8 and 10 below. The economics of slavery and of cattle husbandry have much in common.

The manner of change

All the major riverine crop growing societies of antiquity were located within 30° of latitude of the equator. All the present major crop growing areas of the world are, with one exception, located within 45° of latitude of the equator. The western Europeans of the first millenium of the Christian era were the first, and have so far been the only, people to grow crops extensively more than 45° latitude from the equator. The magnitude of the achievement is not readily apparent.

Denoting:

Y: the yield of crop relative to the seed sown;
s: the amount of seed sown by a cultivator;
S: the full maintenance needs of a cultivator from one harvest to the next;

then a necessary condition for sustaining crop production is:

$$Y.s > S + s \tag{3.1}$$

That is, the produce of a harvest must equal or exceed the cultivator's full maintenance requirements till the next harvest and the seed to plant for that harvest. This conditional statement can be rearranged as:

$$s > \frac{S}{Y - 1} \tag{3.2}$$

A tropical cultivator's full maintenance needs, from harvest to harvest, are taken as:

$$S_r = 100 \tag{3.3}$$

More difficult climatic conditions require body weights to be greater in temperate zones; and, per unit weight, these bodies' upkeep needs are greater than bodies in warmer climates (Clark 1977 pp. 125–128). European harvests normally occur once annually; harvests in riverine valleys within 30° of the equator normally occur twice annually and frequently at shorter intervals. These considerations suggest that the equivalent full maintenance of the European cultivator may be taken as:

$$S_e = 300 \tag{3.4}$$

European travellers of the medieval and Renaissance periods were impressed by crop yields abroad. Father de las Cartes noted that in China the same land gave three crops in a year and each crop yielded at the rate of 40 to 50 grains from one seed sown. A return of 70 to 80 grains of maize per grain sown was obtained in the dry zone of Mexico, while in more favourable areas a return of 150 to 1 was considered low (Braudel 1973, pp. 104, 110). European observers had reason to be impressed. At that time the normal return in Europe was around 3 to 1. It had been 2 to 1 earlier at the time under discussion here, which was the early Middle Ages (Slicher van Bath 1963 p. 18, Duby 1974 p 28).[13] Thus, if the yield of crops in riverine tropical societies Y_r is taken as 51, the yield in early medieval Europe, Y_e, can be taken as 2. The respective planting requirements are then:

$$s_r > \frac{100}{51 - 1} > 2 \tag{3.5}$$

$$s_e > \frac{300}{2 - 1} > 300 \tag{3.6}$$

---

13. The return from grain crops was fourfold on the slave-worked estates of ancient Italy (Finley 1975 p. 83).

The quotient increases with distance from the equator because of a simultaneous increase in the numerator and decrease in the denominator.

The early medieval European peasant had to plant at each sowing season perhaps 150 times as much seed as the cultivators in the tropical and semitropical riverine valleys. As each seed requires roughly as much growing space, the European peasant had to cultivate for sowing an area that was very many times greater than the area cultivated by the tropical riverine peasant. One of the great questions of human development is how European peasants amassed seed supplies that, per person, were vastly greater than those of other cultivators, and how they prepared the extensive areas of land to receive the seed.

The technological explanation is relatively straightforward. Maximum growth occurs under a combination of high temperatures and abundant moisture; hence location of cultivations in tropical riverine valleys. For given high temperatures, yields decline rapidly with moisture. But as temperature declines, moisture requirements also decline, and at low, European temperatures, excess of moisture is the more serious constraint on plant growth (e.g. Devlin & Barker 1971 pp. 266–9).[14]

Cultivators who, in warmer climates, sought low lying moist locations, in northern Europe were forced on to the higher drained and drier land, and of this northern Europe had a virtually limitless supply. Land ceased to be a constraint on production. "Some general estimates of Europe's population in the sixth century have been tentatively put foward: a density per square kilometre of 5.5 in Gaul, 2.0 in England (corresponding to a population of less than half a million) and 2.2 in Germany, where the arable did not cover more than 3.5 to 4 per cent of the total area, even in the most densely settled regions." (Duby 1974 p. 13). Production was instead constrained by the capacity to clear extensive areas of the primeval forest; to rear oxen as draft animals to supplement the entirely inadequate muscle power of the cultivators; to make ploughs and harrows instead of the hoes that sufficed to cultivate smaller areas elsewhere; to make hoes also, to check the weeds that always threatened to smother the slowly growing crops; to make harness for the draft animals and to secure winter fodder for them; to build storage for a larger, single, annual harvest, mills to grind it, and ovens to bake the flour, since rice that is more easily prepared does not grow north of the Alps. All these things and more were done by the barbarians of Europe during the centuries following the collapse of the Roman Empire that are commonly referred to as the Dark Ages.

Massive capital formation transformed the tribal pastoral Europeans of Caesar's day into the crop growers of William the Conqueror's. It was not, of course, the first time capital had been applied in agriculture. Capital, in the form of grazing livestock, is the condition of all pastoral agriculture. But the accumulation of cattle stocks under western European conditions involved savings that were not required in other pastoral situations. European cattle (*bos taurus*) differ critically from the cattle of India (*bos indicus*) in that cows lactate in the absence of their calves, whereas the presence of their live calves is a normal condition of lactation by *bos indicus* cows. Keeping calves alive is therefore a condition of milk production from *bos indicus* cows; rearing the calves of *bos taurus* cows involves a choice between more current milk and more future cattle. Nomadism was more difficult for the more settled pastoralists of western Europe, so the survival of their cattle through the long winters depended more on the provision by their owners of fodder saved during the growing season and less on their access to communal winter grazing. Rearing cattle, therefore, as well as reducing current milk consumption, necessitated incursions into the pastoralists' limited fodder

---

14. Good natural drainage is necessary to prevent waterlogging when rainfall exceeds evapotranspiration, as it frequently does in colder climates. For the effects of excess moisture in a cold climate see Everard & Fourt (1971).

supply to carry the weanling cattle through their first vulnerable winter, especially
Finally, for the settled pastoralists of western Europe after an early date, cattle die
not normally fill the role of money they do with traditional nomads (Chapter 9)
holding cattle implied foregoing other, more liquid forms of wealth, like coins
Investment in hydraulic works by riverine, crop growing societies probably far
exceeded the capital formation of western Europe. But that was social investment
undertaken by the State, or by the Pharaoh, Inca or Emperor who represented it. The
investment that, during the Dark Ages, transformed the pastoralist Europeans of
Caesar's day into the crop growers of William the Conqueror's day was undertaken
and financed, in some miraculous way, by the mass of Europe's hungry, cold and
plundered peasants.

The timing of change

An association, at least, exists between the transformation of western Europe from
tribal pastoralism to a crop based society during the first millenium of the Christian
era and the eruption into, followed by the withdrawal from, western Europe of Roman
influence during that millenium. That association need not have been one of effect
and cause. The transformation of western Europe conceivably might have occurred
without Roman intervention. But Roman influence certainly expedited the
transformation.

First, the pastoralists throughout much of the first half of the millenium were
exposed, as they had not been previously, to crop based culture. They learned of
through trade, through alliances, and through service in the Roman legions. They
were exposed to it in a more general, yet more intimate, way as, with Rome's collapse
the barbarians were sucked in to fill the power vacuum. Encouraged, if not originated
by the collapse of the Empire that was inherent in the dynamics of slave-based
Mediterranean crop growing, the *Volkerwandering* must have induced not merely
greater measure of locational mobility but, associated with that, also more innovation
in social values and institutions. It involved such a commingling of pastoralists and
crop growers as had never previously occurred and that must have strengthened
greatly the forces for change within the primary, tribal pastoral society.

If capital was the key to transforming European pastoralists to crop growers
property was the condition for capital formation. Concepts of property are weak
among pastoralists. That is so with pastoralists in Africa now (Chapter 9); it also
appears to have been the case with European pastoralists in Caesar's day (Caesar
1951 p. 36). Perhaps the single greatest difference between Roman and tribal pastoral
institutions was the insistence by the former on law and, based on law, the individual
rights of property, including especially property in slaves; the latter emphasised
custom and the social interest (Caesar 1951 p. 36, Atkinson 1965 p. 4). Roman
concepts of property were a new influence on European pastoral society and may have
facilitated the accumulation by individuals of property in cleared land, in work oxen
in cultivating equipment, in seeds, in storage space and in milling and baking
equipment under circumstances that were otherwise almost entirely inimical to
accumulation.

The Roman Church, for all its spiritualism, may too have contributed critically to
capital formation. Its doctrine of individual salvation and of its own role as the
intermediary between everyman and his God attributed a new significance to the
individual that did not exist in riverine or tribal pastoral societies (Sills 1968 see
"Christianity"). It opened for the individual the prospect of eternal bliss, to be
achieved by his mundane efforts. Its emphasis on mortification supplied a religious
prescription for saving, while its emphasis on the natural law origins of property
conferred on it a divine sanction that was a bulwark to property in an exceptional

violent and poverty stricken age.[15] The Church's doctrine of indulgences to be gained by those who bequeathed property to the Church offered the best of both worlds: the possibility of being rich in the present yet, more easily than the camel through the needle's eye, of getting entry also to the kingdom of heaven.

The Roman influence in these and other ways was probably decisive in determining the timing of the switch from tribal pastoralism to crop production in western Europe.

The location of change

Forests and woods that now cover one third of the earth's surface are the natural flora of most of it (FAO 1978a p. 45, Times Atlas 1967 Plate 5). Primeval forests ranged from the coniferous forests of the arctic, through the deciduous forests of the temperate zone, to the jungles and rain forests of the tropics. Cattle are the natural fauna of extensive areas of the earth's surface (Zeuner 1963 pp. 9–15 and Butzer 1970). They occurred naturally in much of the Eurasian-African land mass, though not in the extreme north nor in the tropical forests. Neither did cattle occur in the Americas or Australia. Western Europe, however, was the only extensive area that was forested and had cattle as part of the fauna. This unique combination may have contributed significantly to western Europe's being also the only part of the world in which a spontaneous transition occurred from primary tribal pastoralism to capitalist crop production.

Natural forest cover makes difficult the congregation of large masses of people or animals that easily takes place on open steppe, prairie or savannah. People and livestock are forced, in the forest, to percolate and infiltrate in small numbers, each group being more or less isolated from other groups (Bloch 1966 p. 2, Duby 1974 p. 7). Differentiation is possible among forest habitants as it is not among those on the open plains. The isolation of each group permits a degree of deviation from conformity with the dominant type. The forest barrier makes it difficult for dominant groups to control lesser groups.

Political relations in the forest differ from those of the steppes or river valleys as retailing differs from commodity markets. A multiplicity of small obstructions that includes proximity to, and convenience for, customers, provision of personalised credit and delivery services, impedes the operation of competitive forces and makes it possible for many retail outlets to sell similar products at different prices. There is one price only for commodities of similar quality on commodity markets; no seller can exact more, nor need take less, than the current market price. Likewise, the more dominant of two groups is less likely to be so numerically dominant in the forest as on the steppe or in the valley, and it has greater difficulty in exerting its dominance over lesser groups through the barrier of the intervening forest.

The forest made experimentation possible; cattle made it productive. Large numbers, it has been suggested already, tend to force out small numbers, because of their greater weight and their greater efficiency, resulting from more division of labour. This meant in ancient, western European forest society that groups who were successful in extending the cultivated area to support larger numbers survived, and in time became dominant. Extension of the cultivated area depended essentially on private capital formation to clear the forest, to accumulate draft cattle, winter fodder, harness and implements for the cattle, seed to plant the land, etc. Groups who accumulated capital survived and dominated groups who failed to accumulate.

15. "Private property is not opposed to natural law, but is an addition to it." (Thomas 1948 p. 169).

The paramountcy of capital

Capital was the condition of crop cultivation north of the 45° parallel. Neither labour nor land was limiting (Fussell 1972 p. 57–58, Duby 1974 p. 186). Labour without capital could not, as it did on the Mediterranean littoral, maintain, much less reproduce, itself. Though remnants of slavery persisted for centuries after the collapse of the empire, it lacked an economic base once the margin of cultivation moved northwards (Duby 1974 p. 81). The compulsory labour services of feudalism were quite a different phenomenon. Serfs were required to provide their labour on specified days, usually coinciding with seasonal peak labour needs; they were otherwise free — free to starve too, if, without capital, they could not maintain themselves. A profit was not normally to be got from a man's labour after providing for his maintenance. If feudal lords tried, with limited success, to bind dependent populations to the land it was the serfs' capital and not their persons they sought to hold (Duby 1974 pp. 80–87, 178).

A surplus, pauper, ravished population shifted like flotsam through the European countryside, before, during and after the collapse of the Roman Empire and sought to subsist on charity, petty crime and casual labour. Less fortunate than Roman slaves, they would have traded their labour for food and shelter, but normally had no takers. Only when the margin of cultivation again moved southwards, for the growing of sugar, cocoa and other tropical products in the western hemisphere, was labour unequipped with considerable capital but producing exotic products for capitalised Europe, once more able to produce a surplus over maintenance needs. Then, after a lapse of 1000 years, slavery again became profitable and was made the basis of production in the West Indies and in the southern part of North America, as it had been in the Roman Empire.

Land, that was irrigated or that grew grass, limited the output of riverine crop growers and tribal pastoralists. Land was no constraint on western European crop production. The high wooded plains of western Europe were, relative to the ability to exploit them, limitless. "The total cultivated area must have been negligible compared with that of forest, moor and marsh by which each unit was encompassed" (Fussell 1972 pp. 57–58). Production was limited by the amount of capital applied to western Europe's virtually limitless land by a population of whom many were starving.

The more capital European crop growers applied to an area of land, the more productive the capital stock became. Some of the additional capital was used to clear more forest and waste, extending the cropping and grazing land available to the community; more was used for draft animals, implements and seed to operate the cleared land. The larger population able to subsist on the extended area could defend itself better in an age of violence; it could use common services, like milling and baking, more fully and therefore at less cost; and it could support a greater degree of specialisation, resulting in a wider range of products and services for producers and consumers (Duby 1974 p. 206–7).

These consequences of capital formation contrasted with those of open country tribal pastoralism. The Baseri, for example, a typical nomad people from South Persia, "are organisationally equipped only to exploit a natural environment as it is not to labour on it for subsequent more efficient utilization" (Barth 1964 p. 102). Livestock is the only capital formation possible for tribal pastoralists in open country. Increase in stock numbers on the unimproved, communal grazing implies declining average output from stock already on the land. Some, or even all, of the benefit got by the owner of the added stock is at the expense of owners of stock already on the land.

The point, extremely important in pastoral economics, may be illustrated by considering the simplified arithmetic representation of two situations in Table 3. S_t is assumed to be a typical, traditional pastoral situation, as confronts the Baseri in South Persia. S_e represents that confronting north European peasants in the first

Table 3.1.   Effects of capital accumulation: traditional pastoralism and
              European individualism.

	S_t	S_e
Initial positions		
Number of animals	10	10
Total output	100	100
Average output per animal	10	10
Subsequent position		
Number of animals	11	11
Total output	105	115
Average output per animal	9.55	10.45

Source: See text.

millenium AD. The initial position in both cases is assumed to be that 10 grazing
animals, belonging to 10 owners, occupy a given area, and produce in each case a
total of 100 units of cattle products. If an 11th animal is added, then typically in S_t,
while output may increase, the increase will be less than proportionate, from 100 to,
say, 105. An additional animal in S_e, used principally for draft purposes, will, for the
reasons given in the preceding paragraphs, increase output more than proportionately,
from 100 to, say, 115. The owner of the 11th animal gets in both cases the same as
the other owners, or in S_t, 9.55 and in S_e, 10.45. In the former case $(9.55-5=)$ 4.55
of what the owner of the 11th animal gets is at the expense of the owners of the other
animals. In the latter case, the owner of the 11th animal gets only part of the
additional wealth that his animal produces; the balance, $(15-10.45=)$ 4.55, accrues
to the owners of the other 10 animals. Conditions of production, therefore, cause
stock accumulation by individuals to be detrimental to the interests of others in S_t
and to be beneficial to those interests in S_e. Society benefits in the one case from
discouraging, and in the other case from encouraging, individual accumulation.

These different social interests in privately owned capital are reflected in institutional
attitudes towards property. Roman concepts of, and preoccupation with, property
rights were one of the principal, most eagerly adopted intellectual inheritances of
western Europe; under the Salic law of the Franks, for example, "private ownership
was absolute" (Latouche 1961 p. 90–91). Traditional tribal pastoral attitudes towards
property, on the other hand, are much laxer (Chapter 9).

The strong can acquire wealth by appropriating the forced savings of the weak.
This was especially the case in the turmoil that succeeded the collapse of the Roman
Empire. But acquiring wealth in that way had two limitations: first, the expropriated,
if left with insufficient capital, could not reproduce themselves in Dark Ages Europe;
and second, as the strong were not all equally avaricious, property owners could seek
the protection of the less, against the more, avaricious of the strong (Duby 1974
pp. 80, 178). Given the social surplus of capital (Table 3.1), it paid the strong to curb
their avarice so as to attract, rather than drive away, property owners. Powerful
persons who curbed their avarice, or used their own wealth productively, or who
otherwise caused more capital to be formed within their jurisdiction, became more
powerful. The powerful who failed to curb their avarice, or who used their wealth
unproductively, or who otherwise depressed capital formation within their sphere of
influence, became less powerful.

**Capital as a
constraint on the
birth rate**

The paramountcy of capital probably helped western Europe partly to escape from
the fecundity trap. Possession of, or access to, capital being a condition of subsistence,
those without capital were as dependent on the owners of capital as the slave had
been on his owner. This especially meant that children were dependent on parents

who owned property and whose right to dispose of that property was as central to post-Roman European social institutions as it had been to those of the Empire. This right extended even beyond death, allowing property owners to bequeath their property, especially property other than land, to whomsoever they wished (Wittfogel 1959 pp. 79–86).

European parents, through their absolute control of property, could determine when and if their children married. This normally was close to, or after, the death of parents (Hajnal 1965),[16] for while parents could anticipate the benefits of their childrens' labour as an offset to the cost of rearing them, they could not normally expect to benefit from the labour of their grandchildren, though family resources would be needed to rear them. Only on acquiring the family property could young people produce a subsistence for themselves and a family. Marrying, they produced children whose dependence in turn was as absolute, and who could be relied upon at a later stage to produce a surplus over their maintenance by working the parental property. Absolute dependence of children on parents was ensured by the parents' ownership of property and the power even to bequeath it to others than their children — especially to the Church — on their death.

No similar economic restraint on marriage and procreation operated in traditional riverine crop growing society, or in tribal pastoral society. Virile young people, with minimal resources, could produce from fertile, tropical riverine land as much as, or more than, older people, from whom they could therefore gain possession of the land. Possessing land, they could mate and procreate, while older people, forced from the land, perished. Concepts of property are, it has been suggested, weaker for understandable reasons in tribal pastoral, than in capitalist, societies. Young people in these societies could, therefore, normally gain control of grazing livestock at an early age, enabling them also to marry early.

The need to get capital, by way of savings, gift or inheritance, was an economic impediment to marriage peculiar to western Europe. Its absence in tropical riverine and in tribal pastoral societies gave greater scope for birth rates in those societies to tend towards a biological limit. The cultivator's need for capital to grow crops north of the 45° parallel is likely, therefore, to have accounted for some at least of the characteristically low West European birth rate, a balancing low death rate and a correspondingly greater life expectancy that have been noted from the Middle Ages onwards (Hajnal 1965 pp. 130–1).

The Church's role here too was probably important. Its emphasis on filial respect and obedience and its anathema on extramarital sexual intercourse reinforced an institution that deprived people of sexuality when young and most virile. It also provided, through a clerical life in its monasteries and nunneries, material and spiritual succour for the great numbers who, because they inherited no or too little capital, were forced, in any case, to lead celibate lives (Hajnal 1965, Power 1975). That is to say, the Church reinforced with its spiritual sanctions the economic pressures that compelled an extraordinary degree of celibacy, and it simultaneously provided spiritual or psychological succour to those upon whom celibacy was forced.

Capitalist Pastoralism

Late and relatively few marriages were insufficient to curtail population. Europe's population, for millenia, as elsewhere pressed upon the means of subsistence. Europe's

---

16. Capital acquired an even more dominant role in 19th century Ireland, and parents, through their control of it, enforced an unprecedented incidence of celibacy on their children (Crotty 1966 pp. 39–58).

demography was exceptional only in that the means of subsistence were overwhelmingly, and to a peculiar degree, private capital. Fecundity from time to time outstripped saving capacity and the death rate rose to restore balance. Characteristically in bleak, northern Europe, the occasional imbalances between population and resources were manifest in a combination of hunger that weakened peoples and disease that wiped out large proportions of the weakened population. The Black Death of the 1340s was a particularly severe occurrence of this sort that halved the population in much of western Europe (Russell 1972 pp. 54–6).

Halving Europe's population within a few years profoundly changed the capital/labour ratio and greatly increased output per surviving person. People, when their productivity and incomes suddenly rose, raised their consumption also, but not of all products similarly. While consuming more grain on average, they were unlikely to have doubled consumption per person, so that when population halved, total grain consumption fell. Poor people, made suddenly better off, were likely to spend a large proportion of their increased income on clothes, especially under medieval European conditions, when most people had little clothing and when housing gave pathetically inadequate shelter against the prevailing cold, wet weather. These demand changes found remarkable expression in key price changes. Taking prices in 1340 as the base (=100), prices in 1400 were approximately (Lloyd 1973, Brown & Hopkins 1962):

> wages: 150
> wheat: 75
> wool: 150

Much cultivated land, especially where yields were below normal, was abandoned (a) because the smaller amount of surviving labour, with the existing technology, could not cope with it, and (b) because the grain from it was worth less than formerly (Lipson 1959 Ch. 3, Hatcher 1970 Ch. 5, Spufford 1965 pp. 31–7).

The process probably went further than elsewhere in England which, under even favourable conditions, is marginal for grain production. The cold, wet weather that makes England marginal for grain growing, by corollary, favours grass growth, so that land abandoned by cultivators after the Black Death quickly reverted to pasture. If this land, that had been formerly held under individual tenure for cropping, continued under that tenure when it reverted to pasture it could, when grazed with sheep at the high current price of wool, be profitable. It is likely, indeed, that lords of demesne land, who had difficulty in getting villeins to cultivate the land and who sold the grain produced at a depressed price, found that wool, requiring virtually no labour and sold at a high price, yielded a greater surplus. Unsurprisingly, therefore, the two centuries following the Black Death witnessed in England the widespread stocking with sheep of land, in the first place, that had been abandoned by cultivators, but presently also of land that had been cleared of cultivators to make way for sheep. This process, the Tudor enclosures, was truly revolutionary (Lipson 1959 Ch. 4, Thirsk 1967).

It was the first occasion, on a substantial scale, that land had reverted from tillage to pasture while remaining under the individual tenure appropriate to crop growing and not reverting to the communal form of tenure under which grazing land had invariably been held previously. A remarkable combination of circumstances, that can only be touched on here, brought this about.

Advanced concepts of property were necessary. Concepts of property, it has been suggested above, were first developed by Mediterranean crop growers in relation to people as slaves; they were transferred by European crop growers to capital; in England they were transferred to land, when the price revolution following the Black Death made land without people, for the first time, profitable.

Trade on a substantial scale was necessary. Wages, wheat and wool, after some reallocation of resources, would have soon reverted close to their original relative values, even after a halving of the population, had it not been possible to exchange wool for other goods and services. Magnates able to appropriate surplus would as before, in the absence of trade, have been best off maximising the number of persons within their power to exploit. But given especially an international market, it was possible for one part of that market to specialise in a single product without its price declining.[17] Indeed, such being the economies of scale, it was possible for the price to rise with output, as the scale of marketing increased and the skills involved improved.

Substantial differences in production conditions were necessary if a large, continuing trade was to be profitable. These differences arose from England's location on the ancient and medieval margin between pasture and crop production. Coldness and wetness prevented both Romans and Normans from pressing further north or west than England; the Celtic fringes of the British Isles lay, for the most part, outside the control of these crop based cultures. Marginality between crop growing and pastoral sheep production is evidenced today by Britain's having 28.2 million sheep and 3.7 million acres of grain crops, or a sheep/crop ratio of 7.62:1 compared to a similar ratio in the seven continental European Economic Community countries, where substantially similar prices prevail, of 0.93:1. (FAO 1978a pp. 92, 201)

Located on the crop/pasture margin, either activity has prevailed in England with the ebb and flow of Europe's economy and population; the "up horn, down corn" of one epoch has been followed by the "up corn, down horn" of a succeeding one. The Roman and Norman crop growers settled their crop growing cultures and institutions on England, the former during the heyday of the Empire and the latter as Europe's population and economy slowly recovered from the chaos of the Dark Ages. England reverted to pastoralism after the fifth century withdrawal of the Romans (Applebaum 1972 p. 253); and again crops gave way to sheep in the 15th century, when the Black Death had halved Europe's population. Crop growing expanded once more in the 18th century but contracted once again in the face of expanding pasture in the 19th century (Chapter 4).

A powerful Tudor State was necessary for the replacement of men by sheep in 15th century England. The king, at the apex of the feudal hierarchy of exploitation, had a common interest with the producers/savers to curb the avarice of intermediaries, so that more subjects might survive to serve royal interests. Feudal kings sought to curb the barons with laws that protected their subjects' property. The English Tudors found themselves in the inverse position of being required to safeguard the property of their quondam robber-barons against a peasant class loth to respect that property (Lipson 1959 pp. 170–184).

The measure of great men was no longer in Tudor England the number of persons over whom they exercised feudal authority — which was, of course, correlated with the geographical area over which that authority held good. The correlative, land, instead became the measure of greatness. Magnates abandoned their predatory claims on the persons and property of cultivators/savers and consolidated their geographical titles. These titles, by an alchemy of the market place, had acquired value, such as draft oxen, implements, seeds and improvements to land had only possessed previously. Land, having acquired value, could be rented or sold like other factors of production. It was no longer sufficient for prospective users of land to bow to feudal exactions, of one sort or another, by the magnate; they had to pay for the use of land a price in the same way they would have had to pay if they wanted to rent or to buy a plough, an ox or seed. Only the powerful Tudor State, in an extraordinary reversal of what had been the normal role of monarchs, could have succeeded in defending these titles

17. England was not, of course, the only source of wool in medieval Europe. Spain's *mesta*, or traditional nomadic sheep industry, was another major source (See Klein 1964 Ch. 3).

against shocked, outraged and starving peasants who were denied access to the land and protested that "sheep do eat up men".

Two propositions have been advanced here: first, that more populous ousted less populous societies; and second, that western Europe's forests broke up mass movements of people and animals and permitted local differentiation and experimentation. Trade and technological advancement permitted some derogation from the first proposition; surplus produce from an area could be exchanged for products that incorporated the benefits of division of labour, and that could be used to defend a smaller against a larger population. The English Channel, a more effective barrier than the forest, gave exceptional licence to an island people to deviate from current trends on the continental mainland. The protection afforded by it, as well as facilitating the early emergence of a powerful monarch, spared England much of the to-ing and fro-ing of warring, pillaging armies. It shifted the balance in favour of replacing soldier/cultivators with sheep in a less war torn England.

These appear to have been the principal elements in that extraordinary concatenation of circumstances that, in 15th century England, resulted, first, in land becoming once more, as in tribal pastoral and tropical riverine agriculture, the factor that limited output; and second, in the transfer to that land of concepts of property, perceived first by Mediterranean crop growers with respect to slaves, and developed by north European crop growers with respect to capital.

The audacity of the transformation in Tudor England defies comprehension. The predators, whose exactions from the beginning had been the principal brake on capital accumulation and were to continue so over most of western Europe until 1789, found themselves overnight, so to speak, proprietors of an asset more valuable perhaps than the stock of English capital. English magnates no longer, by *force majeure* or by reference to tradition, had to exact from capital owning peasants a tribute that might disappear if the cultivator's survival was undermined by the exactions, or if he moved to the territory of a less predatory magnate. The magnates, sheathing their swords, adopting the usage of the market place and appealing to the very institutions that were designed to protect capital against feudal predators, could trade and contract with those who now sought to use land. The poachers turned gamekeepers. The magnates could, at worst, exploit the land themselves with flocks of sheep that required few to tend them. The magnates were no longer dependent on the peasants; the peasants instead were made dependent on the magnates. They could only have access to the magnates' land if they paid an income equal to, or greater than, the income from sheep flocks. People were forced to compete for land, not with one another as in tropical riverine agriculture, but with grazing animals.

An institution that empowered some to exclude others from land that primordially had been the source of sustenance for all, except on payment of a rent equal to, or greater than, the surplus generated by grazing animals was unprecedented and remarkable. It gave rise to social tensions that strained even the powerful English Tudor State. It lowered the share of England's product retained by producers, so that for four centuries they ate less than before and for three centuries they bred less.[18]

18. Population in England grew more rapidly than in continental Europe before the Black Death and less rapidly after the Tudor enclosures (Slicher Van Bath 1963 pp. 80–81). The most plausible explanations for the relative decline in England's population growth rate in the 16th and 17th centuries is a reduction in marriage rates, and therefore birth rates, caused by the replacement of people by sheep on enclosed land, that also reduced workers' real wages (Brown & Hopkins 1962). A similar, though more acute, depression of living standards, marriage and birth rates occurred in 19th century Ireland when cattle replaced people on land (Crotty 1966 Ch. 2). The birth rate rose in England in the 18th century as economic growth accelerated, employment opportunities increased, and marriage became possible for more (Deane & Cole 1967 p. 127).

The power of some, through the institution of property, to preempt the use of land to others, unless they offered a rent equal to, or in excess of, the profits from grazing animals was a principal concern of English political and economic philosophers like Hobbes, Locke, Smith and Ricardo, and of Marx who was influenced by these.

The institution is indefensible on equity, political or economic grounds. It has been justified pragmatically by its success in England, where two exceptional conditions obtained. First, though English theorists asserted the right of individuals to exclusive use of pastoral land, empirically this right was significantly circumscribed. The late Tudors, but more especially the Stuart monarchs, were concerned to curb the enclosure of land for grazing, that reduced employment and threatened the peace (Thirsk 1967 pp. 214–39). Where people had been excluded from land, a generalised Poor Law system secured for them a subsistence of sorts at the cost of a charge on the local land (Birnie 1955 pp. 119–22). That is to say, private title to pastoral land was exercised in England with due regard to current political realities.

The second condition, of perhaps greater importance in making operable an apparently inoperable institution, was that England was the first, and for long the only, country in which it existed. Uniqueness frequently has its own advantages. England, that at the time of the Black Death, was an outlying part of Europe, an economic backwater, became, within three centuries, the politically and economically most advanced country in Europe. The unique contribution of England's landed gentry to rapid evolution on both fronts is unquestioned; what needs emphasising is that this contribution was made possible by the profits that accrued to a pastoral corner of Europe's otherwise predominantly cropped land. A significant portion of Europe's economic surplus came into the possession of those with titles of ownership of the land that produced the wool from which much of Europe's cloth was woven. Though much of this rental income was consumed, as were all of the feudal exactions of continental Europe's feudal aristocracy, enough was saved and added to the merchants' and manufacturers' capital to make England for a couple of centuries the world's leading nation (Rabb 1967).

The profits, that accrued extraordinarily to the owners of England's pastoral land and that enabled England to take the foremost part in the overseas expansion of capitalism, opened opportunities for some of those who, having to compete with grazing animals, had no longer access to English land. Wages and marriage rates that were depressed for centuries after the Tudor enclosures, would have been lower still but for the opportunities opened in navy, army and colonies by English capitalist expansion overseas through the 17th, 18th and 19th centuries. The lead in capitalist colonial expansion in time set the scene for the English industrial revolution of the 18th century that, after a gestation period of three centuries, recovered for the mass of English people some of the benefits of which they were deprived when land was enclosed and when those without title had to pay for access to land a rent equal to, or greater than, the profits from grazing animals.

The application to grazing land of the individual tenure normal to crop land gave acceptable results in England, because it was the first country in which it happened and — a probably related factor — it was applied there in a politically responsive manner. Neither of these conditions obtained in the neighbouring island, Ireland. The consequence there has been that as cattle prices have risen fivefold relative to grain prices in response to the shift in demand induced by England's industrial revolution, cattle have replaced people on the land (Table 4.6). The people initially starved to death; but, for 150 years, room has been made for expanding cattle herds by the emigration of almost every second person born in Ireland (Crotty 1979a).

The Development of Demand for Livestock Products

Introduction

People have normally lived at subsistence level and have adjusted their diets to the available food. The Germans and Britons observed by Caesar ate mostly milk products and meat because those were the foods most abundantly available. The English villeins recorded in the Doomsday Book ate mostly grain based foods because those too were the foods currently most abundantly available. The Masai of Africa and the Monguls of Mongolia eat mainly livestock products; the Chinese and the Indians eat mainly grain based foods. In all these cases people eat the food most abundantly available.

The relationship between people and their food in these circumstances is physiological. It is not economic; choice is not involved. People eat what is available. Foods are ranked in value according to their nutritional content, usually with small premia for scarcity. The gauchos of the Argentine pampas in the 19th century were reported to have exchanged beef, that was abundant, for smaller quantities of fresh vegetables, that were scarce. The fact that beef constitutes 37% of meat production in countries with the poorest third of the world's population compared to 24% in the countries with the middle third, and compared to 40% in the third with the wealthiest third (Table 2.1) has little to do with the preferences of people in the poorest countries for different meats; it has everything to do with the combination of resources in these poor countries that results in beef being produced in amounts that are large relative to total meat production, but are small relative to population.

The relationship between foods changed with the industrial revolution. The industrial revolution created in Europe a proletariat that was propertyless, like the peasants of riverine crop growing societies; but that, because of its pioneer status, had above subsistence incomes, like the petit bourgeois peasants of western Europe. Its income being above subsistence, Europe's industrial proletariat, like its petit bourgeois peasants, could contemplate the future, as the subsistence level populations of elsewhere could not. But, being propertyless, it could not anticipate gain from the labours of its children on the family assets, as the petite bourgeoisie could, to offset the cost of rearing them. The industrial proletariat was, therefore, the first social class for which having children had a substantial negative net discounted present value. It practised artificial birth control generally and made it possible, for the first time, for capital accumulation to outstrip population growth. It was able to consolidate and to improve its above subsistence incomes (Coale 1969 p. 23).

A large social class, with above subsistence incomes that rose over the long term, was able to exercise choice in the food it consumed. The evolution of this choice, or demand, by the populations of industrial countries has been reflected in changing food prices. These changing food prices, and the evolving demand that they reflect, are the concern of the following sections.

Two principal benefits can accrue from studying the evolution of demand for livestock products over time. First, it can give insights into present and possible future developments relating to livestock production in countries where demand has evolved less. Second, by identifying important differences in demand patterns and price relationships at different stages of economic development, it can also help to identify possibilities for trade in livestock products between DCs (developed countries) and LDCs (less developed countries).

Three broad stages of demand and price evolution are noted. First, an early preindustrial stage that refers to pre-19th century conditions in countries now industrialised, and that coincides approximately with the state of demand for livestock products in countries with lowest incomes now. Second, an early industrial stage that refers to conditions from 1800 to 1939 in DCs and that coincides approximately with the state of demand for livestock products in LDCs with higher incomes. Third, a late industrial stage is noted that refers to conditions from 1945 onwards in DCs. The price data used for illustrative purposes are mostly from Britain, Ireland and the USA, a choice dictated by easy availability over a prolonged period.

Stage 1: Pre-Industrial Subsistence Society

Livestock are scavengers in this society. They subsist on otherwise valueless resources and convert these into useful products. The principal resource that they use is natural pasture, beyond the crop growing margin. Other resources used are crop byproducts like straw and bran, household scavengings — which, being usually more nutritious, are fed mainly to pigs and poultry — and family labour.

Production is technically inefficient; many units of food, land, or labour, are needed for one unit of output. Production, however, is economically efficient, in as much as the inputs used normally have no alternative use. The point is illustrated by Table 4.1.

Table 4.1   Wheat-relative price weights

	Western Europe	North America	Latin America	Near East	Far East	Africa	Oceania and S. Africa
Beef and veal	915	1180	415	425	555	485	620
Pork	720	870	415	625	555	415	835
Poultry	805	695	625	765	625	695	970
Eggs	685	915	555	695	645	655	1195
Milk	90	120	85	160	130	95	105

See FAO 1971b p.48.
Note: Base, 100, equals wheat price.

North American livestock production is technically efficient; little feed or labour is used for a given output. Yet, in terms of wheat, its cost of production relative to that of Africa is:

for beef and veal, 2.43 times greater (1180/485)
for pork   2.10 times greater (870/415)
for eggs   1.40 times greater (915/655)
for milk   1.26 times greater (120/95)

Low wheat-cost livestock production is achieved in Africa and in other LDCs by refraining from using wheat, or other grains, that are relatively expensive in LDCs, and by relying mainly instead on rangeland, surplus family labour, and crop byproducts that would otherwise be waste. The low wheat-relative prices of livestock in relation to those of wheat in LDCs reflect the priorities of poor people, concerned to get from their small expenditure on food sufficient to meet nutritional requirements. They have little surplus to pay premia for palatability or novelty. Prices tend to reflect the relative nutritional values of foods, and this makes it unprofitable to use costly inputs. Persons disregarding consumers' wishes and using costly inputs for livestock production in LDCs will normally find production costs too high to sell at a profit. Their losses are a deterrent against the costly production of livestock in poor countries.

A situation similar to that in LDCs now obtained in Ireland at the commencement of the 19th century (see Table 4.6). Irish prices were determined by exports, most of which went to England, then in the early stages of the industrial revolution.

Stage 2: Early Industrial Society

The sustained income increases in industrial countries brought about by the industrial revolution made it possible for large numbers of people for the first time to exercise choice in the food they consumed. Table 4.2, though reporting on conditions now, shows how the choice was exercised. As peoples' incomes increased, their expenditure on food also increased, but at different rates for different items (Col. 3, Table 4.2). Expenditure on cereals increased much less than that on livestock products.

Table 4.2   Estimated income elasticities of demand[a] for certain foods in the USA, Economic Class I countries (including the USA) and Economic Class II Countries

| | Income elasticities of demand | | |
	USA	Economic Class I	Economic Class II
Cereals	−0.24	−0.24	0.13
Beef and veal	0.50	0.45	0.46
Pigmeat	−0.20	0.20	0.70
Poultrymeat	0.30	0.44	0.89
Eggs	−0.10	0.26	0.78
Whole milk	−0.50	−0.03	0.79
Butter	−0.50	0.01	0.55

See FAO 1971b pp. 130, 133 and 163.
Note: a: Income elasticity of demand is the amount by which demand increases for a 1% increase in income.

This changing demand pattern was manifested in changing prices, of which the most important was the rise in livestock product prices relative to grain prices (Col. 1, Table 4.3).

Table 4.3   British price indices, 1867/77 to 1928 and 1966

	1928 (Base 1867/77 = 100)	1966 (Base 1928 = 100)
Grains[a]	107	238
Butter	149	172
Pork	148	306
Bacon	137	314
Prime beef	125	367
All items	120	337

See: *Journal of the Royal Statistical Society*, Series A, Vol. 92, pp. 240, 250, 251; and Vol. 130, pp. 245–248.
Note a: Unweighted averages of English barley and oats and American wheat and maize.

The price changes were, of course, not due solely to demand; they were also influenced by changes in supply conditions. Generally agricultural productivity appears to have increased at least as rapidly as the overall increase in productivity that has been the source of rising real incomes since the industrial revolution (Kuznets 1966 p. 112). Within agriculture, output per producer of livestock products has at least kept pace with overall agricultural productivity. Indeed, it has been argued above, increased output per person of livestock products, especially cattle draft power and wool, has been central to, and a necessary condition of, the growth of capitalism.

Higher relative prices for livestock products are, therefore, taken to reflect a shift in demand from other foods towards livestock products. The higher prices for livestock products signalled the changes in supply noted, in Britain's case, in Table 4.4. Imports of livestock products increased much more rapidly than grain imports, and there was a shift from grain to livestock in domestic agriculture.

Table 4.4   Changes in British food supplies, 1854–1939

Average	Imports Average annual value in £m.			Home agriculture ($\times 10^3$)		
	Grain & flour	Meat & animals	Butter & margarine	Acres of cereals	Cattle numbers	Pig numbers
1854–58	20.4	3.1	2.0	9958[a]	5209[a]	2638[a]
1896–00	57.3	41.2	18.8	7403	6643	2536
1935–38	71.2	83.6	45.6	5306	7954	3917

See Mitchell & Deane 1962 pp. 78–83, 298–300.
Note a: Average of 1867–68.

English agriculture, located on Europe's margin of crop growing land, changed direction once more. Crop production, that had been expanding from the 17th century onwards, again gave way to pasture, as it had done in the past. The cause of change on this occasion was not, as on former occasions, inadequate local demand for crop products; it was partly because this demand was now being met by imports, and because demand was even more buoyant for livestock products.

The 19th century change in European demand for livestock products differed in at least one important respect from the present demand pattern in LDCs. Prices of the high fat content commodities, butter and pork, rose more than other prices (Table 4.3); and butter and margarine imports rose more than others (Table 4.4), suggesting that demand for these commodities expanded more rapidly than demand for other livestock products. By contrast, in LDCs now, demand is increasing most rapidly for poultrymeat and milk, while demand growth for butter and for pigmeat is relatively sluggish (Table 4.2). Europe's 19th century demand for high fat content animal products was probably in part, an echo of the 14th and 15th century increase in demand for wool as incomes rose; people living in the cold, bleak European climate have a high priority for clothes and high energy foods to keep warm. Additionally arduous physical labour in 19th century factories and mines added to the need for high energy foods. There is, by contrast, little arduous physical labour even in the early stages of industrialisation now and, as well, the countries in Economic Class I of Table 4.2 are located in the tropics and semitropics where consumption of animal fats damages health and most people are lactose intolerant.

Most incomes continue too low in the early industrial stage to permit people to buy other than the less expensive livestock products. Consumers switch from one product to another — from mutton to beef, to pigmeat, to poultrymeat — depending on price and providing religious taboos do not intervene. Prices of livestock products tend therefore to remain fairly closely related. Prices of beef and pigmeat, the principal US meats in the early 1930s, diverged little from each other (Table 4.5). Chicken, however, was a luxury, with very low production and very high prices.

Stage 3: Advanced Industrial Society

Columns 1 and 2 of Table 4.2 indicate the changes in demand for foods that occur as people in large numbers reach the incomes experienced in advanced industrial economies. The shift in demand from grain to livestock is much more pronounced, as people, in fact, consume less grain directly, but much more livestock products. But demand does not increase for all livestock products; demand for milk in particular declines, while demand for the high fat content products, butter and pigmeat, is either weak or declines.

Two physiological factors shape this demand pattern. First, as Adam Smith pointed out 200 years ago, the capacity of the human stomach is limited (Smith 1910 p. 150); if people, whose stomachs' capacity has been reached, eat more of one product, then they must eat less of another. Second, strenuous physical effort has been greatly reduced in modern economies, partly because an increasing proportion of the workforce is engaged in service activities that require little physical effort, and partly because of increased mechanisation and automation in manufacturing and primary industries. The dangers to health from obesity and excess cholesterol require people no longer engaged in strenuous physical labour to curtail their calorie intake, and to curtail especially consumption of livestock products with a high fat content.

Prices of livestock products generally continue to rise relative to grain prices, as in the second stage. Reflecting in part the shift in demand between livestock products, the relative prices of these products also change. This is seen in the British case in Table 4.3, which shows a complete reversal of livestock product prices after around 1928. The price of butter, that rose most prior to 1928, rose least thereafter, and declined in real terms. The price of beef, by contrast, rose least prior to 1928 but most afterwards.

The position in the USA is shown in Table 4.5. The price of beef, that was less than 40% of the price of poultrymeat in the early 1930s, rose to over three times that price in the early 1970s, an eightfold relative increase.

Table 4.5   Corn and livestock prices, USA, 1930–34 and 1969–73.

	Average 1930–34		Average 1969–73	
	Ex-farm price per 100 lb $	Price in terms of 100 lb of corn	Ex-farm price per 100 lb $	Price in terms of 100 lb of corn
Corn	0.92	1.00	2.68	1.00
Hogs	5.12	5.57	25.18	9.40
Steers	5.07	5.51	31.72	11.84
Chickens	13.36	14.52	10.10	3.77
Milk	1.60	1.74	6.11	2.28

See USDA 1940 pp. 46, 356, 373, 441, 464, 1974 pp. 28, 307, 318, 375, 402.

Prices in Ireland have been dominated by conditions in export markets, especially Britain. Relative prices over a period of 170 years are shown in Table 4.6.

Table 4.6   Wheat-relative prices[a], Ireland, 1806–10 and 1970.

	1806–10	1970[b]
Beef	1.99	10.77
Butter	6.41	9.05

See Crotty 1966 p. 283, Ireland, Central Statistics Office 1973 pp. 158, 182.
Notes: a. Ratio of the price of a unit weight of beef or butter
            and the price of a similar unit weight of wheat.
        b. Based on wheat import and butter and beef export prices.

The widening differential between livestock product prices is only partly attributable to the willingness of increasingly affluent consumers to pay premia for preferred products. It is also due to the greater difficulty of expanding output of some livestock products compared to others. The price differentials are the inducement necessary to persuade producers to surmount these production difficulties. Once livestock prices, during Stage 2, reach a level at which it is profitable to progress from scavenging production to commercial production — that is, using resources that have alternative uses — it also becomes profitable to improve technology, with a view to reducing the amount of valuable inputs required for a given unit of output. Technological progress has been easier in some forms of livestock production than in others.

Technological progress has been greater with poultry than with cattle production.[1] Three principal reasons are suggested for this. First, the greater fecundity of poultry has made it easier for geneticists to breed birds better adapted to changed conditions; to adapt from birds capable of surviving and of producing a little from scavengings, to birds capable of converting high quality inputs into large outputs of meat and eggs. Hens commence to lay when six months old and annually lay up to 200 eggs, each of which can be hatched into a chicken. Cattle, by contrast, rarely breed before they are three years old and normally produce less than one calf annually during their breeding lives of around 10 years.

Second, the rising price of livestock products relative to feed costs has benefited grain-consuming poultry more than roughage-consuming cattle. Even without genetic improvement, poultry can convert a given amount of grain into meat more efficiently than cattle. It thus becomes more profitable to use grain for poultry production at a lower meat/grain price ratio than would make the feeding of grain for beef production profitable. The "take off" into intensive feeding is profitable at a lower, earlier livestock product/feed price ratio in the case of poultry than in the case of cattle.

Finally, it seems likely that there has been greater progress, and larger reductions in real costs, in producing grain, on which commercial poultry are mainly fed, than in producing roughage, on which commercial cattle are mainly fed.[2] This is because at least until quite recently, the roughage has come mainly from grazing land, which normally is naturally less productive. Less fertile land normally yields a smaller return to inputs than fertile land. Hence, initially at least, technological improvement tends to be concentrated on the more fertile, crop growing land. It is to this land, and not to the grazing land, that most of the fertilizers, machinery, new seeds, other technological advances, and capital are applied. It is from crop land, at least initially, that most of the increase in output comes. The point is illustrated by experience in the USA since the Second World War; pasture productivity increased more slowly than that of crop land at first, but in recent years has been growing almost as rapidly as crop land productivity. (Table 4.7).

1. What follows is true, to a less extent, of pigs also.
2. This situation may have changed recently (Chapter 7, below).

Table 4.7   Productivity of pasture and cropland, USA, 1945–1969

	Average annual output of pasture (× 10⁶ tons of corn equiv.)	Average annual acres of pasture on farm (× 10⁶ acres)	Average annual output per acre of pasture (ton of corn equivalent)	Change on preceding period %	Average annual index of crop production per acre of cropland used for crops (1967 = 100)	Change on preceding period %
1945–49	104.6	507a	0.206		70	
1955–59	116.8	528b	0.221	+ 7	80	+14
1965–69	148.4	544c	0.273	+23	102	+28
1970–72	154.3	540d	0.286	+ 5	110	+ 8

See USDA 1957 p. 553, 1972 pp. 424, 506, 539, and 1974 pp. 357, 422, 444.
Notes: a. Average of 1945 and 1950;
      b. Average of 1954 and 1959;
      c. Average of 1964 and 1969;
      d. 1969.

There is, in addition to the greater prosperity that makes consumers willing to pay high premia for preferred foods and the technological problems of expanding beef production, a further factor contributing to the wide divergence between beef and other meat prices that has emerged in the third stage. This is that, as demand for beef expands rapidly, demand for milk and milk products declines. The point is considered more fully in Chapter 7. Here it is merely observed that as milk and beef are frequently joint products of cows, a drop in the price of milk may be expected to cause the price of beef to rise.

Partly arising from the divergence in the demand patterns for milk and beef, the supply of calves lags behind the demand for them in the third stage. The price of calves, as a result, rises even more rapidly than the price of beef. It is thus a characteristic of Stage 3 that the price per unit weight of young cattle is higher than the price per unit weight of mature cattle, which is the reverse of the situation which normally obtains in LDCs at the first stage.

Documentary evidence on the changing relative values of young and mature cattle during the evolution of the market for livestock products is scarce, mainly because of the failure to record the very low values of young cattle at earlier stages. The rising trend of young cattle prices relative to mature cattle prices in recent years in the USA is shown in Table 4.8.

Table 4.8   Prices of fat and feeder cattle, USA, 1931–1977

	Average per 100 lb for choice beef steers 1931–1975 $	Average per 100 lb for good and choice steer calves Kansas City 1931–1975 $	Calves per 100 lb as percentage of fat steers per 100 lb %
1931–35	8.72a	6.01	68.9
1941–45	14.47b	13.29	91.9
1951–55	28.22b	26.25	93.0
1961–65	23.51c	24.43	103.9
1966–70	27.36c	31.02	113.4
1971	32.39c	36.84	113.7
1972	35.78c	46.54	130.1
1973	44.54c	59.73	134.1
1974	41.89c	40.84	97.5
1975	41.39c	32.55	78.6
1976	39.11c	41.56	106.3
1977	40.38c	43.60	108.0

See: USDA 1940 p. 356, 1957 p. 386, 1972 p. 324, 1976 p. 306.
    USDA 1958 p. 212, 1968 p. 215, 1973 p. 125.
    USDA *Livestock and Meat Statistics*, August 1976 p. 8, August 1977 p. 15, August 1978 p. 14.
Notes: a Choice and prime, Chicago.   b Choice, Chicago.   c Choice, Omaha.

Speculative forces caused a rapid rise in beef prices and an even more rapid rise in feeder, or store cattle, prices in the USA and other major beef producing countries in the early 1970s. The price decline which followed the ending of the boom in 1973 was much more severe in the case of young cattle than fat cattle and caused, in the USA and other countries, the price per unit weight of young cattle to drop below the price of fat cattle for the first time in many years.[3]

A longer series is available from Ireland, where cow numbers were stabilised at an early date (Fig. 4.1). The break in the relative rise in young cattle prices in the period 1914–1920 was caused by the rapid rise in cattle prices after the outbreak of the First World War. Fat cattle prices were first affected by this rise, but young cattle prices rose in line after a lag.

Fig. 4.1   Ratio of the price of one-year-old and older cattle, Ireland 1887–1929

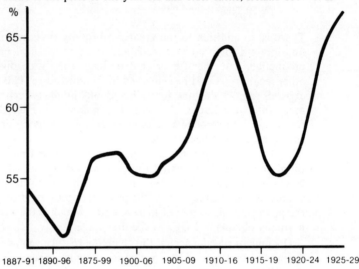

%

| 1887-91 | 1890-96 | 1875-99 | 1900-06 | 1905-09 | 1910-16 | 1915-19 | 1920-24 | 1925-29 |

See Crotty 1966 p. 86.

Calf prices in Ireland have risen from an average of 16.2% of the current price of 2–3 year old cattle in 1914–18 to 28.8% in 1968–72 (Crotty 1974).

Evidence of the low value of young cattle relative to mature cattle in LDCs is impressionistic. Reported values of light and heavy cattle in Kenya are given in Table 4.9.

Table 4.9   Value of cattle by weight, Kenya.

	Weight of cattle kg	Value of cattle US $	Value per kg US cents
Crossbred steers	524	181	34.54
	393	114	29.01
Zebu steers	360	108	30.00
	270	56	20.74

See FAO 1973c p. 11.

3. Crotty (1974) analyses the speculative rise and fall in fat and young cattle prices in Ireland in the early 1970s.

Further evidence of the low relative price of young cattle in Africa is given in Table 4.10.

Table 4.10 Liveweight market price of steers and heifers by ages in Djibo, Upper Volta, 1976–77.

Age	Steers (CFA per kg)	Heifers (CFA per kg)
1	10.85	18.00
2	15.39	25.33
3	19.18	29.63
4	25.22	
5	31.32	
6	37.31	
7	42.25	
8	44.00	

See R. E. McDowell, unpublished work, presented at Seminar on the Improvement of Farming Systems at Bamako, Mali, 20 Feb.–1 March, 1978.

The writer found from field inquiries in north-west Malaysia in 1975 that the price of 600 lb cattle was about Malaysian $1 per lb, while cattle of similar quality but lighter and weighing 300 lb were worth around 85 cents per lb (Chapter 10). Extensive field inquiries by the writer in the Andean Pact countries of South America in 1972 revealed a similar relationship: per unit weight, the price of young, immature cattle was less than that of mature cattle; and the younger, the less mature the cattle, the lower was their value per unit weight.

Diagrammatic Representation

The principal changes occurring in the market for beef and other meats as development moves from the first to the third stage are illustrated in Fig. 4.2.

Fig. 4.2 Supply and demand for (A) beef and (B) pig and poultry meat

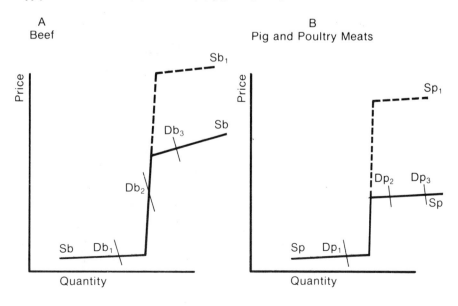

Figures 4.2A and B represent respectively the supply and demand for beef and pig/poultry meats. The horizontal axes are not to scale; the perpendicular ones are, approximately. The supply of beef (S_b) and of pig/poultry meat (S_p) is initially elastic at a low price, corresponding to the scavenging stage of production, during the first stage. D_{bl} and D_{pl} represent the respective demands for beef and pig/poultry meats at that stage.

Fig. 4.3   Changes in price ratios

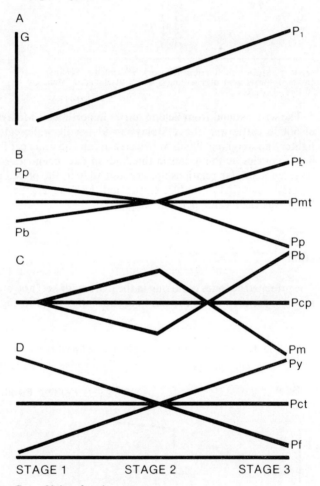

G   : Units of grain.
P_1 : Price of fixed basket of livestock products.
P_b : Price per unit of beef.
P_p : Price per unit of pigmeat/poultrymeat.
P_{mt} : Average price per unit of all meats.
P_m : Price per unit of milk.
P_{cp} : Average price per unit of cattle products.
P_y : Price per unit of young cattle.
P_{ct} : Average price per unit of cattle of all ages.
P_f : Price per unit of fat cattle.

Once production passes the scavenging stage, costs rise sharply. The supply curves would follow the broken lines S_{bl} and S_{pl} but for technological advances which become worthwhile once production moves out of the scavenging stage. The supply curves flatten out when the price of meat in terms of grain (that is, the meat/grain price ratio) reaches a level at which it is profitable to base production mainly on grain. This occurs earlier for pig/poultry meat than for beef for reasons already discussed.

Demand at the second stage is depicted as D_{b2} and D_{p2}. It has raised prices to a level that justifies intensive grain use for pig/poultry meat production. This level has not yet been reached for beef and, because of the continuing responsiveness of consumers to price differences as between meats, the price of beef cannot depart substantially from that of pig/poultry meat.

The price of beef in the third stage breaks with that of pig/poultry meat as demand for beef increases to D_{b3} and demand for pig/poultry meat to D_{p3}. Beef prices in the highest income countries have now reached a level at which supply, based largely on high cost feeds, becomes more elastic; it continues, nevertheless, to be less so than in the case of pig/poultry meat. The prospect of continuing rises in beef prices during the third stage is due to the difficulties of expanding the supply of calves.

Changes in price ratios as the market for livestock products develops from the first to the third stage are illustrated in Fig. 4.3. P_1 in Fig. 4.3A represents the rising level of livestock product prices relative to grain prices in the process of economic development.

In Figure 4.3B, P_{mt} is the average current price of all meats; P_p is the current price of pig/poultry meat; and P_b is the current price of beef. P_p is initially usually higher than P_{mt}, then drops below P_b in the process of economic development, and the price differential between both types of meat widens considerably.

In Figure 4.3C, P_{cp} is the average current price of cattle products; P_m is the current price of milk; and P_b is the current price of beef. P_m rose more rapidly, and P_b rose less rapidly than P_{cp} at the early stages of economic development in countries that are now DCs. This process was reversed about 40 years ago and since then P_b has been rising rapidly and P_m has been falling sharply relative to P_{cp}.

In Figure 4.3D, P_{ct} is the average current price per kilogram of cattle at all stages of growth; P_y is the current price per kg of young cattle and P_f is the current price per kg of fat cattle. P_f is higher than P_y in LDCs, but this relationship is reversed in DCs.

An Economic Model of Decision-Making by Cattle Keepers

Cattle-keepers all over the world at all times have had, and have, command over certain categories of resources which they have combined for the production of cattle products and services in the most beneficial manner. This chapter is concerned to identify (i) the categories of resources so used; (ii) the categories of cattle products and services that result from their use; (iii) how the resources are combined in order to produce various goods and services; and (iv) the combinations of resources and products that are most beneficial to the cattle-keeper. It does so with the help of a mathematical model that purports to represent the decision-making process of cattle owners. The model is normative in that it purports to illustrate how people tend to behave. It "describes not just what *is* but what *should* be." (Brabb 1970 p. 10; see also Boulding 1955 pp. 287, 702–10). The model attempts to identify the direction of change in response to particular causes, through relationships that will be seen to be quite complex. No attempt is made here to use the model to give definitive solutions to specific, real problems. Providing these solutions would involve establishing, by research or guess work, values for a large number of variables and parameters, which the model, however, identifies.

The chapter is abstract. It abstracts from the myriads of complicating detail that make life real; but that is an intellectual device that is necessary if the underlying real relationships are to be identified and analysed. The technique is analogous to setting up experimental conditions in a laboratory in order to examine, in a completely controlled environment, processes that in real life occur in a complex, dynamic environment. Despite the different circumstances, the experimental laboratory results often give useful insights into, and are relevant to, real conditions.

A list of cattle resources, or inputs, could conceivably be infinitely long. But the gains in realism and precision from listing inputs in detail are quickly offset by the loss through increased difficulty in conceptualising and tracing through the use of many inputs. Similar considerations apply to listing the outputs from cattle. A detailed consideration of different inputs and outputs would be particularly inappropriate here, where the object is to explain to readers, some of whom may know little about cattle and others of whom may know little about economics, how cattle owners are perceived to allocate resources with a view to maximising their benefits.

Categories of inputs are here held to the minimum of three that is necessary to conceive the basic relationships. These are: land, time and "other". The category "other" is subdivided into three, the identity of which subcategories will become apparent. Land here has a particular, even esoteric, meaning. It refers to land that is specific to cattle production; that has no alternative use; that, if not used for cattle, will be left idle. This very narrow definition of land is a typical device of economic analysis to abstract from the great complexity of real life in order to identify and to trace through relationships that are themselves complex. It helps, in particular, to specify conditions of *ceteris paribus*; that the land resource is held constant and other inputs are varied as specified. The assumption of a single category of cattle land, fixed in quantity and uniform in quality, can be relaxed to allow consideration of as many increments of land, of as many different qualities as may be desired, but doing so would complicate the analysis greatly, with clarity being traded off on very poor terms for increased realism. The device used throughout the present study is to adhere to the assumption of a fixed quantity of specifically cattle land, which may, however, be added to by the payment of rent for more "noncattle land". The rental payments then figure under the heading of "other" inputs.

The concept of "time" as an input to cattle production may seem strange to noneconomists, and even to some economists. Reflection will, however, make clear its importance. A fattening animal can be slaughtered and consumed now, or it can be held for further fattening and future consumption. A draft animal can be slaughtered and consumed now, or retained to give a flow of draft services over its working life. An animal for breeding, fattening or working can be allowed to mature slowly, or maturation can be expedited by better feeding. A decision on whether to breed or to slaughter a heifer is perhaps the most crucial pertaining to time. Slaughtered, a heifer gives immediate gratification from its consumption; if bred, the owner benefits, in the case of a milch animal, from a stream of milk produced over several lactations, and from calves that can themselves be either future breeding animals, or be reared for slaughter or work. Two categories of time are distinguished here: time used for rearing cattle for breeding, designated "t", and time used for rearing cattle for all other purposes, designated θ.[1]

It is observed that while time is an input for cattle rearing, it is not an input for cattle breeding. This is because the time taken for rearing can be varied; it can be speeded up or slowed down, particularly by varying the nutritional level of the reared animal. The breeding process cannot, however, be speeded up or slowed down; the bovine gestation period of nine months is unaffected by nutritional or other factors.

"Other" inputs include labour, feed, land that is not specific for cattle, veterinary services, and all inputs other than those specified. These individual inputs are assumed to be combined together in the economically most efficient way for the purpose in hand.[2] Three such purposes, each requiring a subcategory of "other" inputs, are recognised: first, rearing cattle for draft or slaughter, requiring "other" inputs designated V_1; second, rearing cattle for breeding and requiring "other" input designated V_2; and third, breeding cows, requiring "other" inputs designated V_3.

It is stressed again that as many different types of "other" inputs as may be desired can be distinguished, if required and if the computing capacity is available for dealing with them. But while such disaggregation may be justified in real situations for policy making purposes, any advantage in terms of increased realism that might accrue in the present context would be more than offset by greatly increased complexity of exposition.

Activities

The discussion on inputs has already identified three categories of cattle activity: rearing cattle for fattening or draft, rearing them for breeding, and breeding cattle. Again, these three categories of cattle keeping activity could be subdivided to any desired extent for greater realism, but doing so would quickly increase the complexity of the exposition. Thus, for example, the model could be expanded to deal separately with a store- (or immature-) cattle enterprise and a cattle fattening enterprise

1. Appendix C contains a list of symbols used.
2. See Boulding 1955 pp. 733–84, for a definition and exposition of the economically most efficient way of combining resources.

Likewise, other enterprises competing for the same pastoral resources, such as camel, sheep and goat grazing or browsing could be introduced. This again would be at the cost of seriously complicating the exposition without greatly increasing realism.

Outputs

The cattle activities have their distinctive products. Rearing cattle for slaughter or for draft gives fat or draft cattle; cow rearing gives breeding cows; and cow keeping gives calves and/or milk.

Some of these products are final products from the viewpoint of the cattle sector (which is also the viewpoint of the present study). The remainder are intermediate products.

Cattle for slaughter and draft cattle are final products of the cattle sector. This is obviously the case for slaughter cattle, but is less so in the case of draft cattle.[3] A draft animal has a certain value at the commencement of its working life, as a slaughter animal has at the end of its fattening life. These values are exogenous to the cattle sector; they represent disposals of products of the cattle sector to another sector (crop growing) or to consumption. Milk, other than that consumed by calves, is also a final product of the cattle sector. Calves and breeding cows, on the other hand, are intermediate products. Calves, produced by the cow keeping activity, are inputs of the fattening and draft animal rearing activities and of the cow rearing activity. Cows are inputs of the cow keeping activity.

The relationships between resources, activities and outputs are illustrated in Fig. 5.1 and described in Table 5.1.

Fig. 5.1   Cattle production: resources, activities, outputs

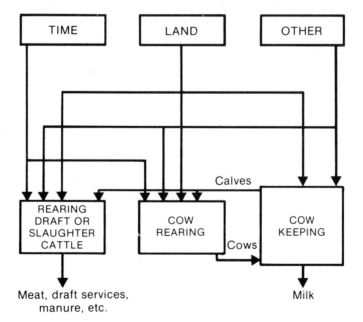

---

3. It is assumed that the draft animals are oxen. The situation is more complex when, as in South East Asia, female breeding animals are used for draft. Chapter 10 examines this situation.

Table 5.1   Activities, resources and outputs of the cattle enterprise

Activity	Resources	Outputs
Rearing cattle for fattening or draft	Time (θ) Land "Other", V_1 Calves	Slaughter cattle or draft cattle (final products)
Cow rearing	Time (t) Land "Other", V_2 Calves	Cows (intermediate product)
Cow keeping	Land "Other", V_3 Cows	Milk (final product) Calves (intermediate product)

Source: see text.

Production Relations

The economic problem, or the problem of choice, confronting the cattle owner is to use that amount of time (t or θ), and that amount of "other" inputs (V_1, V_2, or V_3) so as to give him the most satisfaction. It is necessary, in order to understand how this can be done, first to understand the nature of the relationships between the various inputs and the various outputs, and the relationships between the various activities that convert inputs into outputs. It will be recollected that all activities use land. Cow keeping is examined first.

Cow keeping

Milk production, say M, on the given area of land will tend to increase (i) as the number of cows, say K, increases; and (ii) as other inputs, V_3, are increased. Given conditions of decreasing returns, production will increase less than proportionately for given inputs of cows, K, and/or other inputs, V_3 (Conway 1974). It may be noted here again, at the risk of repetitiveness, that cows, K, are assumed to have in all cases a breeding life of "n" years. Differences in the genetic capability of cows and in the duration of their breeding lives can be built into the model, but again at the cost of making it more complex and more difficult to analyse. Differences in cow quality are however, discussed, particularly in Chapter 11.

The level of cattle activities other than milk production will also affect the latter. These other activities are rearing cattle for slaughter and draft, cow rearing and calf production. These activities use the same resources, to a greater or less extent, as are used for milk production. For any given level of calf production, say C, the longer the calves are held for rearing for draft or for slaughter, or the longer they are held while being reared to become cows, the more herd followers, say F, there will be. Thus, for example, if calves are sold for slaughter at 15 months, as in Italy, and if heifers calve at two years of age, there will be, for any number of calves produced in a year, fewer followers than if cattle are not slaughtered until seven years old, as in South America, and if heifers do not calve until they are four years old. Decisions to increase or to reduce θ or t will result in increased, or reduced, numbers of followers, or F. The more followers there are competing with cows on a given area of land, the less milk will be produced.

Calves, C, and milk, M, are competing products. This is more clearly seen if "calf" is defined not as dropped by the cow, but after receiving at least enough beastings to ensure survival, and if differences in calf quality, size and vigour are recognised. For example, if maximum milk output is required in a temperate zone without reference to calf production, a farmer will keep a limited number of Friesian type cows that are fed well, and he will cross these with a Channel Island bull to breed small calves that are slaughtered at birth and receive no beastings. At the other end of the spectrum, if production of the largest number of strong calves is required for beef production and without reference to milk production, a larger number of beef type cows will be kept and crossed with a beef type bull to produce as large a number of calves as can be reared satisfactorily by suckling their dams.

The competitive relationship between milk, M, and calves C, is illustrated in Fig. 5.2. A cattle owner with given resources can produce OM milk or OC calves, or any combination of milk and calves within the boundary OMKPRCO. He can, for example, produce OM' milk *and* OC' calves.

The relationship between milk and calves is not entirely competitive. If the cattle owner wishes to maximise milk output, OM, MK calves will also be produced in the process. Cows will not lactate without first giving birth to calves, and some cows, of *bos indicus* breeds, will normally only lactate while their calves are alive and in sight.[4] The complementary relationship between calf and milk production represented by the segment RC in Fig. 5.2 is of less practical importance and is shown here principally for symmetry. However, it may be pointed out that it frequently occurs when cows

Fig. 5.2   Milk/calves, production possibilities

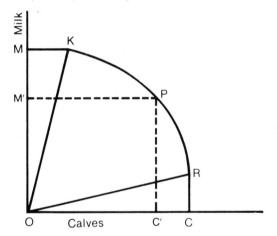

are bred to produce calves only that, immediately after calving, the flush of milk from the cow is excessive for the calf. This excess milk, if not taken from the cow, may lead to scouring and other digestive disorders of a possibly fatal nature in the young calf.

The relationships discussed between output of milk, M, and the inputs K and V_3, and other cattle enterprises represented by followers, F, and calf production, C, can be expressed mathematically as:

$$M = f(K, V_3, F, C)$$

That is, given the technology and given the amount of cattle-specific land available, M is determined by the values of K, V_3, F and C. The nature of the relationship has been identified to the extent that it will normally be expected that:

(i) M will increase, though less than proportionately, as K and V_3 are increased; and
(ii) M will decrease as F and C are increased.

These relationships can be expressed as follows by the well known Cobb-Douglas

4. Chapter 11 develops this point.

function that is frequently used to express similar relationships in economic analysis and that is convenient to manipulate (e.g. Walters 1968 pp. 319–22):

$$M = aK^{\alpha} V_3^{\beta} F^{-\gamma} C^{-\delta} \tag{5.1}$$

The parameters a, α, β, γ, and δ, are unknown, but may be estimated in any particular case by field studies or from the results of earlier studies. They all have positive values (which, of course, implies negative values for $-\gamma$ and $-\delta$); and both α and β are less than 1.

Similar reasoning suggests that the calf producing activity may be represented by another equation:

$$C = bK^{\epsilon} V_3^{\zeta} F^{-\eta} M^{-\lambda} \tag{5.2}$$

where again

b, ϵ, ζ, η and $\lambda > 0$ and ϵ and $\zeta < 1$.

It is pointed out here that the time period for cow keeping is conceived to be a calendar year. M, therefore, is the amount of milk and C is the amount of calves produced in a year. Alternative time periods may be taken, but throughout the present analysis the time period implied for milk and calf production is one year.

The cattle herd is assumed to be in equilibrium, neither expanding nor contracting. If K is the number of cows in the herd and n is the breeding life in years of cows, then to maintain the cow herd constant, K/n calves must annually be directed into the cow rearing activity; and this activity, in turn, produces a similar number of cows for breeding. Again it may be noted that there is an implicit calf mortality rate of zero. This unlikely assumption may be made more realistic if C is amended to represent the annual output of surviving calves rather than total calf production.

If K/n calves are preempted as replacements for the cow herd, C − K/n are available for rearing for slaughter or for draft. Given that cattle reared for slaughter or draft are held for θ years and that cows calve at t years, the total number of followers is given as:

$$F = \theta(C - K/n) + tK/n \tag{5.3}$$

Assuming that on average two followers have the same grazing requirements as one cow, F can be expressed in terms of "cow equivalents" as:

$$F = \tfrac{1}{2} [\theta C + (t - \theta)K/n] \tag{5.4}$$

The following equations can now be obtained by substitution:

$$M = \{ab^{-\delta} K^{\alpha - \delta\epsilon} V_3^{\beta} [\theta C/2 - K(t - \theta)/2n]^{\delta\zeta - \gamma}\}^{1/(1 - \delta\lambda)} \tag{5.5}$$

and

$$C = \{a^{-\lambda} bK^{\epsilon - \alpha\lambda} V_3^{\zeta - \beta\lambda} [\theta C/2 - K(t - \theta)/2n]^{\gamma\lambda - \eta}\}^{1/(1 - \delta\lambda)} \tag{5.6}$$

These equations make explicit that, given,

(i) the amount of land available;

(ii) the technical conditions of production as defined by the parameters, and
(iii) values for K,V_3,θ and t,

then

(i) the maximum values of M and C are determined; and
(ii) the choice of any value of M less than the maximum determines the value of C as a residual; and vice versa.

Cow rearing

t is here understood to mean the time taken to rear a calf to the point where it is ready to commence a breeding life that, for the particular circumstances, is normal with respect to longevity, regularity of breeding, and productivity of milk and/or calves. Heifers can be made to breed earlier than is envisaged here, but their subsequent performance will be below normal with respect to one or more of the criteria mentioned. Again, deviation from this narrow meaning of t can be accommodated in the model, but at the cost of unwarrantably complicating it.

Given the land available for cattle production, t will be determined by (i) the rate of stocking, or K+F, and (ii) the level of "other" inputs devoted to cow rearing, or V_2. This relationship may, for convenience of manipulation, be expressed as:

$$t = g(K + F)^s . V_2^{-u}$$

where F is expressed in terms of cow-equivalents and has the value given by equation 5.4. That is:

$$t = g\{K + \tfrac{1}{2} [\theta C + (t - \theta)K/n] \}^s . V_2^{-u} \tag{5.7}$$

The parameters "s" and "u" imply that the relationship between t and K+F and V_2 may be nonlinear.

Rearing cattle for slaughter

Cattle other than cows may, as noted, produce a range of goods and services, including meat, draft services, blood, etc. No material alteration in the analysis is required to deal with the situation where monetary liquidity is an important output (Chapter 9); or where draft services are the principal product (Chapter 11); or where both draft and meat are produced (Chapter 10).

The rate at which cattle gain weight on a piece of cattle-specific land depends partly on the number of cattle grazing that land. The more cattle on the land, the less rapid is the rate of weight gain per head of cattle (Conway 1974). The rate of weight gain also depends on the amount of "other" resources given to the cattle. If the land is well fertilized, if the cattle get much supplementary feed, if they are well tended and medicated as necessary — all of these factors can expedite fattening.

These considerations suggest:

$$\text{Rate of weight gain (WG)} = hV_1^{w} (K + F)^{-v} \tag{5.8}$$

where "w" is less and "v" is greater than 1.

The simplifying assumption is made that WG is uniform over the animal's life. This would be clearly misleading if liveweight were being considered, because the rate of liveweight gain of young cattle is normally much higher than that of heavier, mature cattle. The assumption of uniform WG is more realistic if carcass weight is the relevant consideration, as it is here. The proportion of meat to liveweight is virtually zero at birth but rises to a maximum when the animal reaches its full, mature weight. The combination of the two characteristics indicates a more or less uniform rate of carcass weight gain over the animal's life.

It is possible in principle to allow for varying rates of carcass weight gain, WG_1, WG_2 ..... WG_n, over the animal's life. The gain in precision is unlikely to compensate for the added computing difficulties.

Fig 5.3   Labour: product and cost

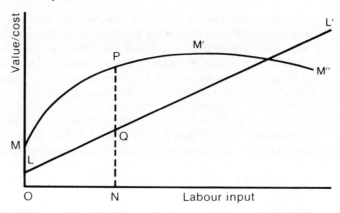

Profit Maximising

Most cattle owners are, and have been, subsistence producers. They produce cattle and milk for consumption by themselves and their families, or for use as draft animals on their own holdings. Subsistence producers, no less than market producers, attempt to organise production so as to maximise their net benefits from the operation.

MM'M'' in Fig. 5.3 represents the response of milk output from a cow (or a herd of cows) to increasing inputs of labour. As more (family) labour is used, milk output increases, though at a declining rate. Conceivably, so much labour can be applied that the cow frets and produces less milk (M''). Inputs of family labour or effort are represented by the straight line, LL', which implies that labour/effort is available in unlimited quantities at a given price. (A more realistic representation would be to show LL' convex to the origin, O, implying that at higher expenditures of labour/effort, the family is less willing to expend more labour/effort.) The distance between MM'M'' and LL' represents, for any level of milk output and labour/effort input, the excess in the utility or benefits of the output over the cost, or disutility, of the inputs. Given the concave downward nature of MM'M'' and the linear, or convex upward nature of LL', a point must be reached, ON, beyond which the benefits or utility of the additional output is less than the disutility of additional labour/effort input. Increasing labour/effort inputs beyond ON reduces the net benefits, QP, that the cattle owner gets from his cow. This result is valid regardless of whether the milk is produced for the market or for home consumption; or whether the labour is family or hired.

The activity considered involves a single resource (labour) and a single product, milk. The problem under examination is considerably more complex in that, despite the drastic simplifying assumptions that have been made, there are four activities (calf, milk and cow production, and rearing cattle for slaughter or draft), using five inputs (V_1, V_2, V_3, θ, and K),[5] with two final products, milk and slaughter/draft cattle.

5. Equation 5.7 shows that if V_2 is given, t is determined and no longer variable.

Yet the same principle of maximising net benefit obtains. The cattle owner is concerned, consciously or unconsciously, so to allocate his resources of V_1, V_2, V_3, θ and K (or calves) as to maximise his net benefit, or his net revenue — say NR.

NR (Net Revenue)

It is necessary to identify NR before considering how to maximise it. It is useful here to realise that net revenue, or NR, does not accrue to intermediate activities. There is, therefore, no NR from cow rearing, though of course the manner in which resources are used for this activity affects NR generated by those activities having final products, viz. rearing cattle for slaughter or draft, and cow keeping. Attention may therefore focus on activities that generate net revenue.

Cattle for slaughter

ADNB of Figure 5.4. represents the changing value of an animal over time, θ, measured on the horizontal axis, at a given stocking rate, K+F, on the fixed area of cattle-specific land, and at a given level of V_1 input. The level of V_1 input is assumed to be such that, following the principle illustrated in Fig. 5.3, the difference between the value of the weight gain and the cost of the input is maximised. Netting out the cost of V_1 gives AQMC, that represents the net value added over the cost of V_1 inputs at different stages of growth. The weight of the animal, and hence its gross value, is assumed to stabilise at some advanced age, T, and heavy weight. But given the continued constant input of V_1, the value added declines after a point, K.

The value of the animal at birth if slaughtered, or if it perishes, is shown as $-OA$. A calf at birth has no meat and therefore has no slaughter value. OA may therefore be taken as representing the cost of disposing of a dead calf. Not until the calf is aged OD does it have sufficient meat to cover the cost of disposal, so that the value of the

Fig. 5.4   Discounting future values

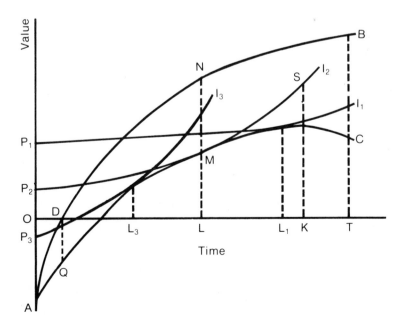

calf for slaughter is zero, though it has incurred costs for V_1 of DQ between birth and age OD.

Two questions arise:

(i) What is the optimum age, θ, at which to slaughter cattle?
(ii) Given that optimum age, what is the net revenue from the enterprise?

Clearly T, or any later age, is less than an optimum age for slaughter.[6] Cattle reach their maximum value net of the cost of inputs, V_1, at age K and beyond that their net value declines. But a producer would only hold cattle up to age K if his rate of time discount were one; that is, if he were indifferent between having a given sum or benefit at some future time and having it now. Normally[7] people prefer a present to a future benefit, and this preference is measured by "i", or the rate per cent per annum at which a future benefit is discounted to the present. Letting $1+i=I$, then I^n is the divisor such that any benefit valued B, to be received n years hence has a present value B/I^n.

It is of great relevance in cattle economics that the poorer people are, the more critical is the time element for them. Subsistence producers in particular are likely to have a very high rate of time discount, preferring a small quantity in the present, to meet their pressing needs, to a large quantity in the future. The ultimate manifestation of the high value that I can attain for poor people is the tragedy of "eating the seed-corn". Starvation is postponed a little, but made more certain and general, by eating the seed for the crops that are the condition of their continued existence.

Cattle owners will not wish to hold cattle beyond the point where the rate of increase in the cattle's net value is less than their rate of time discount. If a cattle owner discounts the future at, say, 10% annually, he will not wish to hold cattle if they increase in net value by less than 10% annually. An animal with a present net value of 100, increasing at the rate of 8% annually, will have a net worth of 108 a year hence. But if the cattle owner discounts this at 10% its present value will be 98 approximately. The cattle owner will therefore be better off by two, approximately, if he sells now rather than holds.

I_1, I_2, and I_3, in Fig. 5.4, represent different rates of time discount of ascending magnitude. They are the loci of points such that, in the case of I_2, the perpendicular distance to the OX axis represents the value at that time which, at the I_2 rate of time discount, has a present value OP_2. Thus, at I_2 rate of discount, a value ML at time L and a value SK at time K have both a present value OP_2.

I_1, I_2, and I_3 are members of three different families of curves. Each family represents a different rate of time discount, and each member of the family represents a different present value. Each of the curves is drawn to be tangental to the net value curve AQMC. The point of tangency in every case represents the time when the rate of increase in the net value of the fattening animal equals the rate of time discount, and so the most profitable time for disposal. When the rate of time discount is I_2, at any time prior to L the animal's net value is increasing more rapidly than the owner's rate of time discount, so it is profitable to retain it. The rate of increase of net value (as represented by the slope of AQMC) is less than the rate of time discount (as represented by the slope of I_2) beyond the point L, so that it is unprofitable to retain the animal. Similarly if I_1 is the rate of time discount, L_1 is the optimum slaughter age; and if I_3 is the rate of time discount, L_3 is the optimum slaughter age.

6. Two further abstractions are noted here. First, the price per unit weight of carcass, Pf, is constant and does not vary either seasonally or over time. Second, calves, like all other cattle, are assumed to be of a uniform quality and all are either reared to the same age, θ, or slaughtered at birth ($\theta=0$).
7. Though not invariably; an important exception is considered in Chapter 9.

If AQMC represents the pattern of net values over time of an animal being reared for slaughter, using optimum levels of V_1 inputs, if I_1 is the rate of time discount, and if the animal is slaughtered at optimum age, OL_1, then OP_1 is the present worth of the profit, or net value, to be made from rearing the animal. OP_2 and OP_3 represent the present worth if, fulfilling similar maximising conditions, the rate of time discount is respectively I_2 and I_3.

Taking I_2 as the rate of time discount and given conditions of perfect competition, cattle keepers will seek to expand their cattle rearing activities up to the point where further expansion costs them OP_2, in addition to the cost of V_1 inputs. The limit to their rearing cattle for slaughter activity is the supply of calves. They will, therefore expand this activity up to the point, but no further than, where the price of calves, say Pc, equals the present discounted net value of rearing cattle for slaughter.

Given the net value curve AQMC, the value of calves will depend on the rate of time discount. If this is low, I_1, the value of calves will be high, OP_1; if the rate of time discount is high, I_3, the value of calves will be low, in this case $-OP_3$. That is to say, cattle owners lose OP_3 for every calf reared, even when slaughtered at the least unprofitable age.

This reasoning holds whether production is integrated, so that producers sell only final products; or whether it is specialised, with some breeding and selling calves and others rearing and fattening them. It holds in the former, less obvious case because of the simplifying assumptions that production parameters, product prices and costs are the same for all producers.

Rearing draft cattle

The path AKBM of Fig. 5.5A represents the net current value of the services provided by cattle at various ages. It represents the value of services net of maintenance costs. The value of services net of maintenance costs is negative until the cattle reach a productive age; it then rises to a peak as the young cattle become fully productive; then it declines from B to M, when the value of services equals the cost of maintenance.

Corresponding to the AKBM curve of Fig. 5.5A, there are capital value curves in Fig. 5.5B, originating at P_1, P_2 and P_3 and terminating at M. Each capital value curve represents the discounted net value of the services forthcoming from the cattle at various stages of life and at various rates of discount, I_1, I_2 and I_3. Thus at time N, the capital net value of the services still to be provided by an animal is NL_1 if the net value of the services is to be discounted at I_1; the capital net value is NL_2 if the discount rate is I_2; and NL_3 if the discount rate is I_3.

The capital value of the animal rises from birth to a peak at time K,[8] when the value of services provided exceeds maintenance costs. Thereafter it declines towards zero at M, when the value of current output equals current maintenance input and the net value of the services provided is zero.

If the animal has a scrap slaughter value, it will be slaughtered before the net value of its current output of services drops to zero. The broken line of Fig. 5.5B represents the value of the animal for slaughter (corresponding to ADNB of Fig. 5.4). It declines after reaching a peak because the slaughter value of working animals declines with age. At a discount rate I_1 the slaughter value equals the work value at age Q_1; at a higher discount rate, I_2, the slaughter value equals the work value at an earlier age, Q_2. It pays to slaughter the animals at age Q_1 or Q_2 as the discount rate is I_1 or I_2.

The value of the cattle rises to a peak after birth partly because of the inputs after birth (represented by the area AKO of Fig. 5.5A) and partly because the animal has grown nearer to its productive life. The value of the cattle at birth is OP_1, OP_2 or

8. This assumes that the animal's productive power increases towards the peak, at age K, more rapidly than the rate of time discount.

Fig. 5.5   Value of (A) draft services and (B) draft animals

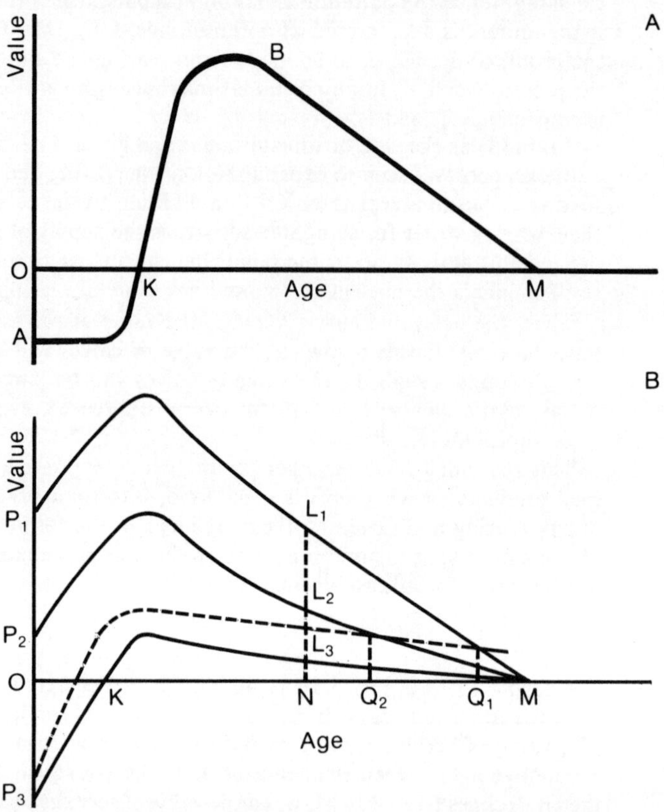

—OP_3, as the discount rate is I_1, I_2 or I_3 These values represent the present discounted net value of the services to be provided by the cattle during their lifetimes. They are the net revenue from rearing draft cattle.

Value of calves

The foregoing shows that the value of calves is the value of rearing cattle for slaughter or draft, net of both the cost of the V_1 inputs and, through the device of time discounting, net of the cost of time, θ. That is to say, the value of a calf, Pc, represents the net revenue of rearing an animal for slaughter or for draft.

Cow keeping

Cow keeping, it has been seen, is a "current" activity. The process of gestating a calf cannot be speeded up or lengthened; time is not an independent variable: neither t nor θ are inputs. The net revenue, or NR(C), from cow keeping consists of Gross Output − Costs. The Gross Output from cows consists (Fig. 5.1) of milk and calves. Denoting the price of milk as Pm, the value of Gross Output from cows is: PmM+PcC.

There are two elements in the cost of cow keeping: (i) direct costs, or the cost of V_3, denoted as PvV_3; and (ii) the cost of replacing the herd, or herd maintenance cost, denoted pro tem as KD (K being the number of cows in the herd).

KD clearly must include the value of calves reared for replacement, and this must equal the value of the calves if reared for slaughter or draft. That is, calves being assumed homogenous quality, their value, Pc, determined by their value reared for slaughter or draft, must also be their value as herd replacements. Denoting Cr the number of calves required annually for herd replacement ($=K/n$),

$$KD = PcCr + X \qquad (5.9)$$

where X is an unknown, positive quantity.

Calves being an intermediate product, their value cannot be included in computing the net revenue from cow keeping. But if the value of calves is to be netted out of the value of the cow keeping product, the cost of calves for herd replacment, PcCr, must also be netted out from the cost of herd maintenance. Thus for cow keeping:

$$NR(C) = PmM - X - PvV_3 \qquad (5.10)$$

Total net revenue

Cow rearing, being an intermediate activity, has no net revenue. Net revenue from other cattle, reared for slaughter or draft, is Pc per animal for $C - Cr$ calves reared, or

$$NR(R) = Pc(C - Cr) \qquad (5.11)$$

Total net revenue from all cattle activities is:

$$
\begin{aligned}
NR = NR(C) + NR(R) &= PmM - X - PvV_3 + Pc(C - Cr) & (5.12) \\
&= PmM + PcC - KD - PvV_3 & (5.13)
\end{aligned}
$$

That is to say, NR for cattle keeping in a given period of, say, one year is comprised of:

(i) the value of milk and calves produced by cows;
(ii) less the cost of herd replacements during that period; and
(iii) less the cost of direct inputs to the cow herd, PvV_3, during that period.

The Value of Calves, Pc

It has been seen that the value of a calf is the present discounted net value of an animal reared for slaughter or draft. Denoting the value of an animal reared for slaughter as VFA,[9] its present value discounted over a time period θ, at I rate of time discount is:

$$\text{Present discounted gross value} = VFA/I^\theta \qquad (5.14)$$

Assuming that V_1 inputs are applied uniformly over the life of the fattening animal and that the cost per unit of these (as for units of V_2 and V_3) is Pv:

$$\text{Present discounted cost of inputs} = PvV_1 \int_0^\theta \ell^{-I.\theta} \qquad (5.15)$$

or approximately, $PvV_1/I^{\theta/2}$. This gives $\qquad (5.15)$

$$Pc = VFA/I^\theta - PvV_1/I^{\theta/2} \qquad (5.16)$$

9. Similar reasoning applies in the case of an animal reared for draft. VFA, of course, includes the value of byproducts, sometimes referred to as the animal's "fifth quarter".

The rate of weight gain by cattle is given by Equation 5.8 as $WG = hV_1{}^w (K+F)^{-v}$ Omitting for ease of computation the animal's weight at birth, its weight at age θ will be:

$$\text{Slaughter weight} = \theta hV_1{}^w/(K + F)^v \qquad (5.17)$$

Assuming that the price per unit weight of slaughter cattle is Pf, then

$$VFA = Pf \cdot \theta hV_1{}^w/(K + F)^v \qquad (5.18)$$

From equations 5.16 and 5.18:

$$Pc = Pf\theta hV_1{}^w/I^\theta(K + F)^v - PvV_1/I^{\theta/2} \qquad (5.19)$$

Herd Maintenance

Fig. 5.1 shows that there are three elements in the cost of producing a cow, say, CC. These are "other" inputs, V_2, the cost of which is taken to be PvV_2; t, the time taken for a calf to reach maturity as a cow and which varies according to Equation 5.7; and Pc, the cost of a calf. These elements are combined to give:

$$CC = Pc \cdot I^t + PvV_2 \int_0^t \ell^{\frac{It}{}} \qquad (5.20)$$

where the variable costs, PvV_2, are incurred at an assumed uniform rate during the rearing of the heifer. This may be restated approximately as:

$$CC = Pc \cdot I^t + PvV_2 \cdot I^{t/2} \qquad (5.21)$$

The capital cost of the herd is, therefore,

$$K \cdot CC = K(Pc \cdot I^t + PvV_2 \cdot I^{t/2}) \qquad (5.22)$$

Cows are assumed to have an exogenously determined breeding life of n years, at the end of which they have no scrap value.[10] The herd's maintenance, therefore requires annually K/n young cows to replace a similar number of valueless cows removed from the herd at the end of their breeding life. The cost of these K/n young cows, or KD of Equation 5.9, is, from Equation 5.21:

$$KD = (Pc \cdot I^t + PvV_2 \cdot I^{t/2}) K/n \qquad (5.23)$$

Substituting in Equation 5.13 gives:

$$NR = PmM + PcC - (Pc \cdot I^t + PvV_2 \cdot I^{t/2}) K/n - PvV_3 \qquad (5.24)$$

Conditions of Profit Maximisation

The phenomenon of maximising net revenue has been discussed above (p. 46) in relation to a single input (labour) and a single output (milk). The same principle obtains when there are more than one inputs (time and "other" inputs) and more than one outputs (milk and slaughter/draft cattle). Cattle owners attempt to maximise their net revenue (NR) from their resources of land, time and "other" inputs by:

---

10. Again, more realistic assumptions about the length of the breeding life and the terminal value of cows could be accommodated by the model, but at the cost of complicating the exposition fairly seriously.

(i) having the optimum number of cows;

(ii) keeping animals for slaughter or draft to an optimum age, θ, (that may be zero);

(iii) using optimum levels of "other" inputs (a) for rearing cattle for slaughter or draft, V_1; (b) for cow rearing, V_2; and (c) for cow keeping, V_3.

These conditions are fulfilled when the first order partial derivatives of NR with respect to the independent variables are all equal to zero (Allen 1938 p. 355). That is, when:

$$\frac{\delta NR}{\delta K} = \frac{\delta NR}{\delta \theta} = \frac{\delta NR}{\delta V_1} = \frac{\delta NR}{\delta V_2} = \frac{\delta NR}{\delta V_3} = 0 \qquad (5.25)$$

Five nonlinear equations for the first order partial derivatives are given in Appendix C. The set of simultaneous nonlinear equations can be solved by computer.

Nature of the Model

The model abstracts from everything other than what are conceived to be the essential economic relationships. Greater realism can be had in the model, but at the cost of rapidly multiplying its complexity. The production process can be disaggregated, for example, to permit individual firms to perform as many specialist functions as is desired. Specialist firms might then rear calves, rear heifers for breeding, rear young stock for fattening, fatten cattle, breed heifers and milk cows. It would then first be necessary to establish a particular set of activity functions and composite bundles of "other" inputs for each type of firm. It would also be necessary to encompass all the firms producing intermediate products into a single firm producing the two end products, milk and meat.

Likewise, as noted above, the composite bundle of "other" inputs can be disaggregated into as many homogenous types of inputs as is desired and as the computing capacity will allow. The vector V_1, V_2, V_3 of "other" inputs would then become a $3 \times j$ matrix of "other" inputs; each element in the V_1 row, for example, representing each of j different kinds of "other" inputs such as labour, feed, medicine, fertilizer, housing etc. used in rearing draft or slaughter cattle. Each of the inputs $3 \times j$ would have its appropriate parameters in the milk production, calf production, heifer rearing and cattle fattening functions.

The model and its operation are complex notwithstanding the abstractions that have been made. It involves four exogenous variables: Pm, Pf, Pv and I; five independent variables: K, θ, V_1, V_2, V_3; and 17 parameters: α, β, γ, δ, ϵ, ζ, η, λ, a, b, g, h, n, s, u, v, w. Even if values for the four exogenous variables and the 17 parameters can be obtained by researching or guessing,[11] several hours of computer time are required to establish the optimum values of the independent variables.

A definitive solution to the problem of maximising profits in a cattle producing situation becomes prohibitively expensive as that situation is defined in other than the simplest, most abstract terms. Yet, daily solutions are worked out by millions of cattle owners throughout the world, rarely using computers and usually without using a

---

11. Actual values for eight of the 22 unknowns can be obtained fairly readily by observing: (1) the number of cows, K; (2) the age at calving, t (to give V_2); (3) the age at slaughter, θ; (4) the price of calves, Pc; (5) the cost of cows, $I^t Pc + I^{t/2} Pv V_2$; (6) the milk yield, M; (7) the calving rate, C; (8) the value of $Pv(V_1 + V_2 + V_3)$, which is the difference between gross output and the rent of land. The observed values are unlikely to be optimal, in the sense of fulfilling the conditions of equation 5.25.

pencil. Daily, cattle owners seek to increase their net incomes by selling or buying stock, by breeding or slaughtering stock, by giving or witholding feed, fertilizer and an almost infinitely wide range of other inputs. They do so frequently when simultaneously the exogenous variables are changing in response to market forces and the parameters are changing in response, especially, to changing weather conditions and also to longer term technological change.

Clearly, at best, a majority of cattle owners may be moving towards an optimum situation, while a minority are making decisions and taking actions that reduce their net incomes from cattle. Conceivably, and even over prolonged periods, a majority of cattle owners may be acting in ways that reduce their incomes.

Millions of cattle owners daily cope with the almost impossibly complex problem of maximising income, for the most part by repeating what they did the previous day, or by marginally changing this action in the light of new weather or price conditions, or in the light of the experience of other cattle producers. Coping with a complex situation, if wise they adhere to proven methods and innovate slowly, cautiously and pragmatically. Given the complexity of the problem, it is probable that any increase in income that would result from computations based on observations of the values of the variables and parameters would in most cases exceed the cost of making the observations and computations.

The model, for these reasons, is likely to be of limited operational use. Estimates of the optimum values of the independent variables would, in a specific case, require a degree of disaggregation that would make computations practically unmanageable. Alternatively, if the computations are to be held at a level that is reasonable in relation to research and computing resources, the degree of aggregation is likely to be such as to provide most cattle owners with generalised recommendations of the type that are normally associated with good and astute husbandry practices.

The usefulness of the model is perceived to lie in helping to understand the principles of pastoral resource use at a time of explosive change, over extensive areas of the world, in an ancient occupation. Individual cattle owners are generally well advised to innovate cautiously and pragmatically; but cautious pragmatism is not a course open to those responsible for public policy in livestock matters at a time of rapid change. Decisions, even by default, cannot avoid having far reaching, fundamental repercussions. The model can help in predicting the outcome of these decisions, and in identifying the direction of response to new stimuli under strange and rapidly changing circumstances.

The model suggests a typology of cattle keeping situations. Each situation is identified with a major producing region. Cattle production in each of the regions is examined in turn in subsequent chapters, with the help of the model, (a) to establish distinctive regional characteristics; (b) to appraise regional cattle production policy; and (c) to identify in each region policies that secure social aspirations more effectively. The exercise has the further purposes of illustrating the model's use and of elucidating the principles of pastoral resource use.

Individual and Communal Tenure

It is necessary, before proceeding to examine cattle production systems, to deal with a matter of fundamental importance that has an overwhelming influence on the relationships that have been discussed. That is, whether the cattle owner has access to grazing land on terms of individual or communal tenure.

Table 5.2 represents the effect on milk production, per cow and in total, of increasing the number of cows on an area of grazing from 1 to 10. It is assumed that V_3 per cow does not change; nor are any resources applied to land, which is assumed to be of

Table 5.2   Stocking density and milk production

Number of cows (1)	Milk per cow (2)	Total milk (3)	Marginal milk (4)
1	3.00	3.00	3.00
2	2.50	5.00	2.00
3	2.20	6.60	1.60
4	2.00	8.00	1.40
5	1.80	9.00	1.00
6	1.50	9.00	0.00
7	1.14	8.00	−1.00
8	0.75	6.00	−2.00
9	0.33	3.00	−3.00
10	0.00	0.00	−3.00

Source: See text.

fixed quality and carrying capacity. The unit of production may be taken as any convenient amount, such as gallons per day, thousands of litres per annum, etc. The cost of keeping a cow in terms of V_3, is assumed to be equal to, say, 0.5 units of output.

If a single person owns all the cows he will realise that by adding, say, a fifth cow, that cow's presence will adversely affect the performance of the other four, causing average output to drop from 2.00 to 1.80 and total output to increase by only 1.00. He will also be aware that if he increases cow numbers still further to six, average yield will decline so much that total output will remain unchanged at 9.00. He will, therefore, not wish to hold more than five cows, however low the cost of keeping a cow is. Given the cost of keeping a cow is 0.5, he will wish to hold five cows; if the cost of keeping a cow were over 1.00, he would only wish to hold four cows.

Fig. 5.6   Weight gain (milk yield) per head

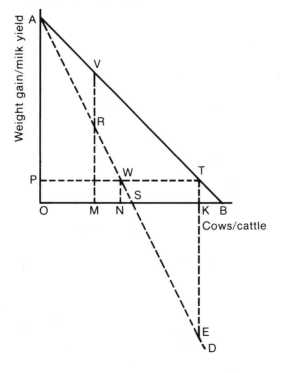

If all the cows belong to different people, they will hold eight. With seven cows on the land, a person putting on an eighth would get a return of 0.75, or 0.25 more than the cost of keeping a cow. Total output with eight cows, at 6.00, is less than with five cows, when it is 9.00. The addition of the seventh and eighth cows reduces output.

Similar considerations obtain in relation to rates of weight gain for cattle reared for slaughter or draft, and to rates of maturation for cows. The schedule illustrates the point that, for a given level of pasture productivity, grazing will tend to be heavier under communal than under individual tenure of the grazing land. The point is illustrated diagramatically in Fig. 5.6.

As cattle are added to a piece of land, the rate of weight gain (milk yield) per head declines, as AB. Corresponding to the average output curve, AB, is a marginal output curve, AD.[12] This shows for any stocking level OM, the average rate of weight gain (milk yield) MV and the corresponding marginal rate, MR.

If the cost of holding an animal is OP, the cattle owner under individual tenure will stock up to ON, getting from the ON[th] a return of WN. Cattle owners on communal grazing will wish to stock up to OK, when each gets a return of KT per head, equal to the cost to him of holding the animal. Because of the depressing effect on the performance of the stock already on the grazing, the OK[th] animal causes total output to decline by KE.

The difference between average and marginal age at maturation is illustrated in Fig. 5.7. The average age at maturation increases with stocking density from OA, along AB. The corresponding marginal age at maturation is AC. At any stocking level OM, the average maturation age is MT, and the marginal maturation age is MR.

Fig. 5.7   Age at maturation

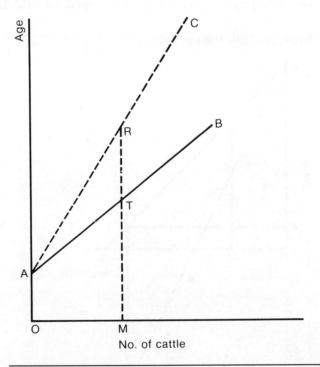

No. of cattle

12. See Boulding 1955 pp. 586–90, for a fuller exposition of the relationship between average and marginal products.

Communal grazing can differ at one extreme from individual grazing as the mountains differ from the sea; they can, at the other extreme, merge towards one another as the land merges with the sea on the seashore. Highly institutionalised forms of communal grazing can approximate to individual grazing. The number of owners with rights of access to the communal grazing may be closely circumscribed by law and custom; and, by similar precept, those with grazing rights may be closely restricted as to the type, age and number of stock each may carry and as to the duration of the grazing season. They may also be required to contribute various inputs to the maintenance or improvement of the communal grazing. Conceivably, at the other end of the scale there may be no restrictions on the numbers entitled to use the communal grazing, nor on the type and number of animals they may graze on it, nor on the timing or duration of the grazing. No contribution to the upkeep of the grazing may be required. It is this extreme, or ideal, type of communal grazing which is considered here for analytical purposes, and for contrast with individual grazing.

The number of cattle on a communal grazing is assumed to be so large that the stock of an individual owner affects the average performance imperceptibly.[13] Referring to Fig. 5.6, if there is a large number of cattle, OM, on an extensive communal grazing area, an individual increasing the small number of cattle which he holds will cause such a slight shift down AB, the average output curve, from V as to be imperceptible. The reduction in average output per head is so slight that, for the small number of cattle which the individual owns, the effect is negligible. The output per head of the added cattle (that is, the marginal output) will be virtually the same for the individual cattle owner as that of the cattle which he already has (that is, the average output). The same decline in output per head will, however, be experienced by all the cattle of the many owners using the grazing area. Summing all of the slight losses in output per head suffered by the many cattle on the communal grazing area, and deducting this from the increase in output obtained by the individual cattle owner per additional animal results in a substantially smaller net gain. This is the gain to the community of an additional animal and corresponds to MR in Fig. 5.6.

Thus, under communal grazing, at a given stocking rate, the average output per head of cattle is the same for the community and for the individual cattle owner; the marginal output per head of cattle for the individual owner is the same as the average output per head; the marginal output per head of cattle for the community is less than the average output. The same considerations obtain in relation to age of heifer maturation.

Algebraic representation

The activities, milk and calf production, slaughter/draft cattle and cow rearing have been represented by the following algebraic equations:

$$M = aK^{\alpha} V_3^{\beta} F^{-\gamma} C^{-\partial} \tag{5.1}$$
$$C = bK^{\epsilon} V_3^{\zeta} F^{-\eta} M^{-\lambda} \tag{5.2}$$
$$WG = hV_1^{w} (K + F)^{-\nu} \tag{5.8}$$
$$t = g(K + F)^{s} . V_2^{-u} \tag{5.7}$$

If, other things being equal, cow numbers are changed, the effect will be:

(i) on M: $\dfrac{dM}{dK} = \alpha . M/K$ (5.26)

---

13. The concept is similar to that of perfect competition, where the impact of the individual is so small that it does not affect price. See Boulding 1955 pp. 45–61.

(ii) on C: $\dfrac{dC}{dK} = \epsilon \cdot C/K$ (5.27)

$\alpha.M/K$ and $\epsilon.C/K$ are, respectively, the marginal products of milk and calves with respect to cows. They are the returns cow owners grazing land individually get when they increase cow numbers. Individual cow owners, under conditions of communal grazing, obtain, as has been seen, the average returns to cows, or M/K and C/K of milk and calves respectively. Given declining returns, so that α and ϵ are both less than 1, $\alpha.M/K$ is less than M/K and $\epsilon.C/K$ is less than C/K.

WG of Equation 5.8 is the weight added by a single animal, or unit of F, in the specified time. The total weight gained by the fattening animals of a cattle owner is:

$$TWG = hV_1{}^w(K + F)^{-v} \cdot F$$ (5.28)

Similarly, t is the time taken by a single heifer, or unit of F, to reach maturity. The total time, in heifer months, taken by all the heifers of a cattle owner is:

$$Tt = g\,(K + F)^s \cdot V_2{}^{-u} \cdot F$$ (5.29)

The effect of increasing the number of followers, F, will be

(iii) on TWG: $\dfrac{dTWG}{dF} = (1 - v)hV_1{}^w(K + F)^{-v}$ (5.30)

(iv) on Tt: $\dfrac{dTt}{dF} = g(1 + s)(K + F)^s \cdot V_2{}^{-u}$ (5.31)

The marginal increase in weight gain is less than the average, in that $(1-v)$ is less than 1. Likewise, the marginal increase in maturation time is greater than the average maturation time, in that $(1+s)$ is greater than 1.

Negative marginal returns

It is common, and frequently normal, even on individually controlled grazing, for producers to stock to the point where negative physical marginal returns obtain. Pasture growth is characteristically seasonal: during the wet season in tropical and semitropical areas, and during the summer in temperate and cold climates. Cattle are subjected to alternating "feast and famine" conditions. Cattle prices reflect the seasonal availability of fodder; they are high at the commencement of the growing season and low at the end of it. There are three ways of reacting to this seasonal variation in prices that reflects the seasonal availability of fodder:

(i) slaughter and preserve the meat of cattle at the end of the growing season;
(ii) conserve fodder for use during the dormant season;
(iii) allow cattle to lose condition during the dormant season which, with "compensatory growth", they rapidly regain during the following growing season.

The most profitable course will depend on the particular circumstances that obtain. Generally, where capital is abundant, it pays to conserve fodder and to get more or less uniform growth throughout the year. Where capital is scarce and, by corollary, grazing land is relatively abundant and inexpensive, it is likely to be more profitable to get the maximum number of cattle through the dormant season. The general rule for maximising returns is: if cattle prices are expected to be high, stock heavily; if they are expected to be low, stock lightly. It occasionally requires nice judgement to stock heavily in anticipation of rising prices without incurring mortalities; and while even lean cattle are valuable when cattle prices are high, cattle that have perished are valueless.

However, while it is common for cattle producers on individual tenure to stock to the point of getting negative physical marginal returns, in the sense that at a lower stocking rate cattle would lose less weight during the dormant season, they expect in doing so to get positive marginal returns in cattle values. If, *ex post*, they do less well from heavy stocking than they would have done from lighter stocking, this is due to miscalculation about the length and severity of the dormant season, or about the level of cattle prices at the commencement of the next growing season.

There are no externalities that convert the gains of the individual cattle owners into social losses when the tenure of grazing land is individual. The position is otherwise in the case of communal grazing. Individual graziers, acting rationally and correctly anticipating seasonal fodder supplies and cattle prices, and maximising their individual net incomes from cattle, may reduce total communal or social returns from communal grazing land. Cobb-Douglas functions, that have been used here to represent algebraically output from cows, cow rearing and cattle fattening, give marginal values for the dependent variables that are either positive or negative for all values of the independent variables. Values are all positive in the present case. There are important reservations to note about this representation under communal grazing conditions. Communal grazing conditions can, however, be represented algebraically by a combination of Cobb-Douglas and quadratic functions.

Inputs under individual and communal tenure

Given communal grazing, with many cattle owners having each a small number of cattle grazing communal land, it will not normally pay any individual to use inputs of a land improving nature. The benefits of these inputs would accrue to all those using the improved land while the cost would be incurred by the individual, "improving" grazier. These inputs might take many forms.

One form of input is refraining from using the grazing land at appropriate times. Timing and density of stocking greatly affect the productivity of grazing land. If land is grazed heavily during seasons of sparse growth, the valuable species that grow during these seasons will be exterminated and the pasture will be populated by less valuable species that grow during the season of heavy growth when there is a surplus of pasture. If part of the land is left ungrazed during the growing season — and preferably a different part every year — the resulting meadow can be conserved and used as fodder during the dormant season, when fodder has a much higher value. The individual grazier cannot hope under conditions of communal grazing, to gain from land-improving abstinence from grazing; rationally, the guiding principle for the individual operating on communal grazing land as understood here, must be: "graze it or lose it". That is, if the individual keeps his cattle off the communal grazing to conserve valuable species or fodder for use in the dormant season, the pasturage that his cattle forego will be eaten by the cattle of other people.

It does not pay the individual cattle owner under conditions of communal grazing as understood here to incur outlays of various types to improve the grazing. Relevant outlays include fodder conservation, drainage, the supply of drinking water, removing scrub and other inferior flora, fencing to permit of rotational grazing, and fertilising. These are standard grassland husbandry measures and account for most of the inputs to cattle under conditions of individual grazing. Outlays of this nature being impossible under conditions of communal grazing as understood here, "other" inputs must take a more restricted form. Much labour and capital is likely to be used by individual cattle owners tending their own livestock; or growing feed on their private land for their own livestock; or buying feed for them instead of fertilizer for the communal grazing. Inputs will not be of the type that improve the quality of pasture.

It has been noted in Chapter 1 that some two thirds of the world's agricultural land is used for grazing. A high proportion of this land, perhaps amounting to half the world's agricultural land, is grazed communally. Institutional arrangements prevent, or at least seriously impede, in the manner described, the application of labour, capital and modern technology to that large proportion of the world's agricultural land that is grazed communally. It is difficult to conceive any single step that would raise world agricultural production by as much as institutional change that would make possible the application to communal grazing lands of "other" inputs up to the point where their marginal productivity on this half of the world's agricultural land is as high as on cropped land and on individually grazed land.

A Typology of Cattle Production Systems

The model suggests a typology of cattle production systems. The most fundamental distinction by far is that between individual and communal grazing. Few situations in the social sciences have given rise to as much widespread confusion as the failure by students, innovators and administrators dealing with cattle to recognise and to appreciate the profound significance of this very basic and quite elementary distinction. Any systematic study of pastoral land exploitation must start from the distinction between individual and communal tenure of the land.[14]

The purpose for which cows are bred gives a second basic criterion for distinguishing cattle production systems. Cows are bred to produce (i) milk, or (ii) milk and calves, or (iii) calves. These are products that can only be got by breeding cows. Combining the two criteria of (a) form of grazing land tenure and (b) purpose for which cows are bred gives a 2×3 cross classification, or matrix, each element of which corresponds to a major cattle production system associated with a particular region or period, as follows:

Form of Tenure	Cow Product	Region
1. Individual	Milk	Northwest Europe and Northeast USA pre-1939
2. Individual	Milk and calves	Northwest Europe and Northeast USA post-1945
3. Individual	Calves	South America
4. Communal	Milk	India
5. Communal	Milk and calves	Africa
6. Communal	Calves	South East Asia

It is hardly necessary to make the point that, in every region/period, cases can be found of all the cattle systems identified here. Indeed, frequently a number of the systems listed will be found on the same farm. That does not invalidate the point that each system is (or was) to be found generally in a particular region and that within that region other systems were exceptional. The classification is, in any case, justified if, and only if, it helps to provide insights into the decision-making processes of cattle owners under various circumstances.

14. The large share of the world's pastures located in centrally planned countries can be considered as held generally under individual tenure. The communist state, in which the pastoral resources are vested, decides on stocking policy for the grazing lands. See, for example, Lattimore 1962 p. 185.

Each of the six cattle production systems is considered in one of the following chapters. The model, along with the statistical data of Chapter 2 and the historical analysis of Chapters 3 and 4 is used to reach an understanding of the distinctive characteristics of each cattle production system. The first systems considered pertain to developed countries (DCs). This order of procedure is determined principally by the consideration that, along with the modern cattle technology that has been transposed from DCs to LDCs, there has also gone something of the institutions, cultures and values of the DCs. It seems important to establish at the outset the influence of these factors on DC cattle husbandry and their limited transferability.

Western Europe and North America, Pre-Second World War: Cattle Grazed Individually; Milk Has Value

Introduction

The cattle keeping systems first treated of, in this and the following two chapters, are based on individual tenure of grazing land. This order of precedence does not imply a judgment of individual tenure as the norm and communal tenure as an aberration; or that individual tenure is more efficient or appropriate. It is rather required by the nature of the inquiry of this work, which is into the consequences of introducing modern technology into traditional cattle keeping situations. That technology originates in the West, where individual tenure of grazing land is the norm. It therefore appears necessary to treat of the conditions of cattle production in the West before proceeding to treat of production in areas to which western cattle technology is being introduced.

The cultural, institutional and broad economic backgrounds to conditions in western Europe and North America have been treated in Chapters 3 and 4. It is only necessary here to restate that, especially from the beginning of the 19th century, incomes in western Europe and North America were rising, raising large groups of people, for the first time in history, above a subsistence level. A manifestation of the rising incomes was an increased demand for livestock products, as reflected in higher livestock product prices relative to grain and feed prices. The concern of this chapter is the manner in which cattle production in western Europe and North America was affected first, by those forces of increased productivity that resulted in overall economic growth and that operated on cattle no less than on other forms of production; and second, by the increased demand for livestock products that resulted from higher incomes.

Choice of Livestock Enterprise

Feed conversion

Livestock in subsistence economies, as scavengers, convert otherwise waste products into useful ones; or as draft animals assist in producing food crops. As incomes increase and the livestock product/feed price ratio rises, it becomes profitable to convert scarce feed into livestock products for consumption. If feed is scarce — i.e. has value — the question of the type of livestock to give it to arises. Should the feed be given to cattle, to sheep, to pigs, or to chickens? And if to cattle, should it be given for milk or beef production? Other things being equal, it is clearly preferable to give the feed to the livestock that will convert it into the largest amount of useful livestock product. Using modern technology, the same amount, in units of starch equivalent, of feed will produce approximately 1.0 lb of butter, or 1.2 lb of beef, or 4.0 lb of pigmeat, or 4.5 lb of poultrymeat.[1]

---

1. Assuming: (a) for cows daily, total digestible nutrient intake, 14 lb; milk yield, 2 gallons, with 0.8 lb butter fat; (b) for other enterprises, feed conversion rates (fcr) and killing-out percentages (kop) as follows:

   chickens   : 2.5 fcr; 75 kop;
   pigs   : 3.5 fcr; 75 kop;
   fattening cattle : 9.0 fcr; 60 kop.

Given the use of modern technology, and the condition of other things being equal, prices of butter, beef, pig and poultry meats will tend to relate to one another according to the amounts of scarce — and therefore valuable — feeds used to produce them. That is, under the specified conditions, 1 lb of butter will tend to have the same value as 1.2 lb of beef, or 4.0 lb of pigmeat, or 4.5 lb of poultrymeat. If the relative prices were otherwise, more feed would be used to produce the relatively more valuable product, and less to produce the relatively less valuable product.

Relative rates of feed conversion are key considerations determining the allocation of scarce livestock feed. But there are others, some of which are touched on here because they are deemed to have importantly influenced the allocation of feed to livestock in western Europe and North America.

Quality and regularity of feed supply

The indicated relative feed conversion rates assume virtually ideal technological conditions. They assume especially that the feed is of appropriate quality and in regular supply. The better feed conversion rates of the nonruminants are attainable only with feeds of high nutritional and low fibre content; limitless feed from natural pastures would not convert into a pound of pig or poultry meat. Likewise a chicken, capable of converting a given amount of low fibre, high energy feed into four times as much meat as a beef animal could, will perish, though a fattening animal in good condition can survive, if deprived of feed for a month. Natural pasture, the most abundant feed, as well as being of high fibre and low energy content, is characteristically available in seasonal glut followed by seasonal scarcity that further limits its usefulness as a feed.

The crop growing basis of western European farming has been emphasised in Chapter 3. Farming in North America is scarcely less crop based; notwithstanding the extensive cattle raising rangelands of the western USA, most of the people were and are engaged in, and most of the output came, and continues to come from, crop growing and ancillary livestock production in the east and mid-west (USA Bureau of the Census 1960 pp. 458, 464, 485, and 1903 plates no. 130, 136). This crop based farming produced feed that was of high quality and — to a large extent, related — in regular supply. Crop growing made available for livestock production feed grains, food grain offals, tubers and root crops, of high nutritional content, suitable for nonruminants. Being of high nutritional value, these feeds are also relatively inexpensive to handle and therefore to store, which increases the regularity of their supply. Furthermore these, and complementary feeds like straw, normally become available at harvesting, the commencement of the dormant season, and this tends to make them relatively abundant then and relatively scarce in the season of pasture growth.

The quality of much of the feed produced by crop based western European and North American agriculture was sufficiently high to permit it being fed to nonruminants. The availability of much of the higher fibre content feeds, like straw and root crops, during the dormant season reduced the seasonality of fodder supply. The more even distribution of the supply of bulk fodders facilitated their feeding to dairy cows. Whereas fattening or draft cattle can draw on stored fat or muscle to carry them through periods of fodder scarcity, dairy cows, that convert feed into milk or calves have less reserves of fat or muscle, and they are therefore more liable to serious and possibly, fatal damage if supplementary fodder is unavailable in the dormant season. The abundance of crop byproducts for feed in the dormant season removed or lessened this risk in western European and North American agriculture.

The availability of quality feeds suitable for nonruminants made possible production of pig-, poultry-meat and eggs. Meat supplies in Europe were further augmented by the slaughter for consumption of a large and expanding number of workhorses at the end of their working lives (Mitchell 1975 pp. 289–305). The emphasis on crop growing by making available in these ways alternative meat supplies, reduced the need to use high fibre content feeds to produce beef. The seasonal regularity of bulk feed supply, that also resulted from the concentration on crop production, made it possible instead to use a large part of the high fibre content feed for milch cows.

Plate 1   Pre-1939 Danish Red cows, tethered to spare grass, against a background of extensive cereal crops

Cost of cow replacement

An initial orientation of cattle husbandry towards milk production had an inherent tendency to become accentuated. Cows were bred to induce lactation and their calves were superfluous. For example, half of France's calves were slaughtered for veal when six weeks old (Yates 1940 p. 263). Because calves were superfluous, their value was virtually zero; i.e. $Pc \approx 0$. Recollecting that the cost of a cow,

$$CC = Pc \cdot I^t + PvV_2 \cdot I^{t/2} \tag{5.21}$$

if

$$Pc = 0, \text{ then: } CC = PvV_2 \cdot I^{t/2} \tag{6.1}$$

Stress has been placed on western Europe and North America being the home of capitalism. This being the case, capital was relatively abundant there and the rate of return on it was low. For example, the annual return on land purchases in Belgium was about 2–2½%, and in France "not more than 2½%" (Yates 1940 pp. 208, 290). If capital was relatively abundant and low cost, the rate at which cattle owners discounted the future, I, must also have been low; and t being low, $I^{1/2}$ was low.

The present discounted value of a scrap cow at the time of its original mating as a heifer has, for ease of exposition, been hitherto assumed to be zero. Though still believed to be substantially true, it was not the case in western Europe in the 19th century. Comparatively young, well fed cows, replaced by heifers of higher milk potential, accounted for a high proportion of all beef supplies (e.g. Jensen 1937 pp. 226–7, Yates 1940 pp. 42, 431). The cost, in that case, of replacing a cow was $I^{1/2}PvV_2-VCA$ where VCA=value of a culled cow. The cost being low, it paid to replace milking cows at an early age with heifers from high yielding cows. This was conducive to the evolution of cows of high milk yielding strains that reinforced tendencies to give feed to milch cows rather than meat producing cattle.

The low cost of, and therefore rapid, replacement of cows made the ranking of cows by their milking capacity important. If $I^{1/2}PvV_2-VCA=0$, then it paid to rear every year the heifer calves of the higher yielding half of the herd, using these to replace older cows and cows in the lower yielding half of the herd. Given annual calving and zero unplanned mortality, this breeding policy implies an average cow life in the breeding herd of four years. The actual average life of cows in Danish herds was four and a half to five years (Yates 1940 p. 42), which, making a small allowance for infertility and for cow and calf mortalities, was consistent with the rearing for herd replacements of all heifer calves from better cows.

Systematic recording of milk yields was necessary to execute this breeding policy effectively. It was especially important to distinguish between those cows in the second and third quartiles, by milking capacity. Heifer calves from the second quartile were reared; cows in the third quartile were culled from the herd.

A similar identification problem does not exist where the cost of cow replacement is greater — because VCA is low, or because Pc>0, or because I has a high value. Fewer heifers are reared for herd replacement; and it is easy to identify the outstanding cows whose heifers are reared, and the usually old, or ill, cows to be replaced. Further, if the cow replacement cost is high (i.e. if CC−VCA is high), reared calves are likely to be valuable for beef or draft. In that case, a cow's capacity to breed calves of suitable conformation may be at least as important as its milk yield, and needs to be considered in selecting heifer calves to be reared as herd replacements. It is sufficient, in these circumstances, to be able to distinguish between the best and the worst milkers in a herd, and competent herd owners do not need to keep systematic records of yield to do that. Danish and Dutch cow owners widely adopted systematic milk recording because it was warranted in their circumstances; other cow owners, though frequently urged and often subsidised to do so, have generally not recorded yields, because the information to be obtained is unimportant for them.

Other inputs

Feed is not converted into livestock products simply by the conjunction of livestock and feed. Other inputs are required, including housing, bedding, veterinary treatment and, especially, labour. But for a given amount of feed converted, these additional inputs are required in different proportions for different livestock. The production, from a given amount of feed, of 1 lb of butter requires many more inputs than the production of 1.2 lb of beef. Or, more simply, milch cattle require more tending than beef or draft cattle.

The populations on the predominantly family farms of western Europe and North America increased through most of the 19th century (Yates 1940 pp. 57, 134, 203, 285, 368, 440; Mitchell 1975 pp. 153–63; USA Bureau of the Census 1976 pp. 139, 467–8). Though average incomes on these farms were, by the standards of the time quite high, good quality family labour was available on them at little cost. This was because the farms operated primarily to support and nourish the farm family and that, given their intensive use of capital, they did well. The result was a good supply of high quality labour available for allocation to its most productive use, according to the principle illustrated by Fig. 3.1.

The regions in question being the heartland of industrial development, other inputs, especially those processed or manufactured, were generally available more readily and cheaply than anywhere else in the world. This applied to such items as transport of farm produce to markets, fertilizers, machinery and buildings. The cost of variable inputs, Pv, was in all these ways held low, and that, given its greater requirements for variable inputs, favoured dairying against other cattle activities.

Demand for cattle products

Two conditions directed demand towards the milk, rather than the calf, product of cows in North America and western Europe. First were those factors noted above that resulted in a relatively abundant supply of other meats, including cow beef and veal, that tended to make the rearing of calves for beef unattractive. Second, the expanding populations of western Europe and North America were located further from the equator than any other major population group, and they were engaged in the heavy, physical toil of early industrialisation. Their need for energy foods to replace lost energy was great and, given their rising incomes, they had the power to translate this need into a firm demand for high energy dairy foods. They also had a high incidence of lactose tolerance (Simoons 1978).

The price of milk, Pm

The price of milk, Pm, relative to the price of beef, Pf, is now low in Europe and North America. It is about 1 : 10 in Europe and North America, compared to 1 : 5 in the rest of the world (Table 4.1). This low milk/beef price ratio is the outcome of a protracted shift in demand to be considered more fully in the following chapter. The ratio was much higher a century ago.

The course of change in the milk/beef price ratio in western Europe and North America is illustrated by the Irish and British experiences, already referred to in Chapter 3. The price of butter, which is a good proxy for the price of traded milk, was over three times the price per unit weight of beef in Ireland in 1810 (Table 4.6). The price of butter rose relative to the price of beef during the following century (Table 4.3), but subsequently declined. By 1970 the price of butter in Ireland had declined to 84% of the price of beef, or to one quarter its 1810 value in terms of beef (Table 4.6). It appears, therefore, that from the beginning of the 19th century to quite recent times, the milk/beef price ratio in western Europe and North America was at least as high as it now is in other regions.

To summarize: while many factors powerfully conduced to milk production in western Europe and North America in the century or so preceding the Second World War, there were other, no less potent, forces operating to strengthen the demand for milk. The net effect of the interaction of these supply and demand forces was a high milk price that, under the circumstances, favoured a large, rapidly expanding output.

Equilibrium Conditions

The low, virtually zero value of calves (i.e. Pc $\approx$ 0) was a distinctive feature of the cattle economy of western Europe and North East America before the Second World War. Recalling that:

$$NR = PmM + PcC - (Pc \cdot I^t + PvV_2 \cdot I^{t/2})K/n - PvV_3 \qquad (5.24)$$

Net revenue from cattle in the circumstances under consideration was:

$$NR' = PmM - I^{t/2}PvV_2\,K/n - PvV_3 \tag{6.2}$$

The marginal product of cows under these circumstances is:

$$\frac{dNR'}{dK} = \alpha\,Pm\,.\,M^* - Pv(I^{t/2}/n + V_3^*) \tag{6.3}$$

where M^* and V_3^* denote respectively average milk yield and variable input per cow. In equilibrium:

$$\alpha = Pv(I^{t/2}/n + V_3^*)/Pm\,.\,M^* \tag{6.4}$$

The nub of the preceding argument is that, in western Europe and North America before the Second World War, the value of the numerator was low and the value of the denominator was high in Equation 6.4, so that the value of the quotient, α, was also low.

Fig. 6.1   Elasticity of milk production

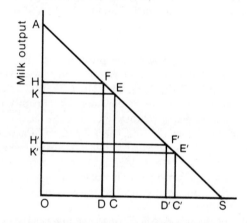

Fig. 6.1 is developed from Fig. 5.6. The elasticity of milk production with respect to cows, or the proportionate increase in milk production, DFEC/OAFD, for a given proportionate increase in cow numbers, DC/OD, is:

$$\alpha = \frac{\text{DFEC/OAFD}}{\text{DC/OD}}$$

or approximately:

α=DC.DF.OD/DC.OAFD=OHFD/OAFD

Similarly, at a higher stocking rate, OD′

α'=OH′F′D′/OAF′D′

where $\alpha > \alpha'$

The favourable production and demand conditions that resulted in equilibrium being reached at a low elasticity of milk production with respect to cows, α, made it profitable to extend cow numbers along OS until a low equilibrium value of α was reached.

The Limitations of the Special Case

The cattle keeping treated of in this chapter obtained in a limited area of the world during a century and a half, at most. It was practised during a stage in the evolution of capitalism in the European heartland and in North America. That stage was one of (a) accelerated capital formation, (b) accelerated population growth due to declining death rates, (c) rapid income growth, and (d) heavy manual labour. These circumstances both facilitated milk production and created a demand for the product. They directed the main thrust of farmers towards milk production, that expanded rapidly in western Europe and North America for a century or more prior to the Second World War (Mitchell 1975 pp. 323–4, Jensen 1937 p. 250, Yates 1940).

Rapid, sustained growth in milk production was achieved principally by keeping more cows, bred and fed to produce more milk. It was a combination of measures frequently regarded as the epitome of good cattle husbandry. The fact that this, which might be termed the classical age of capitalist dairy farming, coincided in time and place with the establishment of many new sciences, including the science of cattle husbandry, has tended to broaden acceptance of pre-Second World War cattle husbandry in western Europe and North America as embodying universally desirable characteristics.

A more than passing treatment of this type of cattle husbandry, that was quite limited in time and place, may be justified — apart from the question of symmetry — by highlighting the special circumstances of the case. Reference has already been made to the different emphasis on milk recording warranted in pre-Second World War western Europe and North American cattle-keeping from that of the general situation, where cow replacement costs are much higher. A lower milk/feed price ratio, greater seasonality in feed supplies and a high incidence of lactose intolerance are other critically important differences between conditions that are widespread in the world now and those that obtained in the time and places dealt with in this chapter.

Possibly the greatest contribution to human wellbeing of pre-Second World War cattle keeping in western Europe and North America was its efficient adaptation to the circumstances of the time and place. Appropriate husbandry adaptations are also required if cattle are to serve mankind equally well under other circumstances that differ greatly from place to place, and from time to time.

Chapter 7

Post-Second World War: Cattle Grazed Individually; Milk and Calves Have Value

Capital Accumulation   The tempo of capital accumulation, that transformed western Europe from the pastoral society described by Caesar to the crop growing society recorded in Doomsday Book, changed from time to time. The more remarkable of these tempo changes were turning points in history. One occurred in the 14th century, when the Black Death halved the population of extensive areas of Europe and doubled the capital/labour ratio. Another was the voyages of discovery at the turn of the 15/16th centuries, that opened trade in products that complemented those of Europe and thereby added to the value of the tiny surplus that Europe generated over and above its subsistence. A third was the industrial revolution of the 18th and 19th centuries, that marked the systematic application of machine power for factory production for national and world markets. Common to these turning points was a sharp increase in productivity and in capacity to save and to invest that made change qualitative as well as quantitative.

Change of a similar remarkable qualitative and quantitative nature has occurred in the capitalist economies of western Europe and North America in the mid-20th century. The perceived distinctive elements of that change are demographic and technological. A sharp decline in the birth rate has caused several countries to approach conditions of zero population growth (zpg); and this, with continued or accelerated capital accumulation, has caused a sharp acceleration in the rise of the capital/labour ratio. The productivity of capital has simultaneously been increased by its easy, accurate and versatile control electronically. These changes have, in turn, caused many changes in cattle production, reflected especially in the rising value of calves, Pc.

Demand for cattle products   Western European and North American populations that grew by 1.2% annually between 1850 and 1910 have recently been increasing by 0.5% annually (Mitchell 1975 pp. 19–24, US Bureau of the Census 1960 p. 7). The national products of the regions have continued to grow at least as rapidly, implying, of course, a sharp increase in output and income per person. Demand has consequently shifted from products the consumption of which is determined by the size of populations to those of which the consumption is determined by wealth.

Aspects of the shift to an income-related demand for livestock products have been considered in Chapter 4. It was noted there that demand for animal fats, that increased with the growth of low incomes in northern countries, declined with further income growth. There are many reasons for this decline in demand for animal fats, including better housing, heating and clothing that reduce the need for nutritious, cold-repelling foods; the switch of the workforce out of occupations requiring heavy physical exertion that had to be sustained by highly nutritious diets; and the concern of increasingly well nourished people with obesity, and therefore the special need to reduce the intake of high energy foods.

Demand expanded less for beef than for other livestock products as populations grew rapidly in the 19th and early 20th centuries (Chapter 4). The stabilisation of populations in the mid-20th century has likewise affected the demand for beef less than the demand for other products. The amount of beef consumed in western Europe and North America is closely related to incomes (Table 4.2), so the rapid increase in incomes that has occurred in recent decades has had a more buoyant effect on the demand for beef than the earlier rapid growth of population. So, as populations stablized, consumers' demand for dairy produce has ceased to grow, or has even contracted, because wealthy, well nourished people, performing little manual labour reduced their consumption of cholesterol-rich foods; simultaneously, as people have grown richer they have consumed more lean beef. Cows' calves have become more needed for conversion into beef at the same time as the milk cows yield on calving is required less.

Capital and grass

The preservation of plant produce from growing season to growing season has been a principal preoccupation of agricultural man. It has been easier with high value, low volume crop produce like grain than with low value, high volume grass. The difficulty of conserving the produce of pastures is a major weakness of cattle husbandry as a means of converting plant growth into forms useful to man; in addition to the gearing losses indicated on p. 63, much — and in some cases all — of the fat and muscle acquired by the grazing animal during the growing season may be lost during the dormant season. These losses must have been especially heavy in pre-capitalist Europe, north of the 45° parallel of latitude, where seasonal variation is more prolonged and pronounced than in areas nearer the equator, where the majority of mankind lives. It has been argued (Chapter 3) that capital formation was the key that permitted western Europe to escape from an especially unproductive pastoralism to crop growing that supported a more populous, more specialised and more productive society. But 15 centuries of capital accumulation, and especially the recent decades of greatly accelerated capital growth combined with zpg, have transformed the capital/land ratio in Europe as well as in North America. These regions, formerly land rich and capital poor, are now capital rich and land poor.

Bulky fodder can, with capital, be preserved from the growing season of abundance for use in the dormant season of dearth. The degree to which preservation is worthwhile depends on (a) the seasonal difference in fodder value, and (b) the cost of capital. Generally, the greater the seasonal difference in fodder value and the lower the cost of capital, the more profitable is fodder conservation. The point is illustrated by two hypothetical situations, of scarce and of abundant capital.

	Scarce capital		Abundant capital	
	Season		Season	
	Growing	Dormant	Growing	Dormant
Unit value of fodder	1	6	10	15
Unit value of capital	5	5	5	5

If it requires one unit of capital to conserve one unit of fodder, it is worth conserving fodder when, capital being scarce, the average fodder: capital value ratio is 7:10 and the dormant season value is six times the growing season value of fodder; or when capital being abundant, the average fodder: capital value ratio is 25:10, and the dormant season value is one and a half times the growing season value.

The fodder:capital value ratio has been raised in western Europe and North America during recent decades especially by the accelerated growth of capital formation and zpg that have lowered the value of capital; and by the greater demand for beef that has raised the value of fodder. Fodder conservation has become more profitable; or it has become profitable to conserve fodder at a lower seasonal difference in fodder value. Some evidence of this trend is conveniently available from seasonal cattle prices in Ireland, the most pastoral, peripheral and, in important ways, least developed part of western Europe (Crotty 1979a). More fodder conservation has lowered seasonal disparities in fodder supply and has reduced pressures on cattle owners to sell in the autumn, when fodder is scarce, and to buy in the spring, when it becomes plentiful. The result has been a perceptible decline in seasonal cattle price variations even within the past 25 years, for which an official series of seasonal cattle prices has become available (Ireland, Central Statistics Office). Peak seasonal prices, that occur in the quarter March–May, were compared with seasonally low prices in the October–December quarter. It was necessary, to avoid distortion from the strong secularly upward movement in cattle prices, to relate each spring price to the average of the preceding and following autumn prices. It was found that, in the first 12 years for which data are available, 1953–1964, the spring price was, on average, 119.02% of the corresponding fall price; and in the following 13 years this percentage had declined, on average, to 116.90%.[1]

Continued capital accumulation results, at the limit, in a virtually uniform fodder supply throughout the year. Seasonal surpluses are conserved to offset seasonal scarcities. This has two important effects on the relative efficiency of ruminants as plant food converters.

First, if fodder is available at all seasons at virtually uniform cost, continuous *ad lib* feeding is sensible, and animals convert a given fodder intake into a higher output than is the case when fodder is rationed to reduce intake during seasonal scarcities. The more seasonally uniform the fodder supply is, the closer ruminants approach to their biological potential feed conversion rates, and the less is the disparity in feed conversion efficiency between ruminants, that traditionally have had to adjust to wide seasonal fluctuations in fodder supply, and non-ruminants, that have traditionally had more seasonally uniform supplies of crop feeds.

Second, the elimination of seasonal variations in fodder supply gives a new economic significance to the botanic superiority of perennial grasses over annual grain crops. Perennial grass preserves its root system through the dormant season and commences to grow as soon as soil moisture or temperature permits. The seeds of annuals, on the other hand, only germinate then, and the plant must first develop a root system before photosynthesis can commence. Effective growth of grain crops ends when ripening commences and the nutrients in the plant concentrate in the grain, that can be handled by man with limited resources. Grass growth continues up to the end of the growing season, with energy being stored in the leaves throughout, though in a less concentrated form that can only be exploited by grazing animals or by man plentifully endowed with capital. These botanic advantages of grass extend the growing season at either end and make it possible, typically, to get for similar inputs of land, capital and labour about two and a half times as much digestible nutrients from cultivated pasture as from grain crops.[2] This superiority of grass over grain, hitherto botanically significant only, becomes economically significant when the fodder:capital value ratio rises to the

---

1. The standard error of the difference of the means being 2.11%, the decline was not statistically significant at the 5% level of probability.
2. For example, grass on Goodwood estate, Sussex, England, in a good year yields 5 tons of dry matter, and spring sown cereals 2 tons per acre (M. F. Dougall, MAFF, Lewes, Sussex 29.8.78 personal communication).

level where it is profitable to eliminate major seasonal variations in fodder supply, and fodder becomes as valuable in the growing as in the dormant season.

To summarise

Pre-capitalist western Europeans were, as observed by Caesar, absolutely dependent on cattle. Capital accumulation made escape to crop growing possible from a sparse, precarious dependence on cattle in a northern climate where the dormant season is pronounced, severe and long. It raised incomes eventually to the level where, in the 19th and 20th centuries, the products of nonruminant, crop-consuming livestock became a major element in diets. Continuous, accelerated, advanced capital accumulation, as well as raising incomes to a still higher level where more costly foods can be afforded, has, in the late 20th century, by offsetting the seasonality of growth in northern climates, changed fundamentally the relative economic efficiency of perennial grass and annual cereals, of ruminant and nonruminant livestock. Cattle, as meat producers, as a result of rising incomes and the increased economic efficiency of grass, are recovering ground lost, during a particular phase of capitalist development, to the nonruminant pigs and poultry.

Bull-beef

The rapid expansion in Italy in recent years of bull-beef production encapsulates and reflects in heightened form many of the changed supply and demand relationships discussed above. The expansion of bull-beef production largely accounts for the changes in Italian beef production shown in Table 7.1.

Table 7.1   Cattle stocks and beef production, Italy, 1961–65 and 1975.

Years	Cattle stocks 1000 head	Beef production 1000 tons	Annual beef production per head of stock, kg
1961–65	9258	679	73
1976	8446	1006	119

See FAO 1977a pp. 197, 206.

Bulls have two principal advantages over castrates as beef producers: they are more efficient feed converters, and they produce a higher proportion of lean to fat meat (e.g. Ireland, Agricultural Institute 1975 pp.20–1). The rising relative value of fodder increases the importance of the former advantage; and the shift of demand from animal fats to protein, of which the shift from milk to beef is an element, increases the importance of the latter advantage. But the realisation of these advantages of bulls over castrates requires certain conditions. First, the animals must reach slaughter weight at an early age, before they become intractable and before their meat acquires the pungent flavour of sexually mature animals. That requires *ad lib* feeding from birth, and rules out the restricted feeding normally practised during the dormant season. That in turn requires the fodder:capital ratio to rise to the point where it is profitable to have a uniform feed supply throughout the year.

A second precondition is taking the fodder to the cattle rather than taking the cattle to the fodder. Progress in handling large volumes of low quality materials on farms has made zero grazing, or cutting and carting grass to the consuming animals, more attractive. The fodder is more valuable *in situ* than heretofore, because of the greater facility with which the growing season's surplus can be conserved. It is therefore worthwhile producing heavier yields. But trampling on the fodder by the grazing animal involves losses and these losses are proportionately larger, the heavier and denser is the grazed material. Because of these larger losses of more valuable material, and because of the greater facility with which low value fodder can now be cut and carted, zero grazing has become more attractive.

Zero grazing further expedites fattening as animals convert into body weight energy that would have been used in grazing. To that extent, it favours the fattening of bulls, enabling these to be disposed of before their flavour deteriorates and they become difficult to handle. Zero grazing also justifies confining the animals closely in feedlots. This is probably essential for coping with large numbers of bulls. Grazing herds of even young bulls are extremely difficult and costly to fence and control; and even if fenced satisfactorily, grazing herds of bulls are an unacceptable danger to attendants.

Plate 2   Fifteen month old bulls of 600 kg in an Italian feed lot (Reproduced by permission of *The Farmers Weekly*)

Change in Demand and Supply

Change in consumer demand for cattle products and change in the facility with which cattle owners can produce these have been considered in the preceding section. Prices mediate these changing demand and supply conditions. Low prices encourage consumption and discourage production, and high prices discourage consumption and encourage production. Price changes must be considered together with consumption and production changes to perceive the underlying changes in demand and supply. These changes are considered for the countries of western Europe and for the USA between the periods 1955–58, when the requisite data become conveniently available, and 1972–74.

Producer prices and the production they influence are recorded in Tables 7.2 and 7.3. These are, of course, not synonymous with consumer prices that influence consumption, which is recorded in Table 7.4. But producer prices may be taken as proxies for consumer prices in the present case when, apart from the United Kingdom in 1955–58,[3] there were no major subsidies or taxes on the products; and where the principal interest is in change between two periods, during which margins between producer and consumer prices are unlikely to have changed greatly — again with the possible exception of the United Kingdom.

Table 7.2   Prices of milk, cattle and pigs in Europe and the USA, in $ US per 100 kg, annual averages 1955–58 and 1972–75.

	Milk			Cattle			Pigs		
	1955–58	1972–75	Change (%)	1955–58	1972–75	Change (%)	1955–58	1972–75	Change (%)
EEC	7.1366	17.9686	152	39.7736	112.1106	182	54.7246	118.6249	117
ROWE[a]	8.9943	21.8762	143	44.7597	139.4031	211	57.3766	120.3185	110
USA[b]	9.0886	16.6725	83	38.3604	79.4766	107	36.8172	79.2562	115

See ECE and FAO 1960 1978, US Department of Agriculture, *Agricultural Statistics* 1967, and 1976.
Notes: a. Rest of Western Europe, viz. Austria, Finland, Greece, Norway, Portugal, Spain, Sweden, Switzerland.
        b. Periods 1953–56 and 1970–73 for the USA.

US prices are lower than European prices in all cases, except milk in 1955–5 (Table 7.2). The increase in cattle prices, though in the USA slightly less than th increases in pig prices, is in all three cases greater than the increase in milk prices.

Table 7.3   Production of milk, cattle and pigs in Europe and the USA (in metric tons), annual averages 1955–58 and 1972–75.

	Milk × 10³			Cattle meat × 10³			Pigs meat × 10³		
	1955–58	1972–75	Change (%)	1955–58	1972–75	Change (%)	1955–58	1972–75	Change (%)
EEC	76 152	99 677	32	4124	6227	51	3965	8366	111
ROWE[a]	18 790	22 835	22	660	1283	94	957	1864	95
USA	56 206	52 914	−6	6872	10 946	59	4884	5715	17

See OECD 1971, 1978a, 1972 and 1978b.
Note: a. Rest of Western Europe, viz. Austria, Finland, Greece, Norway, Portugal, Spain, Sweden, Switzerland.

Table 7.4   Consumption of milk, cattle and pigs in Europe and the USA, (in metric tons) annual averages 1955–58 and 1972–75.

	Milk × 10³			Cattle meat × 10³			Pigs meat × 10³		
	1955–58	1972–75	Change (%)	1955–58	1972–75	Change (%)	1955–58	1972–75	Change (%)
EEC	62 463	78 832	26	4451	6454	45	4915	8382	71
ROWE[a]	14 710	19 120	30	709	1421	100	554	1881	240
USA	49 029	49 594	1	7132	11 650	63	4927	5752	17

See: OECD 1971, 1978a, 1972 and 1978b.
Note: a. Rest of Western Europe, viz. Austria, Finland, Greece, Norway, Portugal, Spain, Sweden, Switzerland.

3. The UK was an exception in the earlier period when publicly financed deficiency payment bridged the gap between free market prices to consumers and higher guaranteed prices t producers. Elsewhere in Europe, high producer prices were secured by protection, tha raised prices also to consumers.

The production changes recorded in Table 7.3 were responses to changes not merely in product prices, but in such phenomena as costs, incomes and the general price level. Notwithstanding this reservation, relating production to price changes, as in Table 7.5, may be useful.

Table 7.5   Percent increases in output associated with a 1 % increase in price, 1955–58 to 1972–75.

	Milk	Cattle	Pigs
EEC	0.20	0.28	0.95
ROWE	0.15	0.45	0.86
USA	−0.07	0.55	0.15

See Tables 7.2 and 7.3.

The increase in milk production was small relative to the rise in price (Column 1 Table 7.5). The likely explanation is that costs in milk production, which is labour intensive, rose, as a result of the rapid increase in real incomes during the period, more than costs in the other, less labour intensive enterprises. A smaller proportion of a declining farm workforce therefore remained in milk production, to which returns in any case rose relatively slowly (Table 7.2).

Change in milk production in the 17 countries covered by the analysis in Table 7.5 (Belgium and Luxembourg being taken as a single country) varied from a decline of 21% in Sweden to an increase of 108% in Greece. Change in output was related to incomes (Appendix Table A) as:

$Y = 183 - 0.014X$ ($r^2 = 0.41$)

where Y : milk production in 1972–75 as a percentage of production in 1955–58; and X : per caput GNP.

Poor countries tended to increase milk production more than rich ones. This supports the view that milk production, which is labour intensive, was least discouraged in those countries where incomes and labour costs are lowest. The buoyancy of milk production in low income countries may also reflect a measure of immobility, of slow response to changing consumer needs by producers, in less efficient, and therefore poorer, countries.

The elasticity of response was twice as high among US as among EEC cattle producers (Table 7.5, Col. 2). This may be due to the greater adaptability of US producers, because of their personal qualities and/or the resources they commanded. It is likely however that part of the greater responsiveness of US cattle producers to consumer needs arose from the relative depression of the US milk price that forced pastoral resources towards beef production.

Elasticity of response to price was much greater in European than in US pig producers (Table 7.5 Col. 3). The likely explanation here seems to be that European pig:feed price ratios rose, during the period under examination, to the critical level where intensive grain feeding became profitable. The European pig supply curve turned the corner to the horizontal stage depicted in Fig. 4.2B, when, during the period, pig prices more than doubled but feed prices rose by 76%.[4] US producers, throughout the period of study, were on the upper horizontal part of the pig supply curve, where the key pig:feed price ratio is the overwhelmingly important determinant of output. The price of corn in the USA rose during the period by 96%, offsetting virtually all of the increase in pig prices. (USDA 1960 p.29, 1976 p.29).

4. This was the unweighted average rise in feed barley prices in 16 western European countries. (ECE and FAO, 1960 and 1976).

Table 7.6   Proportionate increases in consumption divided by the proportionate increases in prices.

	Milk	Beef	Pigmeat
EEC	0.17	0.25	0.61
ROWE	0.21	0.47	2.18
USA	0.01	0.59	0.15

See Tables 7.2 and 7.4

Change in taste, population, incomes and other prices are the important influences shaping demand. Depending on the strength of these demand-determining factors, they may cause consumption to change in a direction similar to the change in price. The increases in consumption recorded in Table 7.6 despite the price rises (recorded in Table 7.2) indicate the relative strengths of the demand-augmenting forces. The demand for beef in every case increased more than the demand for milk (Cols. 1 and 2). Demand for beef in the USA strengthened especially, while demand for milk there increased very little. Demand for pigmeat in the USA was also especially weak.

Production Adjustment and Surplus "Mountains"

The model developed in Chapter 5 illustrates the manner of adjustment in response to the switch in demand from milk to beef. An increase in the price of beef (Pf) relative to the price of milk (Pm) causes a shift of resources from V_3 to V_1, and possibly of calves from cow rearing to cattle fattening (Fig. 5.1). When the supply of free calves (MK of Fig. 5.2) is exhausted, calves acquire value, Pc, as in Fig. 7.1.

Fig. 7.1   Alternative combinations of milk and calf production

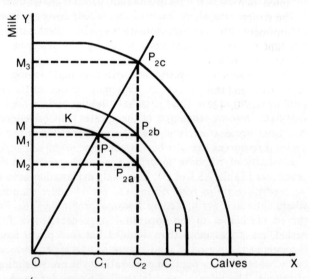

Further increase in calf production, from OC_1 to OC_2 in Fig. 7.1, can be achieved by using for cow keeping:

(i) the same total resources, but less for milk (P_{2a});
(ii) more resources, but the same for milk (P_{2b});
(iii) more resources for milk and calf production (P_{2c}).

Broadly speaking, the first has been the pattern of adjustment followed in the USA; the second that followed in other West European countries; and the third that followed in the EEC.

A high price continues to be paid for milk to farmers under the EEC's common agricultural policy (CAP). The high price encourages production and discourages consumption (Tables 7.3 and 7.4). The excess of production over consumption (M_2M_3 of Fig. 7.1) is bought by the authorities and constitutes the EEC butter and skim milk powder (smp) "mountains".

Adjustment from milk to beef, and from milk to calf, production (from P_1 to P_{2a} in Fig. 7.1) can be difficult and costly. How much so depends on the scale of the OY and OX axes. The more milk and the fewer calves represented by a given distance on these axes, the greater the difficulty of reducing milk and increasing calf production. The adjustment in practice requires farmers to reduce, or give up, their dairy herds and to shift into cattle fattening. Only a reduction in returns relative to other enterprises will induce farmers to leave milk production, as occurred in the USA (Tables 7.2 and 7.3). The simultaneous decline in the supply of, and increase in demand for, young cattle for fattening raises the price of these relative to the price of fat cattle (Table 4.8) and cuts into the profits of cattle fattening.

Adjustment of this nature, though of the essence of economic progress, is often resented and not infrequently resisted. Resistance is the more likely when loss is involved, as in the present case for both milk producers and cattle fatteners. The efficacy of resistance depends on mobilising political power to thwart the operation of market forces. Political circumstances have been especially favourable to resistance to change by EEC cattle owners.

Development and enlargement of a common market has depended importantly on the support of farmers in food surplus member countries, attracted by the prospect of access to the higher agricultural prices of the food deficit countries; and on the neutralisation of the opposition of the farmers in the deficit countries, by commitments to prevent their prices falling. The resulting higher agricultural prices have been accepted as part of the political price of European economic union.

The structure of EEC cattle ownership has been conducive to exploiting a political commitment to higher farm prices so as to shield cattle owners from market pressures to adapt production in line with changing market needs. Most farmers own cattle (though the incidence of ownership is low in Italy, where agricultural incomes are also low). The average EEC herd size is small, less than five cows and less than 15 total cattle, and the average herd income correspondingly small (EEC 1977 pp. 374–6, 1978a pp. 170, 422). Low incomes simultaneously provoke cattle owners to support political action to safeguard these incomes, and evoke a sympathetic response from the electorate and politicians. But poverty is not conducive to political effectiveness. The political ability of EEC cattle owners to resist change arises from the skewness of ownership that results in the majority being poor with few cattle and in a minority being wealthy with many (Table 7.7). The wealthy minority have the resources and the incentive to mobilise the majority for political action that benefits principally the minority.

Table 7.7   Headage and number of holders; cattle and cows, EEC, 1975.

	All cattle		Dairy cows	
	Small herds	Large herds	Small herds	Large herds
Percentage of owners	61.4	3.5	60.6	4.0
Percentage of animals owned	18.0	23.5	20.4	23.3

See: EEC Commission 1978a p. 432–3.

Political action by EEC cattle owners to resist change has been the more feasible because it has been possible to conceal the cost from consumers and taxpayers, who pay for it. High milk prices have required the EEC authorities to buy and stockpile the surplus (equivalent to M_2M_3 of Fig. 7.1) in butter and smp "mountains". Occasional attempts to dispose of these surpluses through commercial channels have given rise to much hostile criticism directed at (a) the use of valuable EEC resources to produce milk products of little commercial value, and (b) the supply of these products to non-EEC consumers at a small fraction of their cost to EEC consumers (*The Times* 22.11.78, p. 7). These embarrassing consequences of disposing of dairy surpluses through commercial channels have been avoided by using them instead as "food aid".

EEC member governments buy dairy surpluses from the stockpile at administered prices that are less than the cost of the produce to the EEC but much above the commercial value. The surpluses are given, and usually delivered, free to LDCs as food aid. The arrangement reduces the financial cost of the dairy policy to the EEC, by transferring part of it to the governments of the member countries, who then treat that transferred cost as a cost of aid to LDCs and not as a cost of aiding their own dairy farmers. The embarrassment of having made explicit the low market value of dairy produce, that costs a lot to produce and for which EEC consumers must pay high prices, is avoided by using the dairy produce as food aid, the value of which the EEC public has little chance of appraising.[5]

The need of farmer support for — or, at worst, tolerance of — EEC development and enlargement, the imbalance of ownership that gave the resources and incentive to a minority of cattle owners to mobilise the discontent of the majority, and the ability to dispose of dairy surpluses with a minimum of embarrassment as food aid — these circumstances have resulted in the EEC's making it possible for its cattle owners to avoid switching resources from milk to beef production in response to changing consumer needs. They have made it possible for EEC cowkeepers to move from P_1 to P_{2c} instead of to P_{2a} in Fig. 7.1. One quarter of the benefits of that policy accrue to 4% of EEC cow owners (Table 7.7), who are also probably among the wealthiest 1% of the population.

The EEC spends 21% of its total budget on disposing of dairy surpluses (EEC 1978b pp. 47, 170). Governments of member countries also contribute to the cost of dairy policy by buying dairy surpluses at above their market value and charging the cost as aid to LDCs. However, the main cost of the EEC dairy policy is the much higher prices for dairy produce that obtain than would be the case if market forces were allowed to compel producers to switch resources from the production of unwanted milk into the production of wanted beef.

The Longer Perspective

The real value of milk produced in the EEC is most closely reflected by its almost zero value if processed for unsubsidised export sale. Political action can cause producers to get more at others' expense. A higher revenue for unwanted milk, as well as adding to producers' profits, induces them to continue keeping cows that produce calves, and deters them from changing to cattle fattening. Calves and young cattle, as a result, cost less to cattle fatteners, who thereby share in the resources directed by political action into the cattle industry.

Political action can easily distort prices, but can less easily change underlying supply and demand conditions. It would appear that only the reversal of trends that have operated in western Europe for millenia can change the decline in the milk/calf

5. But see Chapter 11 below for an assessment of EEC dairy surplus disposal in India.

(Pm/Pc) price ratio that has become manifest there and in North America since the Second World War. Established supply and demand trends in the cattle industry require cow keepers to move from P_{2c} to P_{2a} in Fig. 7.1. Consumers will require still less milk and still more beef, and these consumer preferences will be manifested, by a free market, in high beef (Pf) and calf (Pc) prices and a low milk price, Pm, that will induce cow keepers to breed cows for calf rather than milk production. Cattle keeping will move towards the position where, at the margin, Pm.M=O. Given that Pm.M=O, then

$$NR = Pc \cdot C - (Pc \cdot I^t + Pv \cdot V_2.I^{t/2})K/n - Pv \cdot V_3 \qquad (7.1)$$

Other changes will occur as the supply curve of beef becomes elastic (Fig. 4.2). These will include

(i) A rise in the value of beef, Pf, relative to the cost of variable inputs, Pv, justifying the liberal use of these.

(ii) As a result of the liberal use of variable inputs, the nature of cattle production will change towards that of a "farmyard enterprise", like pig or poultry production, and as feedlotting cattle now is. This will change the production functions suggested in Chapter 5.

(iii) *Ad lib* feeding at all times will cause the maturation age for slaughter, θ, and for breeding, t, to decline towards the biological minimum of, say, one and a half years.

(iv) *Ad lib* feeding will cause the use of virtually equal quantities of variable inputs for (a) rearing a heifer for breeding, (b) fattening an animal for slaughter, and (c) keeping a cow for a year. Effectively then $V_1 = V_2 = V_3$* (variable inputs per cow) and the subscripts may be ignored.

(v) The reduction to zero of the parameters:
Equation 5.1, α
Equation 5.2, ϵ
Equation 5.7, s
Equation 5.8, v
The level of production will be determined by the amount of variable inputs used.

(vi) The calving rate, like the maturation rate, will rise to a biological limit, say, c.
Given these conditions of "factory" beef production,

$$VFA = Pf \cdot \theta h V_1^w/(K + F)^v \qquad (5.18)$$

becomes:

$$VFA = Pf \cdot \theta h \cdot V^w \qquad (7.2)$$

and the value of calves becomes:

$$Pc = Pf \cdot \theta h \cdot V^w \cdot I^{-\theta} - Pv \cdot V \cdot I^{-\theta/2} \qquad (7.3)$$

From Equations 7.1 and 7.3 and from statement (vi) above, net revenue becomes:

$$NR = cK(Pf \cdot \theta h V^w \cdot I^{-\theta} - Pv \cdot V \cdot I^{-\theta/2}) - [I^t(Pf \cdot \theta h V^w \cdot I^{-\theta} - Pv \cdot V \cdot I^{-\theta/2}) + Pv \cdot V \cdot I^{t/2}] K/n - K \cdot Pv \cdot V \qquad (7.4)$$

Denoting net revenue per cow as NR* and assuming (statement (iii)) $\theta = t$, then:

$$NR^* = c \cdot Pf \cdot t \cdot h \cdot V^w \cdot I^{-t} - n^{-1} \cdot Pf \cdot t \cdot h \cdot V^w - cPvV \cdot I^{-t/2} - Pv \cdot V$$
$$= Pf \cdot t \cdot h V^w(c \cdot I^{-t} - n^{-1}) - PvV(c \cdot I^{-t/2} + 1) \qquad (7.5)$$

$$\frac{dNR^*}{dV} = w \cdot Pf \cdot t \cdot h V^{w-1}(c \cdot I^{-t} - n^{-1}) - Pv(cI^{t/2} + 1) \qquad (7.6)$$

In equilibrium, with $\dfrac{dNR^*}{dV} = 0$,

$$wPf \cdot t \cdot hV^{w-1} = Pv(cI^{t/2} + 1)/(cI^{-t} - n^{-1}) \tag{7.7}$$

From Equation 7.2

$$w \cdot Pf \cdot t \cdot hV^{w-1} = \frac{dVFA}{dV} \tag{7.?}$$

Therefore, in equilibrium, under the conditions posited,

$$\frac{dVFA}{dV} = Pv(cI^{t/2} + 1)/(cI^{-t} - n^{-1})$$

$$= Pv \cdot nI^t(cI^{t/2} + 1)/(nc - 1^t) \tag{7.9}$$

Equation 7.9 gives the marginal product of V used in "factory" cattle production. Denoting Pv as the unit of account $=1$, a value of $\dfrac{dVFA}{dV} > 1$ implies that the value of the marginal product of V exceeds the cost $(=1)$. Under normal farming conditions production would continue, with more inputs of V until $\dfrac{dVFA}{dV} = 1$. Cattle, under the factory-farming conditions postulated, would, however, be slaughtered at the exogenously determined age of θ $(=t)$ (Statement (iii)), just as "factory" pigs or chickens are now slaughtered when they reach a conventional weight. The choice is not to keep cattle longer, but to keep more of them.[6]

It does not appear unreasonable, under the postulated conditions of cattle production, to envisage the parameter $w=1$. This implies the introduction of calves in feedlots at a VFA$=$O, and their increasing at a uniform rate to slaughter age when, say, VFA$=100$, and when

$$\frac{dVFA}{dV} = nI^t(cI^{t/2} + 1)/(nc - I^t), \text{ (Pv being 1).}$$

Given that the rate of variable input is, like the rate of increase in VFA, uniform, the quantity $(=$value$)$ of V used is given by:

$$PvV = VFA \bigg/ \frac{dVFA}{dV} \tag{7.10}$$

Given Pv.V, the value of a calf, Pc, can be derived from Equation 7.3. Values of Pv.V and Pc for varying values of I, t, c and n are shown in Table 7.8.

Table 7.8　　Values of Pv.V and Pc for varying values of I, t, c and n.

	(1)	(2)	(3)	(4)	(5)	(6)	(7)
I	1.10	1.05	1.10	1.10	1.10	1.10	1.10
t	2.00	2.00	1.50	2.00	2.00	2.00	2.00
c	0.90	0.90	0.90	0.95	1.50	1.75	0.90
n	10.00	10.00	10.00	10.00	10.00	10.00	15.00
VFA	100.00	100.00	100.00	100.00	100.00	100.00	100.00
Pc	53.23	55.63	54.48	52.19	43.55	40.80	51.71
Pv.V	32.35	36.83	34.58	33.50	43.01	46.03	34.03

Source: see text.

6. The process might alternatively be conceived as Pf being an endogenous variable, the value of which declines rapidly as animals get overfat and so causes $\dfrac{dVFA}{dV}$ to decline to an equilibrium value of one.

The value of calves, Pc, for calving rates of one or less will tend towards 50% of the value of the fat animal, VFA. Even where, as in cases five and six, the successful twinning of cows raises calving rates well above unity, Pc will continue to be high.

Husbandry considerations suggest conclusions in line with those of mathematical analysis. Given circumstances where cows are kept under conditions approximating to feedlotting and with milk having little or no value, it will cost as much to keep a cow for a year as to rear a heifer for breeding or a calf for slaughter. If the cow produces a calf annually, the direct cost of the calf will be the same as the direct cost of fattening it $(Pv.V_1)$. The value of the calf must, in addition, cover the depreciation of the dam over a breeding life in which it produces from 10 to 15 calves.

Calves in western Europe, especially Italy, have been costing up to 35% of the current value of fat animals.[7] A comparable figure for South America might be $3-5\%$. The cost of calves as a proportion of the value of the finished animal, though high in western Europe and North America, is still considerably below the level at which the supply of beef, like that of pig- and poultry-meat, becomes elastic, as in Fig. 4.2.

Assuming:

(i) that it requries the following amounts of feed to produce an additional pound carcass weight of:
  beef   15.0 lb feed
  pigmeat   4.5 lb feed
  poultrymeat   4.0 lb feed
(ii) that the cost per unit of cattle feed is two thirds that of pig and poultry feed;
(iii) that feed costs represent 80% of total rearing/fattening costs, including day pigling or chicken;
(iv) that the cost of 100 lb calves (Pc) is half the value of 1000 lb slaughtered animals (VFA) with a carcass weight of 600 lb (Table 7.8);

it can be deduced[8] that the unit cost of beef will be around four times the unit cost of pig- or poultrymeat. It is concluded, therefore, that in western Europe and North America, given a stagnant or declining demand for milk and an expanding demand for beef:

(i) the price of calves will tend to rise, from about 30% now, to around 50% of the price of the finished animal; and
(ii) the price of beef will tend to rise to around four times the price of pig or pountry meat.

---

7. Hereford bull calves were worth £160–£275 each in Mullingar, Ireland, while the current price of fat cattle was £77.89 per 100 kg (*Irish Farmers' Journal* 28.10.78 p. 65). The mean of the high and low calf-price quotations, £217.50, equals 56% of the current price of a mature, 500 kg animal.
8. Unit cost per lb of beef $= 540 \times 15 \times 100 \times 2/80 \times 600 = 33.75$
   Unit cost per lb pigmeat $= 4.5 \times 1.5 \times 100/80 = 8.44$
   Unit cost per lb chickenmeat $= 3.4 \times 1.5 \times 100/80 = 7.50$.

The South American Case: Cattle Grazed Individually; Calves have Value

Introduction
The countries of South America share a number of characteristics important in relation to cattle production that warrant the continent being considered as one of the six primary types of cattle production identified in Chapter 5. Two of the 14 countries fit the "South American pattern" notably less well; Venezuela's oil and Argentina's extensive, fertile land mark these off from the other countries of the continent. Brazil's size causes it to dominate the continent's statistics almost as much as US statistics dominate the North American scene. These reservations weaken, but do not invalidate, generalisations pertaining to the continent. Those attempted in the present chapter have least validity for Venezuela and Argentina. They have most validity for nine countries, omitting Argentina, Brazil and Venezuela and, for their small size, the Falkland Islands and French Guiana.

Important relevant characteristics of South America are identified in Table 8.1.

Table 8.1   Proportions of world totals accounted for by South America

	%
Population	5.54
GNP	3.57
Crop acreage	6.74
Grassland acreage	14.67
Cattle numbers	17.84
Beef production	14.67
Total meat production	8.08
Milk production	6.11
Cereal production	4.48

See FAO 1977a and IBRD 1975b.

South American incomes are only two thirds the world average, although agricultural land per person is more than twice the world average. Relative to population, cattle stocks are three times and beef production is two and a half times the world average. Production per caput of milk, cereals and total meat is more closely in line with world averages. The continent is a net exporter of 3% of its beef production. Allowing for exports, domestic beef consumption is very high relative to incomes in South America. Per dollar of GNP, it is four times higher in South America than in the world as a whole. Recent changes in these relationships are shown in Table 8.2.

Table 8.2   World and South American growth rates, 1961–65 to 1975.

	Percentage increase	
	World	South American
Population	25.5	37.6
Cattle	21.5	42.2
Beef production	42.5	28.6
Milk production	19.3	46.3
Total meat production	43.9	34.6
Cereal production	37.6	48.8

See FAO 1976b.

South America's population is increasing about half as fast again as the world's. Its cattle stocks have been increasing twice as fast. South American beef production, however, has been growing more slowly than the world's, and more slowly than its own population. Its cereal production per head increased by 8% during the past decade compared to 10% for the world. Milk production per caput has expanded slightly in South America, while declining in the world as a whole.

South America's extensive grazing lands, that have an output equal to the world's average, are held, for the most part, individually, in large holdings, or latifundia. These large holdings rely mainly on hired labour (Tables 8.3 and 8.4).

Table 8.3   Relative number and area of farm units by size groups in South American countries (percentage of country total in each size class).

Countries	Sub-family	Family	Multi-family medium	Multi-family large	Total
	a	b	c	d	Total
Chile					
Number of farm units	36.9	40.0	16.2	6.9	100.0
Area in farms	0.2	7.1	11.4	81.3	100.0
Colombia					
Number of farm units	64.0	30.2	4.5	1.3	100.0
Area in farms	4.9	22.3	23.3	49.5	100.0
Ecuador					
Number of farm units	89.9	8.0	1.7	0.4	100.0
Area in farms	16.6	19.0	19.3	45.1	100.0
Peru					
Number of farm units	88.0	8.5	2.4	1.1	100.0
Area in farms	7.4	4.5	5.7	82.4	100.0

a. Sub-family: Farms large enough to provide employment for less than two people with the typical incomes, markets, and levels of technology, and capital now prevailing in each region.
b. Family: Farms large enough to provide employment for 2 to 3.9 people on the assumption that most of the farm work is being carried out by the members of the farm family.
c. Multi-family medium: Farms large enough to provide employment for 4 to 12 people.
d. Multi-family large: Farms large enough to provide employment for over 12 people.
See Barraclough & Collarte 1973. (Reprinted by permission of the publisher.)

Table 8.4   Distribution of farm families according to socioeconomic status in South American countries.

Status of families in agriculture	Chile 1950	Colombia 1960	Ecuador 1960	Peru 1960
Totals	% 100.0	% 100.0	% 100.0	% 100.0
Upper total	9.5	5.0	2.4	3.0
Operators of large farms	3.0	1.1	0.3	0.9
Operators of medium farms	6.5	3.9	2.1	2.1
Middle total	19.8	24.8	9.5	8.4
Administrators of large and medium farms	2.1	1.5	—	0.6
Owners of family farms	14.8	17.9	8.0	6.1
Tenants with family farms	2.9	5.4	1.5	1.7
Lower total	70.7	70.2	88.1	88.6
"Communal" owners	16.6	—	1.3	4.2
Sub-family-sized farm operators	6.5	47.0	52.3	57.7
Landless farm workers	47.6	23.2	34.5	26.7

See Barraclough & Collarte 1973. (Reprinted by permission of the publisher.)

The Institutional Setting

Chapter 3 gave the historical, social, political and institutional context for the study of the North American and western European cattle economies in Chapters 6 and 7. An understanding of the economics of South American cattle production requires a similar appreciation of its institutional context. This is a profoundly complex subject into which the nonspecialist intrudes with risks both apparent and latent, but unavoidable if the key cattle economy of the region is to be understood. Intrusion in this complex field, though unavoidable in the course of a study of cattle economics, may not be without some merit in its own right. The history, politics and institutions of South America, on the one hand, and the cattle industry, on the other, are interrelated, each acting on, and reacting from, the other. The economics of the cattle industry cannot be understood without reference to the history, politics and institutions of South America; these, in turn, can be but very imperfectly understood without reference to the economics of South America's cattle industry.

The indigenous culture

Three patterns of expansion can be distinguished once capitalism, at the end of the 15th century, spread beyond its western European origins. One of these was the capture and control of trade with the east that followed Vasco de Gama's turning of the Cape of Good Hope in 1497. The European colonial powers for the most part were content to control trade from strategic coastal outposts, like Dakar in Africa, Goa, Madras and Calcutta in India, Penang and Malacca in Malaysia, and Batavia in the East Indies. Masters of the seas, they refrained from involvement in the Afro-Asian hinterlands, until well into the 18th century, when European military progress partly offset the numerical disadvantages of the colonists. Capitalist colonialsm's influence was an alien veneer imposed upon the body of indigenous Afro-Asian cultures and institutions, and its effects only slowly percolated down to bring about fundamental change. The nature of these changes, as they affected cattle, are considered in subsequent chapters.

Columbus's obscure end was a measure of his failure to discover an alternative route to the exotic products of the East (Columbus 1969 pp.16-7). A few unfortunate Carib captives were no substitute for the spices and silks for which Europe craved, and little else was forthcoming for several years. But a remarkable combination of factors transformed Spain's appreciation of its western discoveries and shaped the destiny of Latin America.

The great crop growing societies of the Old World were located several degrees north of the equator; with the qualified exception of Java, the insalubrious equatorial rainforest belt was avoided. The lowland inhabitants of the Americas did not learn to subsist on crops grown in the great subtropical river valleys of the Mississipi and the Paraguay; perhaps their lack of cattle made the transition from hunter to crop grower too difficult. American crop growing instead developed, peculiarly, in the equatorial belt. Most of the ancient world's population, outside the Eurasian-African landmass, subsisted by growing crops on the strip of high land stretching between the Tropics of Capricorn and Cancer in the Western hemisphere. There they had continuous, though not excessive, heat from the sun, and water from the melting snows of the Andean and Rocky mountain peaks. There they extracted gold and silver for decorative purposes from the surrounding mineral-rich mountains. Close to them, the Spaniards landed.

The unmartial ways of the Mezzo-Americans made possible the conquest of a population that was not much less numerous than Europe's by a handful of colonists, who elsewhere avoided hinterland involvement.[1] It may be speculated that the absence

---

1. The combined populations of France, Germany and England at the end of the 15th century were 27 million (Slicher Van Bath 1963 p. 80). "Aztecs, Incas and Mayas totalled between

of cattle and pastoralism from the New World facilitated the work of the *conquistadores*. The indigenous American crop growers had not to defend themselves, like the crop growers of the Old World, against pastoralists; the primitive hunters, the only other culture in the New World, were an irritant but not a threat. The formalised, ritualistic warmaking that evolved under these circumstances was ineffective against Europeans nurtured on violence. Cortes's conquest of the Aztecs was facilitated by his victims' concern to avoid killing their opponents in battle, in order to capture them alive for sacrifice to their insatiable sun god (White 1971 pp.116–8). Pizarro's slaughter of the unresisting Incas in Cajamarca and capture of their leader resembled nothing so much as the butchering of lambs in an abattoir (Zarate 1968 pp. 103–5).

The yawning gap between a highly developed, crop growing culture and primitive hunters appears to have robbed Mezzo-Americans of ability to react to conquest other than by docile acceptance. Lacking flocks and herds, they were rooted to their plots of cultivated land, forced to endure the disastrous exactions of the *conquistadores*. Escape to the savagery of hunting in the tropical forests of the lowlands was not an alternative for these peaceable, cultured, crop growers.

The circumstances of the central American hinterland, close by the Spanish landfall were, then, remarkable. The area contained one of the great concentrations of population of the age, and the only such concentration in the New World. It was a population that had, for decorative purposes, exploited the rich gold and silver deposits of the area, that, even more than the spices and silks of the East, were irresistible to European predators. The absence of cattle from the New World caused these crop growers, though highly cultured, to be unmartial and to accept conquest docilely. These circumstances resulted in the capitalist colonists occupying the land and subjugating its people.

The sparse population of hunters elsewhere in the Americas was incapable of resistance to the European colonists; but the hunters, unlike the Mezzo-Americans tied to their fields, were mobile and could run away to avoid exploitation and "to fight another day". Their land, like all land in the New World, was occupied by the capitalist colonists, and they themselves, like all hunters in the New World, were eventually exterminated.

North and South

Capitalist colonialism, that spread like a veneer over the Old, Afro-Asian World, took possession of the New World, and developed on two disparate lines. Capitalist colonialism in Latin America south of the Rio Grande, backed by the power of the metropolis hungry for the gold and silver of the area, incorporated the large, docile, crop growing indigenous population, and on that base evolved an essentially rentier society. The *conquistadores,* supported by the metropolitan interests of which they were the colonial agents, appropriated all, and more, of what the crop growers produced beyond their subsistence.[2]

The appeal of America north of the Rio Grande to 17th century capitalists was much weaker. It had no obvious store of precious metals to sequester. Its products were likely to compete with Europe's own temperate zone products, when a still immature capitalism sought to trade exclusively in complementary goods, like the silks and spices of the East, or sugar and cocoa from the tropics. North America therefore attracted little European capital and little European military power to protect that capital and to regulate the society in which it was invested. "Salutarily neglected", as Edmund Burke put it, North America was a haven for European

70 and 90 million when the foreign conquerors appear on the horizon; a century and a half later they had been reduced to 3.5 million" (Galeano 1973 p. 50).

2. Above, p. 13. See also Morse 1964 p. 138.

dissidents and nonconformists, for those who, impatient of the exactions of the powerful, transposed themselves and their "penny capitals" to a less demanding environment. It was a process of settlement that was in line with a tradition of development that already stretched back 1000 years to the origins of capitalism in Dark Ages Europe (Chapter 3).

The same economies of scale, the same undermining of political power characterised the spread of temperate zone small farmers across North America as had obtained 1000 years earlier with the transition from tribal pastoralism to crop growing in Europe. The superabundance of land relative to population thwarted every effort to give it value (cf. Le Duc 1966). Land was free to all who would clear, cultivate and seed it. The capital required by the individual settler was small or large, according to the standard used. It was small by comparison with the metropolitan-owned capital that cleared and planted land to sugar in the Caribbean;[3] it was enormous by comparison with the tiny stock of seed from which the Mezzo-Americans received a sixty fold and more return (above p. 16).

The settler, hacking out his farm from the North American wilderness, had the same relationship to his fellows as his progenitors in Europe 1000 years earlier. Acquiring virgin land for crop production, he entrenched in no way on the land of his neighbour — for land was free for the taking and clearing. His presence added to the security and productivity of earlier settlers, because larger settlements could better repel Indian attacks, and they could provide better communication, transport, schooling, commercial, manufacturing and other services. If political power became excessively exacting, the settler, like his European progenitor, could move his livestock, equipment, seed, and other assets to a politically less exacting environment. Political bodies, like Europe's feudal lords, competed for the settler, whose coming added to the wealth and strength of those already present.

The pattern of family farm settlement in North America was that of the growth of capitalism in Europe, but unencumbered with the accretions of 1000 years of history, and on a scale that was vast by comparison with Europe's markets, hedged about as these were by the boundaries of petty kingdoms, and limited as they were by the poverty of their peoples. The full flowering of capitalism's productivity was realised when that culture was translated from Europe to the new, cattleless land of North America, uncluttered as that land was by any earlier culture sufficiently strong to withstand extermination by the pioneers; or sufficiently wealthy and docile to make it profitable and possible to conquer and to assimilate it into a system of colonial exploitation.

The two principles at the core of capitalism, property and freedom, developed unequally when capitalism was translated from the Old World to take possession of the New World. South of the Rio Grande, supported by the power of metropolitan states, property was elevated, and freedom and enterprise were correspondingly subordinated. The result was a rentier-dominated society. North of the Rio Grande, freedom and enterprise flourished and property was subordinated. The result was an entrepreneur-dominated society.

Slavery, though an important part, was not an essential part, of the North American economy, as it had been of Mediterranean crop growing, or as it was of West Indian plantation production. Mediterranean slavery depended on the surplus over subsistence generated by labour applied to unproductive European land; the system required continuous replenishment of the labour force by captives from campaigns of empire expansion (Chapter 3). West Indian slavery operated on the same principle; the plantation economy depended on extracting a surplus from the slave's labour over his

---

3. A contemporary estimate of the finance required to establish a sugarcane plantation in the West Indies in the 18th century was £3515 for a small one and £10710 for a large one (Sheridan 1974 p. 265).

bare subsistence. Insufficient costly provisions were allowed to the slaves to enable them to reproduce themselves, so that the workforce had to be continuously replenished by slave imports.[4] The North American slave population reproduced itself from an early stage. Slaves aged 10–54 years increased from 551 000 in 1802 to 2 461 000 in 1860, without augmentation from imports after 1808 (Conrad & Meyer 1964 p. 76).

Slavery in North America was a device by which landowners supplemented the inadequate powers of a weak state with racial prejudice in order to restrict access by black workers to virtually limitless, productive land. Owners of plantation land, after providing a full maintenance for their slaves, derived a surplus they would not have had if the plantation workers had been free to acquire their own land. Slavery augmented landowners' income. The land, without slavery, would have been valueless and, like other land in North America, available for appropriation by homesteaders. If slave labour generated from this land a surplus over full maintenance, selfemployed family labour could have done likewise. Production of the plantation crops, cotton and tobacco, without slavery, would probably have developed less rapidly and their price would have been higher (Conrad & Meyer 1964, Fogel & Engerman 1974 pp.4–6); the West would have been opened less rapidly; population would probably have been smaller and incomes might have been somewhat lower. But the general outlines of North American development would probably have been the same.

Spanish America was governed for three formative centuries from Lima. The Empire of the Indies was governed for the extraction of the gold and silver, that at first gave Spain command over Europe's productive forces, and that subsequently became essential to maintain its consumption when its own productive capacity, made flabby by the inflow of precious metals, failed. A Spanish and Creole ascendancy, backed by Spanish arms, governed the colonies in the interest first of Spain, and then of the ascendancy agents of Spain. The *encomienda* system, under which grants of land and the disposal of its indigenous inhabitants were made to the *conquistadores,* was the key instrument of exploitation. Agriculture was a secondary sector, feeding the workers in the primary gold and silver mining sector. The grantees, their heirs and their assignees appropriated the surplus over the maintenance of the cultivators, or *campesinos,* for their own consumption, or for transfer to the primary mining sector (Morse 1964 p. 147–9).

The economy was, from its origins, "dependent".[5] It depended on Spanish arms for the establishment and maintenance of property in land and the land's inhabitants. It depended on exports of precious metals to the metropolitan country to pay for its imports of fabricated goods. Profits generated were consumed by the State, by its functionaries, or by the rentier-landowners. Investment was, for the most part, absent and the level of economic activity depended mainly on export demand for metals, and on the application of imported technology.

The contrast with North America was striking. There, metropolitan political and capital involvement were minimal. Production was primarily for local subsistence or local profit. North America's competing temperate zone agricultural products infiltrated European markets indirectly, notwithstanding the protection European countries gave their own agriculture during, and beyond, the age of chronic agricultural surplus until the "industrial revolution" of the late 18th century (Glamann 1977 Slicher van Bath 1963 p.318). Salted cod, meat and grain were sold by the North Americans to the slave plantations in the southern parts of North America and in the West Indies. There the temperate zone products of family farms were transformed

---

4. "By 1790 Barbados, Jamaica and the Leewards had taken a total of some 1 230 000 slaves from Africa in order to achieve a collective black population of 387 000" (Sheridan 1974 p. 314).
5. For a recent exposition of the dependency interpretation of economic underdevelopment see Valenzuela & Valenzuela 1978 p. 535–57.

by the slave labour they maintained and reproduced, into tropical and semitropical products that complemented, and did not compete with, Europe's own temperate products, and were therefore welcomed in the metropolitan countries. North American entrepreneurs, through their ability to procure low cost provisions and to supply these on credit, frequently secured financial control over the whole process (Pares 1956 pp.139–63, 1966 pp.38–50). The homesteaders of North America also exported wheat to La Plata in the 18th century (Worcester & Schaeffer 1970 Vol. 1 p. 350).

Though the Spanish-Creole ascendancy was particularly associated with, and centred on, the Mezzo-American crop growing plateau, its influence permeated the Western Hemisphere from the Rio Grande to the Straits of Magellan. Even where, as in the southern cone of South America, the indigenous culture was hunting and it had been exterminated as elsewhere in the New World, it was replaced by a system of rentier landownership. By the mid-19th century, "as a result of the distribution of vast tracts of public land by Rivadavia (to secure collateral for a British loan) and Rosa (to reward his supporters) the large private estancia had become an established feature of the country" (Pendle 1963 p.40).

Land that in North America, as in northern Europe during the Dark and Middle Ages, was free, was in Latin America, as in England after the Tudor enclosures, not freely available to labour and to capital. The Latin American situation differed, however, from the English situation in at least three important respects. First, with an externally controlled Spanish army to support it, the Spanish-Creole ascendancy could afford to be less politically responsive to the conditions of the *mestizos* and Indians; nothing like the Elizabethan Poor Law was established in Latin America to prevent millions dying from starvation and disease after the conquest (Galeano 1973 p. 50). Second, England was an integral part, and soon became a leading part, of European capitalism as some of the profits of sheep farming were invested; the rentiers' profits in Latin America were either consumed or repatriated to Spain. Finally, the yeomen cultivators of England's enclosed lands were themselves persons of some substance, capable of saving and investing. The Latin American *campesinos*, who harvested 60 grains for one sown (Braudel 1973 p. 110) were without resources and were incapable of investment.

The Latin American land tenure system, though profitable, was inefficient. The agriculture based on it was incapable of supporting its population, which declined after the Conquest. North America's agriculture, by contrast, not merely supported a rapidly expanding population but, even in a mercantilist age, exported to finance essential imports. The system of property in land, created and maintained by Iberian arms, had major structural defects.

The Latin American tenure system implied the appropriation of the surplus over the cultivator's subsistence by an inherently consumer class of rentier landowners. Landowners, like capitalists and workers, have the incentive of higher incomes to use their resources efficiently; but they are not subject to the deterrent of loss from using it inefficiently. If capitalists are inefficient, their capital becomes obsolete, unproductive and valueless; if labour is inefficient, it starves. Land values rarely depreciate. They appreciate if there is trade and capital accumulation or population growth, irrespective of the landowner's action. Action by landowners is not normally necessary to preserve the value of their assets. If they wish to increase it, they have the choice of investing in the land they have, or of acquiring more land. Normally, and especially when land value appreciation is reckoned, the latter is the more profitable outlet for savings.[6]

---

6. See, for example, the Downshire estates in Ireland. Rents on the Downshire estates increased by 562% between 1740 and 1840, when the capital value of land was equal to 25 years' rent. The annual return to land owning was, therefore 4% in current income and an average of 1.9% in capital appreciation. This return compared favourably with British Government stocks, the alternative outlet for rentier funds (Maguire 1972 p. 39).

But land purchase involves no net investment; it implies the buyer's savings financing the seller's dissavings.

The paradox of property is that the more valuable land becomes relative to other resources, as a result of population growth, capital accumulation, or the securing of property rights, the less efficiently it is likely to be used. This is partly because the rentier-consumer-owner is under less pressure to use his resource efficiently if his income is large and his asset valuable; it is partly because as land values appreciate, persons with little capital and no land, who are most likely to use land effectively, are least likely to acquire it. The market, that ensures an efficient allocation of capital and labour, brings about inefficient land use.

Property in land causes it to be used to maximise profits from it. Free land, or socially owned land, is used to maximize output from it (Fig. 3.1).

	Value of Output	Cost of Input	Profit
Labour intensive use	1000	950	50
Labour extensive use	100	10	90

If land is valuable and privately owned, it will be used for the second, labour extensive, purpose in the above example. Specifically, in the South American case, it was more profitable for landowners to produce small amounts of relatively high priced beef, for a malnourished mining population then to produce large quantities of low cost grain, as in North America, for consumption by an expanding urban population, or for processing into provisions for sale to slave operated plantations. Though South American landowners had more profit, and consumed more from the smaller output than they would have had the land been free, the South American landless had neither abundant, low cost food and raw materials, nor a buoyant demand from an exporting agricultural sector.

Finally, property in land creates an ambivalent attitude towards exports. An inefficient latifundia agriculture has not normally exported. Post colonial governments, in those cases where exports have materialised, are under pressure from the substantial majorities who are landless consumers, and have tended to discourage them, because agricultural exports benefit only the minority who are latifundia owners. Argentina, with possibly more productive land per head of population than any country in the world, has carried these agricultural export restrictions to greatest lengths, but most South American countries practise them (Schumacher 1975 pp. 237, 245). Agricultural exports in North America, by contrast, benefited all agriculturists, and these in the economy's early days were a substantial proportion of the total population (USA, Bureau of the Census 1960 p.74). Now an economy, that developed initially on the basis of an efficient family farm agriculture and for which the ex-farm value of agricultural production is relatively unimportant, is unconcerned about ex-farm prices.[7]

Independence

South America was enveloped by the paroxysm of revolution that, in a half century commencing in 1776, embraced almost every corner of capitalist Europe and of the territories, principally in the New World, of which capitalism had taken possession. Revolution originated in North America where the colonies, as they developed, chafed

7. US agricultural output is only 3% of GNP (UN 1977 Vol. 1 p. 1153). About one eighth of it is exported (USDA 1976 pp. 419, 571).

against metropolitan tutelage. The area of conflicting colonial and metropolitan interest increased as the colonies grew; simultaneously the value of the defence services provided by Britain diminished, as the threat from external enemies to the growing colonies faded. Revolution, that in America was political, in the sense of seeking to change the control of power though not the social order power upheld, in France was socioeconomic, in that power was seized to change the social order — to free Europe finally of the feudal predators who, since the Dark Ages, had preyed upon, and hampered the growth of, capitalism. The aspect of revolution was again different in Ireland, the only part of the Old World occupied and possessed by capitalist colonialism as were the Americas. Approaching the precipice of political independence, the Anglo-Irish, Protestant ascendancy perceived that English arms, however irksome, sustained their privileges against the indigenous, hostile, Catholic masses, who outnumbered them five or six to one. Perceiving, they drew back, and secured their privileges for another century by an Act of Union with England (Bolton 1966 pp. 214–22).

The wave of revolution passed over the West Indies,[8] where the white ascendancy, outnumbered ten to one by their black slaves, were unaffected by the fever of the times, and were content to accept metropolitan tutelage as the price of defence against the dangerous enemy within. Revolution erupted again in the southern cone of South America and in Venezuela on the northern coast, where the Creole populations were conscious of Spanish impositions and, like the settlers of North America, were unchallenged by the indigenous hunters, whom they had already exterminated or were in the process of doing so.[9] Spanish exactions, on the other hand, were balanced for the Creoles of the Peruvian heartland of South America, by the support Spain gave to its ascendancy agents against the overwhelming mass of crop growing Indians, whom they exploited and over whom they lived as a privileged ascendancy. The ascendancy class of the heartland of South America reluctantly accepted an independence that freed it from Spanish suzerainty, but also deprived it of Spanish arms to uphold its privileges against *mestizos* and Indians.

Political instability, synonymous with postcolonial South America, expresses the incongruity of a social order based on differential access to land when the external force that established, and for three centuries sustained that order, is withdrawn. Most countries have military governments. Government in Bolivia has been changed by revolution over 120 times since it became independent in 1825.[10]

The Economics of South American Cattle Production

The exogenous variables: price of milk (Pm); price of beef (Pf); cost of variable inputs (Pv); and rate of time discount (I)

The ratios between, and not the absolute levels of, product prices and input costs are important. The lowest regional wheat-relative prices for beef and milk in the world (Table 4.1) for Latin America are consistent with the prevalence of the hacienda, labour-employing farm in the region. Family subsistence is the primary purpose of family farms, and for that milk and meat are important and valued. Consumption of milk and meat on farms makes available family labour at low cost that can then undertake relatively labour intensive enterprises like crop growing (Fig. 3.1). Profit or rent for the owner is the primary purpose of the hacienda. Landless, unemployed peons cannot pay for milk; it is better to sell beef off the hacienda at any price. Cattle

8. Haiti was an exception, due to the loss of control by the French metropolitan power which, at war with Britain, was unable to reinforce its West Indian garrison.
9. "The independence of the Spanish South American countries was achieved under the auspices of the creole elites in the more outlying regions" (Morse 1964 p. 160).
10. "Thus the social and spiritual structure of the past is preserved under new forms . . . its political and legislative forms and its international status change" (Morse 1964 p. 162).

are more profitable than the payment to peons of wages that must, at least, cover maintenance, if not "full maintenance" (Chapter 3) for the growing of crops. So few crops are grown and their cost is high. These circumstances tend to make the price of milk, Pm, and the price of beef, Pf, low relative to the cost of inputs, Pv, insofar as inputs consist of hired labour.

Two other factors depress demand for milk in South America. Most of its population lives closer to the equator than the populations of Europe or North America; even if their incomes were higher and their demand for energy greater, demand for high energy dairy products would probably continue relatively weak. Finally, the indigenous population of the Americas appears to be lactose intolerant. A high proportion of Indians and of those of mixed Indian-Iberian descent probably suffer from digestive disorder when they consume milk or milk products (Simoons 1978 p. 964).

A high level of industrial activity in Europe and North America ensures a good supply of farm inputs at low cost, while the relatively low level of this activity causes the cost of these inputs to be higher in South America. Typically, and particularly important for cattle production, South America's output of fertilizers is low (Table 8.5).

Table 8.5   Cattle stocks and fertilizer output, 1974.

	Cattle stocks $\times 10^6$	Fertilizer output $\times 10^3$ tons
Europe	135	31 584
North America	193	24 768
South America	212	998

See FAO 1976b pp. 230, 231, 285.

The rate at which owners discount future values of cattle, I, appears to be clearly higher in South America than in North America or Europe. Field observations in Colombia in 1972 by the writer of arrangements between graziers and financiers for the purchase of cattle to fatten suggested that the normal return expected by the financier was 50% per annum. (Further details about this practice are given on p. 109). This is confirmed by Timermeier as a normal rate for borrowing in Colombia outside the formal banking system, which supplies only a small proportion of agriculture's capital requirements. Smallholders in Bolivia are normally charged 8–10% per month for credit, while in Chile the average cost of borrowing to smallholders was found to be 63% per annum, after allowing for inflation (US AID 1973 pp. 103, 56, Nisbet 1967 p. 156).

There are many apparent causes of the high value of I in South America, all of which tend to reduce to the rentier nature of the society. Latifundia owners are rentiers who consume rather than invest. Farmers in pre-Second World War Europe and North America (Chapter 6) were entrepreneurs with titles to land that were of low value relative to current incomes; they were compelled to save and invest, or to make way for those who did. European and North American farmers, following a 1500 year old tradition, saved, and invested their savings in assets directly under their control, including especially livestock. South American latifundia owners who save have more attractive investment opportunities than cattle. (That is, assuming that they invest their savings rather than use these to finance the profligacy of others, as happens when they buy the properties of other latifundia owners who are realising their assets in order to maintain consumption at a higher level than their incomes warrant.) Many latifundia owners are absentees, living in towns that are frequently distant from their land.[11] The absentee, urban dwelling latifundia owner's knowledge of off-farm investment opportunities is likely to be at least as good as his knowledge of farm investment opportunities, and his capacity to monitor and control may be better for off-farm investment than for farm investment.

Livestock, though the principal agricultural investment for latifundia owners, have particular disadvantages for them. First, hired labour, on which latifundia depend, is particularly unsuited for handling livestock that require above all the "tender loving care" of the owner and his family. The return that absentee latifundia owners get from livestock, tended by unskilled, poorly paid, hired workers, cannot be high. Second, and related to the land tenure system, South America is, as noted above, politically unstable, and this instability raises I. Unconstitutional changes of government, frequently accompanied by property confiscation, are common. Cattle are particularly liable to confiscation because they cannot be concealed, because they are located in rural areas where law and order is most liable to disruption, and because they have all those qualities of utility and liquidity that cause them to be money in many traditional societies.

The rentier nature of South American society, the alternatives that the saving rentier has of buying more land rather than of investing in the land he has, the further alternatives that he has of investing off-farm rather than on-farm, the dependence of the absentee latifundia owner on hired labour, the vulnerability of property in livestock in politically unstable conditions — these are circumstances peculiarly associated with South America that raise I, the rate of time-discounting future cattle values.

The endogenous variables, milk output (M); calf output (C); rate of weight gain (WG); and age of maturation (t)

Agriculture is much more pasture oriented in South America than in North America or Europe. The point is illustrated by Table 8.6.

Table 8.6

Crop/pasture relationships, by continent.

	Cropland (ha)		Cereals and pulses produced (tons)	
	Per ha of pasture	Per head of cattle	Per ha of pasture	Per head of cattle
Europe	0.81	1.56	0.93	1.81
North America	0.77	1.44	0.73	1.35
South America	0.23	0.43	0.16	0.30

See Table 2.1.

This implies much greater seasonal variation in fodder supplies in South America, because, relative to cattle stocks, crop byproducts for dormant season feeding are much scarcer. South American cattle are, therefore, much more subject to the traditional feast/famine cycle of cattle production. This means, in terms of the production functions:

$$M = aK^\alpha V_3^\beta F^{-\gamma} C^{-\partial} \qquad (5.1)$$
$$C = bK^\epsilon V_3^\zeta F^{-\eta} M^{-\lambda} \qquad (5.2)$$
$$t = g(K + F)^s \cdot V_2^{-u} \qquad (5.7)$$
$$WG = hV_1^w(K + F)^{-v} \qquad (5.8)$$

11. See Barraclough & Collarte 1973 pp. 97 (Brazil), 179 (Colombia), and 261 (Peru). Claveran writes of "an ancestral fear of investment in animal production" under these circumstances (Claveran 1975 p. 194).

that in South America the parameters a, b and h tend to be lower and the parameter g tends to be higher than in Europe or North America. Cattle that gain weight during the growing season are unlikely to do so — and may lose weight — during the dormant season. The overall, average, rate of weight gain, WG, is low and the age at which heifers mature, t, is high. The consequences of seasonality of fodder supply are more serious for lactating cows (Chapter 6), so the parameter a is likely to be particularly low. These production conditions are reflected in Table 8.7.

Table 8.7   Annual production per head of cattle by continent.

	Beef kg	Milk kg
Europe	68	1053
North America	67	348
South America	29	101

See Table 2.1.

Seasonality of fodder supply, that acts through the parameters a, b, g and h to reduce cattle performance, implies in turn that for any level of milk or meat output, cattle stocks, or F, will be large. This, as equations 5.1, 5.2, 5.7 and 5.8 make clear, still further depresses output.

Finally, the productivity of South American cattle is probably adversely affected by low long term investment in land improvements. Here again, the rentier nature of the society and the greater attractions of alternative investments — including land purchase — are relevant.

The price of calves, Pc

Many things combine to make the price of calves, Pc, low in South America. First, although the age at slaughter, θ, is generally high, weight at slaughter is not (Table 8.8).

Table 8.8   Extraction rates and carcass weights by continent (1975).

	Cattle slaughtered annually per 100 head of stock	Average carcass weight kg
Europe	36	214
North America	28	246
South America	15	199
Ditto, excluding Argentina, Chile and Uruguay	13	183

See FAO 1976b, pp. 230, 231, 239, 240.

The low extraction rate confirms frequent observations that slaughter age in South America is frequently upwards of five years. De Miranda, for example, gives the slaughter age for the continent as between four and five years, and the calving rate as between 40% and 60% (De Miranda 1975 p. 8). The Economic Commission for Latin America gives for Colombia the calving rate at 50% and the extraction rate a 13%, which implies a slaughter age of 4.6 years. ECLA's estimates for Uruguay are a 14% extraction rate and a 60% calving rate, which implies a slaughter age of 5.2 years (ECLA & FAO 1962 pp.20, 58).

The value of a calf, Pc, from equations 5.18 and 5.19 is:

$$Pc = VFA/I^\theta - PvV_1/I^{\theta/2}$$

For a given VFA, if I, θ, and Pv are high, then Pc must be low relative to VFA. It is a common feature of agricultural economics that it is difficult to establish the value of items that have in fact little value. Rates of wages for hired labour are normally available, though the value of the much more common, though less costly, family labour cannot be easily established. Prices of artificial manures are usually well known, though the value of farmyard manure, from which more crop nutrients are frequently obtained, is much less well known. Grain prices are readily available, though not the price of straw. Likewise in South America, as in other areas where they have little value, data on the value of calves is not easily available.[12] Apart from a small number of dairy farmers close to cities, calves are not normally traded.

A value for calves may be imputed by comparing the values of two similar cows, one with a new born calf at foot and the other barren, or having lost its calf.[13] The impression obtained from comparisons of this nature is that the value of calves in the continent is normally less than 5% of the current value of a fat animal (VFA). The equivalent proportion in western Europe is around 25–35% and, as noted, the tendency is for this proportion to increase towards 50% (Chapter 7).

Age at slaughter, θ, and cost of capital, I

The model poses, and helps to reconcile, the paradox of a cattle economy where cattle are slaughtered at an advanced age, θ, though the rate of time discount, I, is high. According to the analysis illustrated by Fig. 5.4, if I is high (I_3), cattle are slaughtered early, at age OL_3; but if I is low (I_1), cattle are held longer and slaughtered at age OL_1. Fig. 5.4 represents varying costs of capital within the same cattle-producing conditions.

AQMC represents net value added (nva) in Fig. 8.1, as in Fig. 5.4. Here it is taken to represent nva in South America, while AQ′M′C′ represents nva in Europe or North America. Current costs, PvV_1, being assumed in both cases to be incurred at a constant rate over the animal's life, the differential rates of nva reflect differential rates of weight gain. At a high rate of time discount, I_2, cattle in South America are slaughtered at age AL, to give calves valued at OP_2. If a similar high rate of time discount obtained in Europe and North America, cattle there would be slaughtered at age OL′, to give calves valued at OP'_2. The lower discount rate, I_1, that obtains in Europe and North America results in cattle there being slaughtered at age OL″, younger than in South America, but heavier and when they have come closer to their full mature weight at age OK′. South American cattle are slaughtered at a more advanced age, but when they are still growing quite rapidly and are far (LK) from their full, mature weight. Cattle in South America characteristically are killed when they are still unfinished by European or North American standards (Table 8.8).[14]

---

12. The want of official statistics of calf prices, perhaps the most important variable in cattle economics, is not confined to Latin America. Feeder cattle prices, but not apparently prices of new born calves, are available from the USA. The EEC does not require member countries to report calf prices among the otherwise very comprehensive agricultural returns which it collects. One result of this was the dropping of the calf price series published by the Irish Department of Agriculture's monthly *Farm Bulletin*, when Ireland joined the EEC in 1973.
13. A difficulty of this approach is that it is sometimes found in the Region, where it is usually illegal to slaughter female cattle, that the barren cow is more valuable than the cow with calf at foot. The owner may be able to get a certificate of infertility from the veterinary authority, which permits him to market the animal through legal channels for slaughter. The cow in this case is likely to be of greater value for slaughter than if it were fertile and used for breeding.
14. Compare and contrast the cattle in Plates 2 and 3.

Fig. 8.1   Weight at slaughter

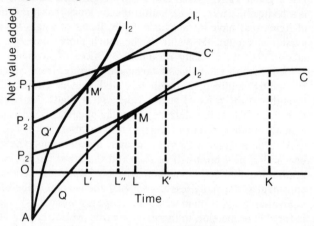

To breed or to slaughter

It follows from the foregoing that the value of cattle gross output, PmM+PcC, is chronically low in South America. If losses are to be avoided, variable inputs, V_1, V_2, and V_3, must be held low. But if the variable inputs are held low, cattle productivity will also be low. The farm or latifundia management implication of this situation is that it will normally be more profitable to slaughter than to breed heifers.

Denoting VBH as the value of a heifer fit for breeding, and VFH the value of the same heifer if used for fattening and slaughter, heifers will normally be bred if, and only if, VBH ⩾ VFH. The condition for breeding a heifer, therefore, is:

$$\text{VBH} - \text{VFH} \geqslant 0 \tag{8.1}$$

The value of a heifer for breeding, VBH, is:

(i) the sum of the future products of calves and milk of the heifer;

Plate 3   5–6 year old steer of 440 kg in a Colombian abattoir (reproduced by permission of FAO)

(ii) plus the animal's scrap value when finished breeding;
(iii) less the heifer's maintenance cost;

all discounted to the time when the heifer is successfully mated.

The product of most mated heifers in South America, where milk is of little importance (Table 8.7), may be taken as suckled yearling calves, denoted as Y. Few cows are salvaged for scrap in South America, and, in the interest of simplicity without departing greatly from what is understood to be the actual position, this factor may be omitted. Denoting PvV_1* the annual inputs to a heifer pre-calving, and PvV_3* the annual inputs to a cow after calving (which includes inputs other than milk to calves at foot), and c, the probability of a cow breeding and rearing a calf in any year during a 10 year breeding life; then:

$$VBH = -PvV_1{}^* . I^{-1} + (Y - PvV_3{}^*)I^{-2} + (cY - PvV_3{}^*) \sum_{i=3}^{11} I^{-i} \qquad (8.2)$$

Assuming that cattle are slaughtered at θ years of age, when they are worth VFA, and that heifers are normally mated at three years of age, then:

$$VFH = VFA . I^{-\theta+3} - PvV_1{}^* . I^{-1} - PvV_1{}^* \sum_{i=2}^{\theta-3} I^{-i} \qquad (8.3)$$

That is, the value of a three year old heifer for fattening for slaughter at θ years of age, equals:

(i) the value of a θ year old fat animal, discounted over $(\theta-3)$ years, less
(ii) the discounted cost of annual inputs to the heifer, PvV_1*

The value of a yearling, Y, reared for slaughter at age θ is:

$$Y = VFA . I^{-\theta+1} - PvV_1{}^* \sum_{i=1}^{\theta-1} I^{-i} \qquad (8.4)$$

Assuming that $PvV_3{}^* = 2PvV_1{}^*$ (p. 44), and denoting

$$\sum_{i=3}^{11} I^{-i} \text{ as } N^*,$$

$$\sum_{i=2}^{\theta-3} I^{-i} \text{ as } N^{**}, \text{ and}$$

$$\sum_{i=1}^{\theta-1} I^{-i} \text{ as } N^{***},$$

the conditional statement (8.1) can be restated as:
heifers will be bred if
$$[N^* + 2(I^{-2} - I^2] \div \{I^{-\theta+1}[I^{-2}(N^{***} + 2) + N^*(cN^{***} + 2) - N^{**}]\}$$
$$- PvV_3{}^*/VFA \geqslant 0 \qquad (8.5)$$

Maximum values of PvV_3*, for VFA=100, c=0.5, and for various values of I and θ are given in Table 8.9.

Table 8.9   Maximum value of PvV_3* for various values of I and θ to satisfy Equation 8.5.

I	$\theta = 5$	$\theta = 6$	$\theta = 7$
1.10	13.30	11.39	9.85
1.15	9.26	7.74	6.51
1.20	5.38	4.39	3.59
1.25	1.65	1.31	1.05
1.30	−1.95	−1.51	−1.17

Source: see text.

The significance of the data tabulated in Table 8.9 may be understood by considering the element in the third column of the third row, 4.39. This shows that if:

(i) the value of a fat animal is 100;
(ii) 0.5 calves are reared per cow per year;
(iii) the age at slaughter is 6 years;
(iv) the rate of time discount is 1.20;

then an annual expenditure on variable inputs per cow not in excess of 4.39 is warranted. If conditions (i)–(iv) are not fulfilled, then at that expenditure on PvV_3^* or higher, VFA>VBH; in other words, it is more profitable to fatten heifers for slaughter than to breed them.

It is important that, in deciding whether to expand, maintain or reduce his breeding herd, the latifundia owner, explicitly or implicitly, is guided by the marginal number of calves reared per cow and the marginal age at slaughter, and not by the average values of these variables. He realises that, by reducing his herd by a cow, the number of calves reared per cow will increase for the remaining cows, and the time taken by the calves to reach maturity will decline. Thus, though the average number of calves reared per cow, $c=0.5$, the marginal rate will be lower, or some ϵc (Equation 5.2); and if the average time for yearlings to reach slaughter weight is five years, the marginal time will be *more than* $5/(1-v)$ years (from equation 5.30). The time taken would be $5/(1-v)$ years if the marginal quality of yearling cattle was as good as the average quality. But, because of the declining output of milk in relation to cows (Equation 5.1), the quality of the remaining yearlings reared will be higher if he removes a cow, and so further reduce the time taken for them to reach slaughter weight. A marginal annual output of 0.5 calves per cow is therefore consistent with a higher average calving rate, and a marginal slaughter age of six years is consistent with a lower average slaughter age.

Minimising costs

The institutional circumstances dealt with above help to explain the predominance of beef cattle in South American agriculture (Tables 8.1, 8.7). The analysis of South American cattle economics explains the need to minimise costs. A cattle economy where inputs are minimized understandably results in a low output agriculture.

It is misleading to perceive South America's low agricultural output as due to want of knowledge or ability on the part of its practitioners. Indubitably, more knowledgeable, ambitious and energetic persons would produce more, even under South American conditions; but if they had these qualities, they would be better advised and likely, to exercise them in a less daunting environment.

High farming is no answer to low prices. Neither is it an answer to chronic political instability. A latifundia owner, concerned to minimise costs, will reduce his stocking rate and his inputs of V_1, V_2, and V_3. At lower stocking levels, cows breed more regularly, suckle their calves better, and cattle mature quicker, for a given level of variable costs. The latifundia owner can hope, by retrenching, to move into a profit making situation. Retrenchment by latifundia owners, while causing the price of beef Pf, to decline in the short term as heifers are slaughtered rather than mated, will, in the medium term, cause Pf to rise, and so also the value of fat cattle. A higher VFA combined with a lower stocking rate, will further conduce to profitability and help to achieve equilibrium.

However, as noted above, the consumer price of food is a politically sensitive issue in South America, where characteristically governments have an ambivalent attitude to agricultural exports. These, generally, are permitted subject to prices being held at an acceptably low level for consumers. The price of beef is a particularly sensitive issue. This is at least partly because meat accounts for an exceptionally high proportion of total food consumption of people with relatively low incomes, and beef — regarded in South America as synonymous with meat — accounts for an exceptionally high proportion of total meat consumed (Table 8.1). This political sensitiveness of the price of beef, Pf, explains the common resort to "meatless" (i.e. beefless) days in South America. This crude form of rationing, discussed more fully below, attempts to equate an insufficient supply of beef with an excess demand at prices controlled at a politically acceptable level.

Given that the price of beef is a politically sensitive issue in a politically unstable continent, it is reasonable to posit a functional relationship between Pf, the price of beef, and I, the rate of time discount, or the cost of capital for cattle production: as Pf increases, political tensions also increase, and with that, the willingness of capitalists to invest in politically vulnerable cattle stocks. It is at least conceivable that, as the value of fat cattle, VFA, increases, I may also increase sufficiently rapidly so that $(VBH-VFH)$ declines, and it becomes less profitable to breed heifers. For example, in the case considered on p. 99, a rise in VFA to 110, other things being equal, would justify raising PvV_3 by a similar proportion, to 4.83. But if a 10% increase in the price of the beef staple caused sufficient political unrest to raise I from 1.20 to 1.21, a 13% reduction in PvV_3 would be required to fulfill the condition $VBH-VFH \geqslant 0$. This decline in variable inputs would cause a further reduction in cattle output, higher beef prices, and so on.

Given a sufficiently close relationship between the price of beef, Pf, and the cost of capital for cattle production, I, it is conceivable that equilibrium can be reached only through destocking, with cattle being withdrawn from less fertile land and stocked less heavily on fertile land, so that, at the margin, milk output, M, calving rate, C, weightgains, WG, and heifer maturation age, t, reach adequately high levels of productivity to offset very high values of I associated with high values of Pf. It is conceivable, under South American conditions, that as the price, Pf, moves towards infinity, output of beef may move towards zero. As observed earlier, high farming is no answer to low prices, or to the political instability endemic in South America. But neither, in the institutional context of South American agriculture, are high prices the answer to low farming.

A tendency for food prices to rise towards infinity and for food output to decline towards zero is inherent in the socio-economic institutions created in South America by Iberian capitalist colonialism and since substantially retained. South America, with the most favourable man/land ratio in the world, has low incomes and low per caput food consumption; excluding Argentina, the continent is a net food importer. An agriculture incapable of supplying abundant low cost food and raw materials to the nonagricultural sectors, and incapable of generating, as a result of sales on home and export markets, a demand for the products of other sectors, is an inadequate base for endogenous, sustained growth. Manufacturing industry, as a result, is inefficient and can survive only with protection or public subsidy, financed in the final analysis by foreign borrowing. The "dependent" character of South American economies is inherent in the structural defects of South American agriculture.

External Influences

It has been argued above that the socioeconomic institutional framework established by Spanish arms and which embodied a large, servile, indigenous population, tends to a situation of zero output and infinitely high prices. It is a conflict that, left to itself, would sooner or later resolve itself by radical institutional change. But the essence of the South American situation for almost five centuries has been its incorporation into a world capitalist system. One aspect of this incorporation has been the supply of arms, first by the Iberian powers and more recently by western capitalist countries, to local oligarchies. Another has been the continuing, increasing demand by these countries for South America's primary products. Capital accumulation and technological innovation have, typically, resulted at the Potosi silver mines in the tailings being reworked and reworked, first to extract silver, and later to extract the tin that was valueless to the original miners but became valuable when a rail link with the coast was established (Osborne 1954 pp.75–7). South America, however economically undynamic, could not insulate itself from external influences. Of these, preventive medicine is especially important to the economics of Latin American cattle production.

Elementary measures of preventive medicine applied in LDCs, with birth rates tending to their biological limit, cause rapid population growth. Preventive medicine means especially that people survive at a lower nutritional level. Per caput meat consumption in South America is declining (Table 8.2). A larger labour supply at lower consumption levels means, in terms of the model, that the cost of variable inputs, Pv, — in so far as these refer to labour — declines relative to the value of the outputs, milk (Pm) or beef (Pf). A decline in the Pv/Pm and Pv/Pf ratios tends to justify the use of more lower paid labour, notwithstanding the increases in VFA and I discussed above.

Preventive medicine is not limited to human populations. Application of its elementary principles to cattle reduces mortality spectacularly at low cost. Cattle performance improves, for a given level of variable inputs, with the application of elementary principles of preventive medicine.[15]

The combination, resulting from the application of preventive medicine, of a decline in the Pv/Pm and Pv/Pf ratios that make the use of more lower cost labour profitable, and of an increase in the effectiveness of variable inputs, brought about an expansion in cattle output notwithstanding those forces inherent in South America's institutions tending to depress output. The overall effect has been an expansion in beef output less than the expansion in population, and a decline in per caput consumption (Table 8.2). There are more, and more poor, people; and there are more, and more powerful guns to control them.

Assessing Policy

Concern over the status of the cattle industry, especially about its failure to expand beef supplies in line with rapidly growing populations, is widespread in South America. This public concern is manifested in various public actions that are designed to increase beef supplies and that include the provision of extension and veterinary services, the supply of capital at advantageous terms, prohibiting the slaughter of female cattle, compulsory meatless days, and restrictions on exports of cattle and beef. The appropriateness of these policy measures is considered in the light of the cattle producers' decision making model developed here.

Extension and veterinary services

Institutional, factor cost and demand conditions in South America result in a unproductive cattle industry. The proximate causes of this low productivity can be readily identified as departures from husbandry practices normal in situations where higher levels of cattle productivity are appropriate — i.e. North America and Europe. Cattle technologists, in these circumstances, can plausibly argue that dramati-

---

15. But see important reservations in subsequent chapters.

increases in output can be got for small increases in input. But, as has been seen above (pp. 99–100), even outlays that are very small relative to fat cattle values may not be warranted.

This situation is particularly likely with respect to measures to increase young cattle production. The value of these being especially low in South America by comparison with North America and Europe, little effort is made, or expense incurred, to produce young cattle; or, when they are produced, to keep them alive. There are, therefore, startling differences in calving rates, calf mortality and reared calves per cow in South America and in North America and Europe.[16] These differences invite intervention by governments and by international agencies, eager to achieve spectacular results at little cost.

The temptation to intervene to assist young cattle production is the greater in that, broadly, young cattle are produced by poor farmers and are fattened by wealthier farmers. There are two reasons for this: first, less capital is required for breeding and rearing young cattle that are of relatively low value than in fattening these cattle, which become increasingly valuable as they approach the marketing stage; second, for biological reasons, to be developed presently, breeding and rearing tend to locate on poor land, usually held by poorer farmers, and fattening on better land, usually held by wealthier farmers. Governments and aid agencies assisting young cattle production can point to palpable success in increasing the output of poorer farmers. Producers of young cattle, meanwhile, are likely to welcome these services if they are given free or at very low cost.

Assistance given by governments and aid agencies increases the supply of young cattle. The demand for these being typically price inelastic, their price declines more than proportionately to the increase in the quantity produced, and the total value of young cattle output declines.[17] Individual producers are caught on a treadmill. If they reject the proferred assistance, their young cattle production remains low, while the price is depressed by use by other producers of the facilities offered. If they use the facilities, their young cattle output also increases, contributing to the depression of prices. The individual producer has no option but to accept facilities offered free, or at little cost, and to adjust his production to the subsequent lower price for young cattle. This he does by reducing his variable inputs. A new equilibrium is approached in which inputs provided by government or aid agency are substituted for other inputs; where, for example, drugs manufactured in, and provided by governments of, DCs replace local labour in young cattle production. Technical performance in young cattle production continues low, but relatively high on farms using much assistance. Continued, increasing, intervention by governments and aid agencies appears warranted.

Concessionary loans

Many official and quasi-official institutions in South America direct finance into cattle production. There are *cajas* and *bancos agricolas* and *fundos ganaderos*.[18] Most of these institutions favour cattle breeding and rearing; cattle fattening does not normally get finance on concessionary terms (e.g. US AID 1973 pp.43, 46). Preference in the allocation of finance is given to breeding and rearing because (a) it is reasoned that beef production cannot expand until more calves are born and reared, and (b) breeders

---

16. Compare, for example, Irish calving rates of about 85% (Ireland, Central Statistics Office 1977 pp. 78–9) and rates for Colombia and Uruguay (above, p. 96).
17. This is the corollary of the point made in Chapter 7 that, because of the inelastic supply of young cattle, an increase in the demand for them in DCs leads to an increase in their value relative to the value of mature cattle.
18. For a review of this see US AID 1973 pp. 7–106; also Schumacher 1975 p. 250.

and rearers as a group are poorer than cattle fatteners. Concessionary loans to cattle breeders thus effectively means subsidising to fatteners the cost of young, or store, cattle, which are already cheap.[19] If, as seems likely, cattle fatteners are reluctant investors, little of the increased profits that they receive as a result of the lower cost of store cattle will be reinvested in cattle production. Public resources directed into the cattle industry to expand young cattle production are likely to be withdrawn from it through the increased profits and savings of cattle fatteners, that are invested outside the industry, or even outside the country.

If finance is to be made available to the cattle industry on concessionary terms, it would probably do most good if used to expand existing fattening facilities. This would increase the demand for young cattle, raise the price of these and make it profitable to expand cow keeping and calf production. Producers of calves and young cattle would be made better off.

The higher throughput of fattening cattle would lower the price of fat cattle and beef to consumers, or make it possible to reduce the number of meatless days. The profit rate on fattening would be reduced because cattle fatteners would be compelled to pay more for store cattle as a result of greater competition from the newly created fattening capacity, and because of lower prices for fat cattle if there were no change in the number of meatless days.

Restricting female slaughter

Prohibiting or restricting the slaughter of female cattle is a common method of attempting to maintain or to increase cattle stocks. It is assumed here that the prohibition is absolute and successful.

A successful prohibition of female cattle slaughter implies that the value of a heifer for slaughter declines to zero, and (VBH−VFH) increases. All heifers are bred, cattle stocks increase, and cattle productivity declines. That is, in terms of equations 8.2, 8.3 and 8.4, c declines and θ increases. Further, because cattle owners can no longer sell females, their ability and willingness to invest in cattle decline, or I increases. The combination of a decline in c and of increases in θ and I implies that, if cattle keeping is to remain profitable, or if condition 8.1 is to be fulfilled, PvV_3^* must decline towards zero.

Governments can, with more or less success, prohibit cattle owners from selling heifers for slaughter. They have not attempted, and would almost certainly find it impossible, to compel them to maintain variable inputs. Prohibition of female slaughter causes the substitution of cattle numbers for other variable inputs in the production process, resulting, for example, in European farmers using 50 times as much fertilizer per head of cattle as South American farmers (Table 8.5). Attempting to prevent female slaughter deals with the chronic tendency for VBH<VFH, or for the value of a heifer to be less for breeding than for slaughter. It exacerbates the institutional, structural, and factor supply defects of which this price relationship is a symptom.

Meatless days

The relationship between the price of meat, Pf, political stability, and the rate of time discount, I, has been considered above. Meatless days attempt to reduce the demand for meat and hence lower Pf. A reduction in Pf, implying a transfer of resources from latifundia owners to meat consumers, could be expected to reduce political tension and hence I. This would, under circumstances discussed (p.101), increas

19. The process is analogous to the EEC subsidising cattle fatteners through butter and skim milk powder "mountains", which raises the returns to milk producing, increases the supply of cows and so reduces the cost of calves.

(VBH−VFA), make cow keeping more profitable, and result in more cows and more beef production.

There are dangers, recognised in South America, that meatless days might benefit rich consumers more than poor ones. Wealthy consumers are better placed to finance the purchase of several days meat in advance on the selling days and to draw on stocks during the nonselling days. They can also better afford refrigerators to store meat bought on the selling days for use on meatless days. The Peruvian tactic of having two consecutive meatless weeks deals with this difficulty in part, (Anon 1972) though even here wealthy consumers able to afford freezers and to buy two weeks' supply in advance have an advantage over poor consumers who must buy on a day to day basis, because of inadequate funds to finance larger purchases and because of inadequate storage. A more formal system of rationing might be more effective in getting a more equitable distribution of meat at a low price, though here again administering a formal rationing system would be a serious imposition on South America's limited administrative capacity.

Export restrictions on beef and live cattle may also be justified on the same grounds as meatless days. Unrestricted exports, while maximising foreign exchange earnings in the short term, may result in lower beef output and less foreign exchange earnings in the longer run.

Policy options

Part A: institutions as a datum

The obvious difficulties of South America's cattle industry — low cow fertility, high calf mortality, slow maturation and, reflecting these, low cattle productivity — are seen as stemming from deep seated structural weaknesses. These include the land tenure system, the unimproved quality of the land, the poverty of the people and their rapid increase in numbers, and political instability that is, to an extent at least, related to high meat prices. Simplistic measures, like feeding breeding cows better to increase fertility and feeding young cattle better to reduce calf mortality rates, are more likely to aggravate than to relieve a difficult situation. Normally approaches of this nature involve the use of scarce resources to increase the supply of young cattle, which is already excessive in relation to the demand for them.

The present problems of the cattle industry, being rooted in South America's underdevelopment, are unlikely to be resolved until the more fundamental, causal problem of underdevelopment is resolved. The economic development of South America is, to a large extent, both a necessary and a sufficient condition for the development of the continent's cattle industry; and that economic development, it is held here, is contingent upon institutional change to achieve more efficient land use. It would, however, be unduly pessimistic to suggest that improvements in cattle production must await institutional change of a fundamental nature and overall economic development. This part of this section is concerned with measures that can be taken to increase cattle production within existing institutional and overall economic limitations.

Operating on WG

An increase in the fattening rate, such that a given value at slaughter, VFA, is reached at a lower age, θ, will have consequences as illustrated by Table 8.9. It will become profitable to use more variable inputs and to retain more heifers for breeding. The fattening rate can be expedited (a) by the more effective use of South America's limiting cattle fattening facilities, and (b) by expanding those facilities.

Existing cattle fattening facilities can be used more effectively by more specialisation in cattle production according to land quality. Good land has a comparative advantage for fattening and poor land has a comparative advantage for breeding and rearing. Increased total output can be achieved by restricting breeding and rearing to poor land and using good land exclusively for fattening. The point can be illustrated arithmetically.

Assume that there are two ranches, A and B; two cattle over one year have the same grazing requirements as one cow; calves less than one year have insignificant grazing requirements. Operating as separate, integrated firms, the ranches have the following carrying capacity (all cattle being assumed sold for slaughter at a uniform weight):

	Ranch A	Ranch B
Cows	100	142
Calves	60	71
Cattle 1 to 2 years	60	71
Cattle 2 to 3 years	60	71
Cattle 3 to 4 years		/1
Cattle 4 to 5 years		71
Cattle 5 to 6 years		71
Total cattle, exclusive of calves	220	497
Cow equivalent	160	320

Total annual output of fat cattle: 131.

If the two ranches join forces, B specialising in breeding/rearing and A in fattening, their stocking and output would be:

	Ranch A	Ranch B
Cows	—	320
Calves	—	160
Cattle 1 to 2 years	160	—
Cattle 2 to 3 years	160	—
Total cattle exclusive of calves	320	320
Cow equivalent	160	320

Total annual output of fat cattle: 160

Annual output is increased from 131 to 160 fat cattle using the same resources but with each class of land specialising on that use for which it is most productive. Specialisation of this nature is the rule on cattle producing farms: the best land is reserved for fattening purposes; the next best for milking cows; and the poorest for growing cattle. But the intrafarm scope for such specialisation is very limited by comparison with the scope for interfarm specialisation. There appears to be at the official level and among the agencies operating in the cattle industry in South America a prejudice against interfarm specialisation in cattle production. For example, IBRD cattle projects normally envisage integrated cattle breeding, rearing and fattening enterprises.[20] The reasons are varied though ill defined. Fear is expressed that one or other party will suffer from specialisation — probably the breeder, who is already poorly off. There is fear that specialisation will benefit only middlemen who will, through it, be able to bleed the industry and consumers. There is fear that movement of cattle between farms will spread disease, and fear that specialisation will lead to unbalanced growth in the short term, and so greater instability and slower growth in the long term. There is fear that the values created by trade are "false values", in some way inferior to the "real values" created by the integrated breeding, rearing and fattening of cattle. Preoccupation with these and similar fears arise from a failure to appreciate the overwhelming importance of "the division of labour" in economic development.

The key development role of communications and transport that make specialisation possible is recognised. A very imperfect marketing system for cattle, especially at the preslaughter stage, raises the transaction cost of trade, hinders specialisation and reduces the fattening rate. Specialisation in cattle production can be achieved by reducing existing impediments and discouragements to cattle trading, fairs and markets. The encouragement of cattle auction marts would be especially conducive to increasing specialisation in production, because marts reduce the disadvantages of the farmer, who rarely buys or sells cattle, vis-à-vis the cattle dealer, who buys and sells daily.

Public intervention is likely to be needed to pioneer cattle auction marts. Their cooperative establishment by cattle owners can easily be undermined by established traders offering the cooperative leaders favourable terms to revert to the established trading system. The establishment of a pioneer cattle mart as a commercial venture is risk laden, without prospect of reward: if the venture is profitable, imitation will reduce returns to the normal level, leaving no reward for risk taking.

The development of auction marts for cattle would also increase the liquidity of cattle of all ages and sizes, by creating a ready market for them at publicised prices. Increased liquidity would make the financing of cattle production at all stages easier than at present, by making it easier to raise credit on the security of cattle held. It is difficult, if not impossible, at present to borrow on the free market to purchase cattle other than cattle near to slaughter, which have a fairly high liquidity. A well run system of cattle marts would confer the same degree of liquidity on cattle of all ages and sizes.

Efficiently operated, well supported cattle marts and fairs, so far from being sources of infection for cattle, could be made into an important part of the disease control system in South America. The display of cattle at marts and fairs could be made conditional on the production of acceptable evidence that required preventive or control measures for diseases or pests had been taken with the cattle. The more efficiently operated and the more highly developed cattle marts and fairs become, the more eager will cattle owners be to use them. The more eager cattle owners become to use cattle marts and fairs, the more stringent the standards pertaining to disease and pest controls which it will be possible to impose as a condition of displaying cattle.

---

20. IBRD cattle projects frequently envisage the purchase of feeder cattle during the "development stage", but normally not afterwards. This is reflected in the Bank's computer programme for simulating herd expansion. "After the development period, the number of animals produced internally equals the carrying capacity, but during development the ranch's capacity may exceed the number of animals produced internally" (IBRD 1972 p. 2.11).

Expanding fattening facilities

It has been suggested above that "other" resources committed by governments to cattle production should be directed to fattening rather than breeding or rearing. An expansion in fattening facilities would increase the present inadequate demand for young cattle and make it profitable to produce more of these.

Probably the quickest, easiest and most profitable way to improve fattening facilities is by improving the better pastures through the usual techniques of better fencing, stock watering and fertilising. The improvements are more likely to be successful if carried out on the better land, where returns are normally better than on poor land, and if the improved pastures are used exclusively for fattening. Much of the benefits will be lost if the improved pastures are used to carry suckling cows and growing young cattle, for which there already exists adequate capacity on the poorer, unimproved pastures.

An expansion of fattening facilities that included the use of high cost feeds might be profitable despite the low meat/feed price ratio that obtains in South America, as in LDCs generally. The meat/grain price ratio is the basic determinant of the profitability of commercial pig/poultry meat production. The relevant relationship in cattle fattening is not the ratio between the price per unit weight of cattle and the price per unit weight of feed; it is the ratio between the value of an incremental unit weight of cattle and the cost of feed. Thus if a 500 kg fat animal is worth 1000 units of account in a DC and the cost of a 300 kg "store" animal is 750 u.o.a (or 25% per kg more than the fat animal), the relevant output criterion for the fattening process is not the average value of 200 u.o.a. per 100 kg, but the marginal value of 125 u.o.a. per 100 kg of added weight. If an animal of similar weight in an LDC is worth 500 u.o.a., or half the current DC value, and the cost of a 300 kg "store" is 225 u.o.a. (or 25% less per kg than the fat animal), the value added per 100 kg is 137.5 u.o.a. If the absolute cost of feed for fattening is the same in the DC as in the LDC, fattening cattle will pay better in the LDC than in the DC, even though the price of fat cattle is only half as high in the former. The average price of fat cattle overstates the costs that can be profitably incurred in fattening cattle in DCs and understates these costs in LDCs, because of the "store" cattle price factor. As noted in Chapter 4, the price per unit weight of immature cattle is lower than that of fat cattle in LDCs and it is higher in DCs. The low cost of "store" cattle in South America makes cattle fattening profitable at a lower beef/feed price ratio than would be the case in DCs.

Operating on I

Cattle are capital that generates flows of milk, meat, other commodities and services. Emphasis has been placed on capital shortage as the chief constraint on cattle production in South America. Relieving that shortage and reducing the rate of time discount, I, are matters largely of general economic development, to be dealt with in the following Part B of this Section. There are, nevertheless, steps that can be taken in relation to the cattle industry to enable it to contribute more effectively to welfare, within existing capital constraints.

The cost of capital to the industry, I, can be lowered by remedying administrative defects that increase the degree of arbitrariness or uncertainty affecting the industry or that divert capital from cattle production to less productive outlets; or that divert capital from more profitable to less profitable forms of cattle production. Action of this nature will benefit cattle production on two accounts: directly by reducing I for the industry; and indirectly by fostering, through an expanded cattle industry, economic growth in South America that will further reduce I for the industry.

Uncertainty could be reduced by the more ready availability of more and better information pertaining to the industry. Uncertainty exists because of the absence in much of South America of elementary, reasonably reliable statistics pertaining to the livestock industry. Because of this people are uncertain whether they should buy or sell cattle; they have little idea whether more or fewer cattle, at lower or higher prices, will be on offer on the market in the near future. This raises I.

This type of uncertainty can be reduced by the provision of better, more reliable information. Little is required for this but a concern to establish the truth through the systematic collection, collation and prompt publication of statistics. Sampling techniques developed for counting cattle and wildlife from the air may have relevance in South America for the regular provision of low cost, reasonably accurate, up to date estimates of cattle stocks (Adams & Wilson, unpublished work, presented at the International Institute for Aerial Survey and Earth Science Symposium, Netherlands, 1976).

Arbitrary action by governments in relation to the industry is a hazard in South America that raises I. Arbitrary action, to limit meat exports or imports, to control or to subsidise meat prices, to assist or to penalise specific actions, and so on, is due, in part, to an inadequate understanding by governments and their advisors of the economics of meat production. This, in turn, to a large extent, appears to be due to a lack of basic data, necessary for rational policy making. Sounder, less arbitrary policy decisions can be made with the help of skilled interpretations of appropriate statistics that show the probable effects of contemplated actions or omissions.

Reducing I, the effective rate of interest, is slow, complex, difficult and unspectacular. That it is so reflects the complexity of achieving economic development under the circumstances that obtain in South America. It is a delusion to imagine that the process can be aided, much less accelerated, by economically ill conceived, spectacular measures of jungle clearance, or of fencing large tracts of worthless range lands.

An important gap remains notwithstanding the great multiplicity of credit institutions in South America. It is a common, though undocumented, phenomenon in South America for farmers to borrow funds to finance cattle fattening from individuals of their acquaintance. The usual procedure is for the financier to buy the "store" cattle, and to divide the gross margin between buying and selling prices in an agreed proportion, determined, among other factors, by the quality of the grazier's land, his creditworthiness and the current, local availability of capital. These transactions are carried out under more or less free market conditions, effective interest rates paid being such as to equate the supply and the demand of loanable funds. The transactions appear to be mutually beneficial to lenders and borrowers. The imputed interest rates are substantially higher than the preferential rates charged by the official lending agencies, that are, however, normally only available for breeding and rearing operations. Transactions observed by the writer at cattle markets in Colombia in 1972 implied interest rates in the region of 50% per annum. Financiers received more if actual performance was better than expected, and less if it was worse. Producers prefer to pay high interest rates for finance for profitable fattening than to pay concessionary, low rates for unprofitable breeding/rearing.

These informal transactions are limited, on the one hand to cattle producers acquainted with persons who have loanable funds, and on the other hand to lenders who are acquainted with cattle producers who require funds. It would be surprising if there were not many cattle producers and many holders of loanable funds in South America who do not fit either of these categories, who indeed are likely to constitute a very small minority. That is to say, despite the existing plethora of agricultural credit institutions, there appears to be scope for one to act as broker between cattle producers who wish to borrow, and fund holders who are prepared to lend, with supply and demand determining the rate of interest.

The type of institution envisaged would not at all be concerned with providing low cost capital — which almost guarantees its wasteful use in South America where capital is scarce and expensive. Its purpose rather would be to facilitate those cattle producers who wish to borrow to obtain funds at the lowest rate at which fund holders are prepared to lend these; and to facilitate savers to find outlets for their funds at the highest interest rates that creditworthy borrowers are prepared to pay. The institution would use, in a systematic fashion, those skills and judgements that lenders and borrowers now operating on this market must possess if they are to make profits rather than incur losses. It would be surprising if such an institution, efficiently operated, did not increase the supply of capital to the industry, at rates of interest lower than those that now effectively obtain. The institution envisaged might be expected to mobilize for livestock production funds that now are used for other, less productive purposes because their owners have no way of directing them into high-yielding livestock ventures. It might also be expected to generate new savings by offering to the public more attractive returns on these savings than those now easily available.

Operating on Pc

Capacity to produce young cattle is abundant; there is a firm demand for fat cattle. The limiting factor in South American cattle production is capacity to fatten young cattle. Calf values, Pc, as a result are only 3–4% of the value of fat cattle, compared to 25–35% of the value of fat cattle in DCs. It is more profitable, because of the low value of young cattle, to eat, than to breed, female cattle.

South America has little foreseeable prospect of expanding cattle fattening facilities or of reducing the cost of capital, sufficiently to raise the price of young cattle substantially relative to the price of fat cattle — that is to say, to increase Pc relative to VFA. In the absence of a substantial increase in Pc/VFA, it will continue to be more profitable to eat than to breed heifers; cattle production will continue to lag and South America's extensive range areas will continue to fail to make a worthwhile contribution to welfare. Given the key role of the Pc/VFA relationship and South America's inability, for cogent structural reasons, materially to alter this relationship it is appropriate to consider the feasibility of raising Pc through an export trade in calves and young cattle.

Fig. 8.2   Young mature cattle trades

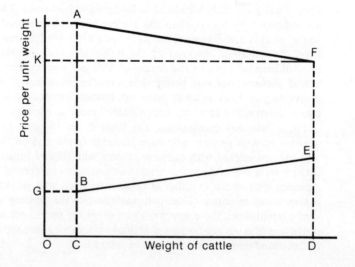

It has been seen (Chapter 7) that in the process of economic development, the cost of calves, or Pc, has in DCs become an increasingly important element in the cost of beef production; Pc can be expected to rise towards VFA/2. Conditions of under-development in South America and especially the problem of raising capital stocks in line with a rapidly growing population, cause Pc/VFA values there to be low. It is a situation where, a priori, the benefits of trade are likely to be substantial.

Let AF and BE in Fig. 8.2 represent the price per kg of cattle of different weights in DCs and in South America respectively. The price per unit weight, as the weight of cattle increases, declines in DCs and increases in South America for reasons already discussed. The potential benefits of a trade in fat cattle, or beef, from South America to DCs is FE. If the transfer could be effected without cost, the value of fat cattle in the Region would rise proportionately by FE/ED. The potential benefits from a trade in young cattle are greater: AB/BC. As between the two trades and abstracting from transport and other costs, a trade in young cattle is potentially more beneficial than one in fat cattle or beef as AB.ED/BC.EF.

The obstacles to a trade in young cattle from LDCs to DCs are discussed in Chapter 12. Here it is assumed that the obstacles can be overcome and that the effect of a trade is to raise the value of young cattle relative to the value of mature cattle in South America.

The effect of a trade that raises the value of young cattle, or Y, relative to the value of mature cattle, VFA, can be analyzed with the model on p. 99. The greater the increase in Y relative to VFA, the greater the increase in variable costs that is warranted. The increase in PvV_3 warranted over those given in Table 8.9 are shown for different values of I and θ in Table 8.10.

Table 8.10   Percentage increase in PvV_3 warranted by a 50% increase in Y, the value of yearling cattle, VFA unchanged.

I	$\theta = 5$	$\theta = 6$	$\theta = 7$
1.15	64	39	19
1.20	111	72	40
1.25	362	261	184

Source: See text.

The proportionate increases in variable inputs warranted for a given proportionate increase in the value of young relative to mature cattle are high for the rates of time discount believed to obtain in South America.

Part B: institutions variable

Need for change

Part A of this Section has been concerned to identify ways, within the existing socio-politico-economic framework, to expand cattle production. Here is raised the more fundamental question of the contribution a more profitable, expanding cattle industry would make to South American wellbeing.

Given existing institutional conditions, an increase in the profitability and output of cattle would be unlikely to cause total agricultural output to increase, or to alleviate poverty, or to contribute to political stability and moderation. There are two reasons for suggesting this. First, an increase in the profitability of cattle, while initially leading to expanded cattle output, would also result in a shift of land to cattle from other activities with a higher gross output (p. 92). The increase in output from land now idle and from land used for cattle production, could exceed, or could fall short of, the decline in output from land diverted from crops to cattle.

Second, and probably more important in the long run, is the paradox of property: the more valuable it becomes, the less efficiently is it likely to be used. A more prosperous cattle industry would make land more valuable, while tending to depress wages as land is transferred from labour intensive crops to labour extensive cattle. It will be made easier for inefficient rentier landowners to continue in possession, taking some, or all, of the increased value of land in the form of increased leisure, security, and resistance to innovation. It will simultaneously be more difficult for the young and landless, who can use land most efficiently, to acquire land as its price rises and their incomes decline. The smaller amount of land reaching the market, as pressures to sell are relaxed, will be bought by the old with much land, and therefore savings or credit to buy more, though they can make little use of it, other than to hold as its value appreciates. A more prosperous cattle industry would accentuate the fundamental difference in capitalism south of the Rio Grande, and north of it and in Europe from the Dark Ages. A prosperous cattle industry would make access to land more difficult for labour and capital, as land grants to *conquistadores* have done in the past.

Striking parallels make the Irish experience seem relevant. Ireland, like the Americas but unlike the rest of the Old World, was possessed by the European capitalist colonialists. Its pastoral people, unlike the hunters of the New World, were not exterminated, but were incorporated into the colonial regime, like the Mezzo-American Indians. An ascendancy class, in both cases, dominated the conquered, indigenous people and exploited them in the interests of the metropolitan country. Race distinguished the Iberian ascendancy and Creoles from the indigenous Indians in the one case; religion distinguished the English, Protestant ascendancy from the indigenous Catholic Irish in the other case.

Irish cattle prices have risen continuously relative to most other prices since the beginning of the 19th century. Specifically, the beef/wheat price ratio has risen from about 2 : 1 to just 11 : 1 (Table 4.6). This has caused a more or less continuous shift of land from crop growing, where output per acre is high, to cattle, where output per acre is low. The net result has been that the volume of Irish agricultural output has remained virtually static for 150 years (Crotty 1966 p.220).

If substantial increases in the profitability and output of South America's cattle industry, attainable within the existing institutional framework, are unlikely to increase agricultural output, and if increased agricultural output is required, then it becomes necessary to consider the institutional framework. It has been contended here that Latin America's land tenure system has been instrumental in preventing the sort of development that has taken place north of the Rio Grande and in western Europe during the past four and a half centuries. Precluding an efficient agriculture the land tenure system causes excessive land to be used wastefully for cattle production. The more efficient mobilisation of the continent's cattle potential, so far from lessening would heighten the need for adaptation of the tenure system.

Extending ownership

Not all changes in the land tenure system are likely to increase agricultural output. The view taken here is that collectivist type changes are unlikely to do so. Communist collectivism has been coercive and inefficient, whilst cooperative collectivism has been utopian and inefficient. Soviet Russia's agriculture has been as unsuccessful as South America's, and agriculture does not appear to have progressed much in Guyana since the foundation there of the Guyana Cooperative Republic.[21] The tenure change

21. Production of cereals has been expanding at one third, and of sugarcane at less than one half the South American rate, in Guyana, where these enterprises account for most of the country's agricultural output (FAO 1977a pp. 89, 161).

envisaged here are those aimed at giving "land to the tiller", whether by increasing the security and reducing the rents of tenants, or by redistributing land from latifundia owners to peons.

The indicated tenure changes would probably decrease political instability in rural South America and they might lead to some increased agricultural output. They would, however, fall far short of reproducing the key relationship between land, labour and capital that has existed in western Europe since the Dark Ages and in North America since Columbus; that is, a low value of the occupier's interest relative to the value of labour and capital. Agriculture would therefore continue inefficient, with low output, and the economy would retain its dependent character.

Here again, the Irish experience seems relevant. One of the most thoroughgoing changes in land tenure systems was executed in Ireland a century ago; tenants were made owners of the land they worked, subject to payment of very moderate annuities. The reform was administered with a competence and honesty that would be difficult to equal. Had South American agriculture, without tenure reform, performed as badly during the past century as Irish agriculture has, with tenure reform, South American poverty would be far worse than it is.[22] Tenure change that widens the base of privileged access to land broadens political support for the system, but does not rectify its economic defect of securing land for those who are not competent to operate it and of excluding from it those who are.

There are cogent political reasons in capitalist societies, and in more traditional societies influenced by capitalist colonialism, for broadening the land ownership base. Large numbers of persons with proprietorial interests in land are a conservative influence in political situations of great change and instability. Broadening the base of landed proprietorship also has appeal in that it implies a move away from an obviously inequitable monopoly of natural resources by an oligarchy. Finally, equity appears to walk hand in hand with efficiency in that family farms are at least no less efficient than large farms, while the western European and North American family farm has contributed notably to the dominant position these regions have in the world economy.

These political, equity and economic attractions of a broad based landed proprietorship are more short term than long term, more apparent than real. The political disadvantages of creating one in Ireland were long concealed by the emigration of every second person born there; but with the recent blocking of traditional emigrant flows and the consequent build-up of the casualties of "tenure reform", Ireland now experiences, per square mile of territory or per 1000 population, more political violence than South America.[23] The inequity of tenants paying rack rents to landowners is obvious; less obvious but more inequitable is the situation of that rapidly increasing proportion of the world's population who missed out in the allocation of proprietorial rights in land, and who, in increasing hundreds of millions all over the world, can no longer get land on any terms, because peasant proprietors do not lease land, and because landlords are reluctant to accept tenants whom the law might convert into owners. Though small landowners are protected from competitive forces by a smaller proprietorial interest than large ones, their incentive to retain land they cannot work effectively increases as the condition of the landless deteriorates. They are also more likely than large landowners to attempt themselves to operate their land inefficiently than to lease it at rack rents to efficient operators. The chance of the efficient landless

---

22. See Crotty 1966 Chapter 4, on the effect of land reform in Ireland. If South American agricultural production had not increased for the past 150 years, like Ireland's, its population, which has increased almost 25 fold meanwhile, would now be starving.
23. The equivalent of Ireland's annual average of 40 sectarian assassinations per million population would, in South America with a population of 200 million, be 8000 politico-economic assassinations annually.

acquiring land to work effectively declines as ownership of land becomes more diffused and less of it is leased at rack rents, and their poverty deepens. Broadening the base of landed proprietorship, like so many policy measures that seek simultaneously to achieve a variety of ends, advances neither the cause of equity nor efficiency; nor, in the long run, is it likely to reduce political instability.

Land use and development

The common, underlying characteristic of economic undevelopment is a poor endowment of capital per person that, for many reasons, has an inherent tendency to perpetuate itself. The land/labour ratio of LDCs is much less unfavourable than the capital/labour ratio. Using GNP as a proxy for capital stocks, per caput GNP in North America is US$4500 and in South America $800. There are 1.9 ha in North America and 2.3 ha in South America of agricultural land per person (Appendix A). Per person in North America, GNP is 5.4 times as great, but agricultural land is only 0.8 times as great, as in South America. It is critically important for LDCs, if they are to offset their inherently self-perpetuating relative weakness in capital stock, to use their relatively abundant land efficiently.

The most important condition for efficient land use is that the user be efficient. Allocating land to, or securing its possession by, people who are poor, old, widowed, blind or physically handicapped will almost certainly ensure its inefficient use. Only if land is allocated to the efficient can LDCs hope to produce the goods and services to relieve the poverty ubiquitous in them. The necessary and sufficient condition for land to go to the efficient is that land users should pay the market price for its use. That price is most accurately reflected by rack, or competitive, rents.

Exaction of the market price for land's use requires the appropriation of this price by the State. Failure to appropriate results in proprietorial rights in land, held either by its immediate users, or by superior landlord interests. Land in either case, because of the paradox of property, will be inefficiently used. If the market price is unappropriated, users will use land inefficiently, or landlords will lease it to inefficient users.

Exaction of land's market value will ensure efficient land use, and therefore an abundant supply of purchasable goods. It will also provide the State with resource to pursue other objectives, including equity. A land tax revenue can relieve poverty giving to the weak or infirm money to buy consumer goods, instead of land to produce them. A land tax makes it possible to give land to the efficient and money to the poor.

Efficient use of land, with which LDCs are relatively well endowed, can help to redress the disadvantages that they now suffer from an inadequacy of capital coupled with inefficient land use. Efficient land use makes three major contributions to non-agricultural growth: first, by supplying the non-agricultural and export sectors with abundant, low cost food and raw materials; second, by creating, through domestic sales and exports, a buoyant agricultural sector demand for the products of the non-agricultural sectors; and third, by the revenue from a land tax, that if maximised is the necessary and sufficient condition for efficient land use, making possible lower taxes on labour and capital.

The case for taxing land in LDCs is overwhelming and incontrovertible. Yet land is taxed nominally, or not at all, in LDCs.[24] The reasons appear to be twofold: first, owners, who are powerful, oppose it; second, social scientists ignore it. The opposition of owners is self-explanatory; its neglect by social scientists may be attributable to the sociology of social scientists.

The vast majority of social scientists are urban born and based. This can be partly

---

24. See Bird 1974, for a review of the subject.

accounted for by the preponderance of urban populations in DCs, that have most of the social scientists. The preponderant agricultural populations of LDCs produce few social scientists, partly because poorer, remoter LDC populations produce disproportionately few higher educated persons; and partly because persons of rural origin in LDCs who receive a higher education usually opt for professional-type training, leaving the more academic, liberal, social sciences to less mundane, urban scholars. Social scientists, as a result, have a preponderantly DC and urban perspective.

Efficient land use was, and is, not a DC problem. This, in the past, was because of those circumstances discussed in Chapter 3, or referred to already in this chapter, that caused land values to be low relative to incomes in western Europe and North America, thus avoiding the paradox of property that causes valuable land to be used inefficiently. DCs now characteristically have low population growth rates and low income elasticities of demand for land intensive food. Moreover, with their commanding economic power, they can easily obtain from LDCs the food they lack. Agricultural land, as a result, continues to be of relatively low economic importance in DCs, where the preoccupation is with its equitable, rather than its efficient, use. The USA has a "land bank" and the EEC aims to create one, in order to reduce food production and to raise lagging agricultural incomes (USDA ERS 1969; ECC 1968 pp.41–3).

These DC considerations underlie the approaches of policy makers to land tenure in LDCs. Typically, their preoccupation is with the more equitable allocation of land (e.g. Lipton 1974 p.270). This preoccupation suggests, at the limit, equal shares in land for all, adjusting quantity for quality in some indefinable way. This equitable allocation would be efficient if everyone had an equal ability to operate land, which is patently not so. Men, on the whole, are likely to operate it more effectively than women; people in their prime will operate it better than young or old people; people skilled in farming will operate it better than unskilled people; people with a high preference for surplus and a low preference for leisure, security and stability are also likely to operate it more productively than others. An allocation of land that even approximately satisfies the norms of equity, that are the preoccupation of social scientists concerned with land tenure in LDCs, is likely to be highly inefficient. Inefficient land use in LDCs, that lack capital and have rapid population growth, is a prescription for the disaster that threatens many and that has overwhelmed some.

Social scientists, coming mainly from DCs, have, for the most part, a superficial understanding of farming, of the relationship between people who live by cultivating land and that land. Knowledge of farming is limited, in the case of the vast majority of social scientists, to what they read, and what they read is normally what has been written by other social scientists. A minority of social scientists inform themselves better of these matters by observing farmers. Hardly any social scientists have acquired the understanding of farming that comes with the merchant's returns, showing that, deducting the cost of crop inputs, a balance of debt remains due after a season; or that comes when the last shovelful of earth has been replaced on the grave of a promising cow, or of a bullock that pined instead of fattening. Hardly any social scientists have experienced, or are members of families that have experienced, these moments of truth that illuminate the unspannable gap between farming practice and academic theory.

The inadequacy of social scientists' understanding of farming matters and their DC perceptions are perhaps most clearly illustrated by their neglect of the institutionalisation of the efficient allocation of land among users. Their preoccupation is with measures to undo the harm done by an inefficient allocation of land: with high farm product prices or low farm input costs, with extension services, with credit, etc., to induce inefficient persons to use efficiently that share of society's land that they control.

Conclusion

The predominance firstly of cattle farming and, secondly, of inefficient cattle farming in South America are seen as reflecting a socially inefficient land tenure system that is the result of the peculiar manner in which capitalist colonialism intruded on South America. The land tenure system precludes efficient land use and, therefore, economic development. Increased cattle output is attainable within the present tenure system, mainly by improving the inadequate demand for young cattle. Any improvement effected, however, is unlikely to increase total agricultural output, that will continue to be low, costly, and therefore, to preclude economic development. Maximising net land tax revenue is seen as the necessary and sufficient condition for efficient use of South America's land resources, that are abundant relative to its capital stock. Efficient land use, including an appropriate allocation between cattle and other enterprises, is seen as a precondition for economic development and political stability.

The African Case: Cattle Grazed Communally; Milk and Calves Have Value

Introduction

This chapter deals with what is perceived to be classical, traditional pastoralism. It is a form of husbandry in which people are dependent mainly on livestock that normally graze on communal pastures. It is, as noted in Chapter 3, the oldest form of production after hunting and gathering. It occurs widely in more or less traditional form. There are in western Europe areas like the Scottish Highlands where people derive their living mainly from sheep grazed communally on hillsides. Similar groups exist on the Altiplano in South America, and others occur in South West Asia (e.g. Bowman 1916 pp.45–7, Barth 1964). Africa, however, is the continent most closely associated with traditional pastoralism. Its culture and institutions appear to be most influenced by that form of production.

Data quoted presently illustrate Africa's exceptional dependence on pastoralism. But that dependence, though exceptional, is not universal within Africa. Chapter 3 referred to the widespread incidence of lactose intolerance in Africa, indicating a long established independence of pastoral products. The inhabitants of the great tropical rainforests, of the crop bearing volcanic soils of Mount Kilimanjaro and of the Nile valley, have traditionally depended little on grazing livestock. The observations that follow do not hold for these and other groups within Africa who are not pastoralists.[1]

Africa is the poorest of the continents. GNP per caput is $292 compared to $414 for Asia, the next poorest continent, and $1239 for the world as a whole. Population is growing one and a half times as rapidly as the world's population (Tables 9.1 and 9.2).

Table 9.1 Percentage of the world's total accounted for by Africa

Population	10.2
GNP	2.4
Arable	14.3
Grassland	26.4
Cattle	12.6
Beef	5.4
Total meat	4.1
Milk	2.6
Cereal + pulses	5.3

See Appendix A.

The continent, with one tenth of the world's population, has one quarter of its grassland and one eighth of its cattle. Per acre, beef production is one fifth and milk production is one tenth the world average. Per head of cattle, African beef production is two fifths and its milk production is one fifth the world average. Though cropland per person is above the world average, African output per head of cereals and pulses is only half the world average, and only three quarters the Asian average.

---

1. See Simoons 1973, especially map on p. 594, for an indication of the prevalence of nonpastoralist societies in Africa.

Table 9.2   World and Africa growth rates (%), 1961–5 to 1974.

	World	Africa
Population	21	30
Cattle stocks	19	12
Beef production	35	17
Milk production	20	29
Total meat	40	22

See FAO 1977a.

Cattle stocks are growing less rapidly than in the world as a whole (Table 9.2). Beef and milk production are both expanding faster than cattle stocks so that production per animal, though very low, is reportedly increasing slightly. Beef and total meat production per head of population, which is already very low, is declining. Milk production, however, is reportedly keeping abreast of population.

The Cultural and Institutional Background[2]

Traditional pastoral society manifests three distinctive characteristics that are especially important from the point of view of economic analysis. These are: first, a general acceptance of all pastoral products unqualified by such reservations as the rejection of milk by lactose-intolerant crop growers, or the rejection of beef by cow worshipping Indians; second, a preference for livestock as an asset to hold, comparable to money in other societies; and third, the communal grazing of stock. This third characteristic was shared by all owners of grazing livestock in the Old World prior to the evolution of capitalism (Chapter 3). It continues to be the normal grazing system throughout the Old World, apart from Europe. Concepts of property, less well defined than those of western society, are also an economically important characteristic of traditional pastoral society. An economic basis for this difference in attitude to property has been suggested above (Table 3.1).

The survival in Africa to an exceptional extent of traditional pastoralism appears to be due mainly to the nature of that continent's resource endowment. Its principal rivers, apart from the Nile, are located in the equatorial rainforest belt, an insalubrious environment that precluded dense population until the introduction of modern preventive medicine. The Nile itself flows through desert that restricts cultivation to a riverine strip. Pastoralism dominated most of the continent, other than the forested areas, where trypanosomiosis excluded cattle. Crop growing was confined, for the most part, to narrowly circumscribed, favoured locations like the volcanic soil of Mount Kilimanjaro and the Nile valley, or to the rainforest, where an unproductive slash and burn husbandry was practised (e.g. Kottak 1972, Simoons 1973).

Not only was Africa less favoured in its river systems than India or China, but also because of the Sahara buffer, it interacted less with Mediterranean crop growing than did Europe. The Roman legions were restricted to Africa's northern coast where they penetrated to the heart of Europe, taking there the seeds at least of crop based culture. It is unlikely, even if Africa had been as well impregnated with Mediterranean

2. This section is based on secondary sources, including the following: Davidson (1974) Dyson-Hudson (1966), Evans-Pritchard (1940), Gulliver (1955), Monod (1975), and Rigby (1969). More recent publications have been Dahl & Hjort (1976); and Konczacki (1978) The above contain extensive lists of works cited, which have been supplemented by the bibliography on "Livestock Production and Range Management in Tropical Africa", in a mimeograph, by the International Livestock Centre for Africa (1975).

concepts of law and property, that they would have blossomed as they did in Europe where it has been argued (Chapter 3) that the combination of forest and cattle, in the presence of the catalyst of Mediterranean culture, provided an uniquely favourable milieu for the transformation of tribal pastoralism into capitalist crop production. No similar miracle of societal interaction occurred in Africa.

Demand for cattle products

A wide diffusion of cattle ownership implies a good demand for milk and beef as subsistence foods for cattle owners and their families. Though production may be rarely geared for the market, milk is required and relished by the cattle owners and beef is an important if irregular item of diet. The wheat-relative prices for beef and milk in Africa are, respectively, 485 and 95 (Table 4.1). These relatively high wheat-relative prices for cattle products in Africa are the more remarkable in view of Africa's very low incomes and the very poor availability of grain there. Blood, urine and dung are outputs of cattle also valued by Africans, the first as a food, the second for ablutions and the third as a fuel.[3] Account must be taken of their value in the analysis.

Cattle as cash

Anthropologists and sociologists emphasise the many roles of cattle in African pastoral society.[4] Their role as money does not exclude other roles, but rather fits them the better to fill these also. The borrowing and loaning of cattle, or *mafista*, is seen as — inter alia — a means of cementing friendships. That the cattle in question have, in addition to the normal capacity to produce milk, calves, blood, etc., the quality of being money, adds to, and does not detract from, their friendship-creating capacity.

Cattle have important advantages as money in a predominantly pastoral society. They are directly useful, as sources of milk, blood and meat, and do not have to be first converted, like coins, into consumable products, that may not always be available in a vast continent, with poor communications and little commerce. Like money on deposit, they increase and multiply, at little cost or inconvenience to the owner; but unlike currency, they have an inbuilt hedge against inflation. Perhaps of greatest importance to a people who, especially in the past, were frequently and necessarily nomadic, cattle are mobile; while other stores of wealth, including coins, must be transported from place to place, cattle move themselves and can, if necessary, transport other forms of wealth also.[5]

Cattle, on the other hand, have no serious disadvantages for pastoral people that are not shared by other forms of money. Pastoralists are sparsely settled and practise little division of labour. Their trading is, therefore, limited and can be managed without a specialised money form in a manner that would be inefficient and involve loss and inconvenience for a sedentary, crop growing society with a high degree of specialisation and, consequently, much trading.

Cattle, for these reasons, are an attractive asset for pastoralists to hold. This very attractiveness adds an additional element of attractiveness to cattle as an asset: it confers on the holder of cattle in a pastoral society security and status, as money in the bank does in sedentary societies. The use of cattle as cash by African pastoralists reflects, first, the almost universal social need for money; and, second, that, under African conditions, cattle were the most appropriate money form.

3. For reference to use of cattle blood as a food, see, for example, Forde 1934 pp. 295–6; for ablutionary use of cattle urine see, for example, Huntingford 1950 p. 51.
4. See, in addition to those referred to on p. 18 note 2, Schneider 1957, and Vincent 1971 pp. 119–25.
5. See photograph of nomads on the move in Adams & Hales 1977 p. 762.

Communal tenure

Traditional tribal pastoralism has, from early in agricultural history, been excluded from two regions: the equatorial belt, where lush year-round growth either smothers out grasses, or permits the growth only of species with low nutritional value; and the riverine crop growing valleys, where more populous crop growing excludes cattle. Traditional pastoral cattle keeping has, therefore, had to adjust to pronounced seasonal variations in growing conditions — the feast of the wet, or warm, growing season being followed by the famine of the dry, or cold, dormant season. Traditional, tribal pastoralism has not had, as cattle production in Europe and North America has recently had, the benefits of crop byproducts to help animals through dormant seasons.

The principal resort of cattle keepers for dealing with inherently variable fodder supplies has been mobility, shifting stock from pasture to pasture according to season. The degree of mobility required varies inversely with the quality of the resource base. The poorer the resource base and the greater the dependence on pasture, the more mobility is necessary. Pastoralists in the Sahel must range widely to find pasture refreshed by recent rainfall; cattle in Europe may be moved within the same farm boundary, from low lying, marshy pasture in the summer, to higher, better drained pasture in the winter. The principle is the same, but in practice the cattle of the noncapitalist, non crop growing, traditional pastoralist occupying less productive land must be more mobile. Conceivably, a well functioning cattle market could effect the necessary cattle movements; in its absence, cattle owners must retain control of the cattle and of the land the cattle graze throughout the year. This is practical over long distances, as in Africa, if the operating unit is large — that is, if the grazing herds are large and grazing is extensive.

This repeats a point made earlier (Fig. 3.1): that returns to labour in pastoral agriculture decline rapidly. A second person herding 100 cattle will add much less to output than the first, and a third will add much less again. Husbandry activities, like milking and feeding young stock, that yield a high return to labour, can be executed in corrals, where the stock can be handled individually although grazing in large herds. The poor resource base of pastoral societies compels them to produce in the most efficient manner, and that is normally in large units.

Maximum profit from pastoral land is made by employing OT workers at a full maintenance wage, OL, to give an output OTRG, of which OTRL goes on wages and LRG is profit (Fig. 3.1). An owner of pastoral land in a capitalist society would try to operate on these lines. Two questions about such a course of action would occur to an individual in a traditional pastoral society. First, how could he, or any society of which he was a member, retain possession of land with OT people when other societies, competing for possession of the land, supported on a similar area ON or more people, and, therefore, more efficient people (p. 11)? Second, even if the individual could retain possession of the land and its product, what use could he make in a precapitalist, non-trading society, of the surplus, LRG, that would be better than supporting TN followers, who could provide personal services and defence?

The politics of tribal pastoralism required the product to be widely diffused; and if the product was to be widely diffused, control of the producing cattle needed to be diffused. The case for diffusion of control of cattle was the stronger in that there was no countervailing consideration from the point of view of production. The difficulty if not impossibility, of positive disease or breeding control under communal grazing was unimportant; natural selection was the most effective disease control and breeding policy with the existing technology.

Communal grazing of the many small, individually owned herds in the group combined the economically most productive and the politically most stable method of exploiting grazing land by precapitalist pastoralists. It made possible grazing in large units, which minimised effort, while simultaneously it permitted a wide diffusion of livestock assets and grazing product, which minimised social tensions. Communal grazing has been the norm in all parts of the world where cattle and other domesticated grazing species are indigenous, with the exception of capitalist Europe. Individual grazing has existed in Europe, to a greater or less extent, since the establishment there of capitalism. It has been the predominant form of grazing practised in the New World, to which cattle and pastoral farming were introduced by Europe's capitalist colonists.

Property attitudes

The diffused form of cattle ownership in Africa has been observed by many authorities. Typically: "In this connection, ownership of stock must be clearly distinguished from the exercise of certain rights against them. There is a basic 'stock-owning unit' in each tribe — the 'house' in Jieland and the 'nuclear family' in Turkanaland — within which, subject to the privileges of seniority, rights are largely communal and egalitarian, and administered by the head of that unit" (Gulliver 1955 p.247). Reasons given for the diffusion of property interests include the need for owners of large herds to delegate responsibility for the care of some of their animals; the spreading of risk from disease or fodder shortages by locating animals in different places; and cattle's role in fostering and strengthening social relations. Another reason has been suggested above where the difference in the social effects of property in tribal-pastoral and capitalist crop growing societies was noted (Table 3.1). Individually owned property in a traditional pastoral situation yields a product less than the owner receives, and therefore results in a social loss; property in a capitalist society yields a product greater than the owner receives, from which society benefits. This, it has been suggested above and is repeated here, engenders very different social attitudes towards property: capitalism elevates property to the focus of social existence; tribal pastoralism subordinates it to the convenience of persons.

A non-exclusive attitude towards property in cattle is, in any case, a necessary corollary of the diffused control of grazing livestock and diffused enjoyment of their produce. Exclusive, capitalist type property in cattle must, in time, result in concentration of livestock ownership, and therefore in the benefits derived from grazing cattle, that would be impossible to contain within the weak institutional framework of traditional pastoral society.

The Economics of Traditional Pastoral Cattle Production

Cultural and institutional conditions largely determine the values of the exogenous variables relevant to cattle owners' decisions. They also influence the process of decision-making. This section treats of these variables and of the manner in which they determine the form and level of traditional cattle production in Africa.

**xogenous variables:
ice of meat (Pf);
ice of milk (Pm);
st of inputs (Pv);
d rate of time
scount (I).**

The high esteem in which milk and beef are held by pastoralists has been noted, and implies high values for Pm and Pf. Cognisance can be taken of the values of cattle blood, urine and dung by introducing separate terms for these products. Alternatively, and more simply here for expository purposes, these values can be allowed for implicitly by an appropriate upward adjustment of milk and beef values. Labour, being self employed and with little alternative employment, is abundant, low cost and of good quality for tending cattle. The cost of "other" inputs, that are composed largely of labour, is, to that extent, low.

The most distinctive and crucial characteristic of African cattle production is its implicit low value of I. Cattle being cash and therefore a good which, of itself, it is desirable to hold, it is at least conceivable that I may have a value less than one. As liquidity considerations induce people in advanced economies to hold cash instead of interest bearing bonds, traditional African cattle producers may wish to hold cattle even if these yield neither meat nor milk. Further, as people in advanced economies are prepared to hold assets as a hedge against future wants though the current value of the assets is declining, so it is conceivable that Africans, wishing to increase their status in society or to provide against the needs of the future, would hold cattle even though they were losing condition and value. I in such cases would be less than one; a given stock of cattle a year hence would have a present discounted value greater than a similar stock of cattle held now.

Cattle had important advantages as cash in traditional African society. It is not irrational, under changed circumstances, that their traditional cash role should survive, just as gold survives as money in other cultures. And as with gold, cattle can be a better hedge against the depreciation of other forms of money than interest bearing bonds. Given the role of cattle as cash, it is not inconceivable that $I < 1$.

Plate 4   Masai herdsman with cattle in Tanzania (Photo: Colorific)

Endogenous variables: milk (M); calves (C); and weight gain (WG):

The difference for the owner of cattle grazed under individual or communal tenure of pastureland in the relationships between cattle numbers, on the one hand, and milk and calf output and weight gain, on the other hand, has been discussed above (Fig. 5.6 and 5.7). It was seen that the effect of changing stock numbers for cattle owners was to change the output of M,C and WG by an amount equal to the marginal value of these variables when the tenure is individual and by an amount equal to the average values when the tenure is communal. Given conditions of decreasing returns average output is greater than marginal output.

Output of meat and milk per head of cattle is lower in Africa than in the rest of the world (Table 9.1). This lower average output per head of cattle stock in Africa may, however, be as high as, or higher than, the marginal output per head of livestock outside Africa, and for that reason may represent as good, or better, an incentive to increase stock numbers as exists outside Africa.

Similar reasoning applies in the case of calf production. Though the average calving rate in Africa may be lower than elsewhere, the marginal calving rate for the individual cattle owner, though not for society, need not be lower than in the case of individually grazed cattle elsewhere.

The non-slaughter roles of cattle, age at slaughter θ, and the price of calves (Pc):

Cattle in Africa have a value over and above their value for meat. The source of this additional value is readily perceptible in the case of female cattle as their capacity to produce milk and calves. The less perceptible above-slaughter value of male cattle arises from their capacity to produce blood, an important food for some Africans, and from their role as money. Traditional African reluctance to slaughter male cattle, even of mature age, is evidence of this above-slaughter value of cattle. The phenomenon is illustrated and analysed with the help of Fig. 9.1.

Cattle, through their lifespan OD, provide a flow of benefits: blood and monetary liquidity. The value of these services, net of the animal's maintenance cost, is related to the age and size of the animal. An animal's blood producing capacity diminishes to zero at death at age OD. An animal's liquidity value or value as money reflects, in part, its alternative value for slaughter. A prime animal, at age OQ and weight QB, has a greater liquidity value than one aged OP and similar weight PC. FB is greater than GC because of the greater life expectancy, QD, during which the animal can produce blood and act as money. Likewise an animal at birth has a liquidity value which, in proportion to its weight, is greater than its liquidity value at age OQ, because of the longer life expectancy, OD, at birth. That is, OE/OA>QF/QB>PG/PC. If the line OABCD is the path of the animal's weight

Fig. 9.1   Slaughter age in traditional pastoralism

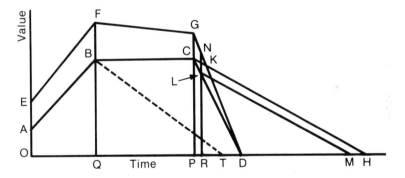

over its life, OD, the line OEFGD may be taken as representing the path of blood and liquidity values, net of the animal's maintenance cost, produced by the animal if held from birth to natural death at age OD. The area OEFGD represents the total of these values produced by the animal in its lifetime, OD.

Live cattle generate flows of blood and act as money. If slaughtered for a communal feast they earn for their owner prestige and debts of gratitude, which may be conceived also as a flow of future benefits, diminishing with time and proportionate to the weight of the slaughtered animal (Gulliver 1955 p.198). QBT represents one such flow of benefits to the owner of an animal slaughtered at age OQ for a communal feast, and weight QB. PCH represents a similar flow for an animal slaughtered at age OP and weight PC. Because PC=QB, PCH=QBT. The cattle owner will attempt to slaughter cattle at a point such that the total of the blood and monetary liquidity benefits and the prestige and gratitude benefits are maximised. Assuming that the blood and monetary liquidity benefits and the prestige and gratitude benefits are on the same scale, he will slaughter at age OR such that the blood and monetary liquidity benefits, OEFGNR, plus the prestige and gratitude benefits, RLM, are a maximum. The animal if it dies at age OD would yield OEFGD blood and monetary liquidity benefits but no prestige and gratitude benefits. If slaughtered at age OP it would yield OEFGP blood and monetary liquidity benefits plus PCH prestige and gratitude benefits, which is DKH − GKC greater than OEFGD. When slaughtered at age OR the animal yields OEFGNR blood and monetary liquidity benefits, and PCH−(PCLR+CHML) prestige and gratitude benefits. The optimum slaughter age is such that the rate of decline in blood and monetary liquidity benefits equals the rate of decline in prestige and gratitude benefits.

There are two consequences. First, it is advantageous for the individual cattle owner to hold cattle until an advanced age, θ, so the number of followers, F, tends to be high. Because the grazing is communal, this does not seriously affect the return per animal owned by the individual, though of course it lowers returns for the community (Fig. 5.6). Second, the price of calves, Pc, tends to be high, not merely because I is low (Equation 5.16), but also because of their role as "young money", that tends to raise their value over and above what it would be as a potential source of meat — that is, from OA to OE in Fig. 9.1.

Net revenue from cattle (NR)

It is recalled that:

$$NR = PmM + PcC - (I^t . Pc + I^{t/2} . PvV_2)K/n - PvV_3 \qquad (5.24)$$

and that NR for the individual cattle owner is influenced by:
K: the number of cows he keeps;
θ: the period for which he keeps non-breeding cattle;
V_1, V_2 and V_3: variable inputs to fattening cattle, heifers being reared and cows, respectively.

Pm, M, Pc and C tend to have high values, and PvV_2 and PvV_3 tend to have low values for reasons suggested in the preceding pages. I has a value possibly below one. NR therefore has a chronic tendency to be positive, encouraging cattle owners to increase the values of the independent variables, K and θ. But increasing K and θ will have little influence on output per head of M, C or on Pc for the individual cattle owner, and there are limits beyond which these variables cannot be increased. The limit for θ is the point D in Fig. 9.1, when male cattle perish; and the limit for K is when all female cattle are bred.

If all female cattle are bred, the value of female, or heifer, calves, Pcf, ceases to be derived from the value of slaughter or draft cattle (Equation 5.16). It is higher, and derives from the value of a new-milched cow (NMC), or a cow calving down for the first time. That is, following the reasoning leading to Equation 5.16, in equilibrium,

$$Pcf = NMC/I^t - PvV_2/I^{t/2} \qquad (9.1)$$

The value of a new-milched cow, NMC, is the capitalised present value of the stream of future values produced by the cow as a breeding and milk producing animal, and its scrap value when finished breeding and milking. Making the simplifying assumptions (that do not substantively affect the argument) that the cow's performance is uniform through its breeding life of n years, and that it has no scrap value, then

$$NMC = AMC/I + AMC/I^2 + \ldots + AMC/I^n \qquad (9.2)$$

where AMC is the value of the gross annual output of a cow, less the cost of direct inputs. The sum of the geometric series gives:

$$NMC = N \cdot AMC \tag{9.3}$$

where

$$N = (I^n - 1)/I^n(I - 1) \tag{9.4}$$

From Equation 5.13:

$$AMC = PmM^* + \tfrac{1}{2}C^*(Pcf + Pcm) - PvV_3^* \tag{9.5}$$

(where the asterisks denote milk and calf output and variable inputs per cow and Pcm is the value of a male calf).

From Equations 9.3 and 9.5, in equilibrium:

$$NMC = N\left[PmM^* + \tfrac{1}{2}C^*(Pcf + Pcm) - PvV_3^*\right] \tag{9.6}$$

From Equation 9.1:

$$NMC = I^t Pcf + I^{t/2} PvV_2 \tag{9.7}$$

From Equations 9.6 and 9.7:

$$I^{t/2} \cdot PvV_2 = N(PmM^* + \tfrac{1}{2}C^* \cdot Pcm - PvV_3) + Pcf(\tfrac{1}{2}NC^* - I^t) \tag{9.8}$$

When $n = 10$ years, N varies with I as follows:

I	N
1.50	0.97
1.05	7.72
1.00	10.00
0.95	13.42
0.80	41.57

Given that:

(i) PvV_3^* is very small and not substantially different from zero;

(ii) $I \leqslant 1$

(iii) $C^* \geqslant 2/n$, or 0.2, so that the herd reproduces itself; then both terms on the right hand side of Equation 9.8 will be positive and

$$PvV_2 \gg PmM^* + \tfrac{1}{2}C^* Pcm \tag{9.9}$$

It follows that equilibrium is reached when the cost of rearing a heifer, PvV_2, equals approximately PmM^*, the value of milk from a cow. The principal component of PvV_2 under these circumstances is, of course, the milk used to rear the heifer calf. So, equilibrium is approached when the amount of milk a cow produces declines towards the amount required to rear a replacement heifer calf.

Most heifers in western Europe and North America are slaughtered at birth (Chapter 5), or for meat without breeding.[6] All heifers normally appear to be bred in Africa. They are more valuable in Africa than males because of their capacity to

---

6. The number of heifers in calf in Ireland is normally only about one tenth of the number of total cattle aged one to two years. This implies that only about one fifth of all heifers reared are mated. Three quarters or more of heifers reared in Ireland are slaughtered without mating, though the proportion varies if the national herd is expanding or contracting (Ireland, Central Statistics Office 1977 pp. 78–9).

breed: "Large sums of money can be obtained for beef cattle only; breeding cows, for instance, are virtually never sold informally and would be 'priceless' if they were".[7] Liveweight market prices of cattle in Djibo, Upper Volta in 1976–77 also reflect the demand for heifers for breeding (Table 4.10).

The relationship between heifer and steer prices in Ireland is the inverse of that in Upper Volta, the explanation being that in Ireland, as in western Europe and North America, heifers are valued for their beefing rather than breeding qualities.[8] Heifers are less satisfactory than steers for beef production. The fact that Pcf has a high value, combined with a low value for I, makes the value of NR higher still, making it still more attractive to breed heifers, causing Pcf to rise still further, causing NR to rise still further, etc.[9]

An economic equilibrium, as defined in Equation 5.25, is difficult to attain under what are perceived to be traditional pastoral cattle keeping conditions, where all cattle products are valued, cattle are money, and grazing is communal. Traditional African and other pastoralists can never have sufficient grazing livestock; however many they have, they will wish to hold more.

The predominance of family labour and the dearth in pastoral societies of alternative uses for that labour, combined with the money quality of cattle in these societies implies that, for the members of those societies, the cost of keeping cattle is very low. In terms of Fig. 9.2, that reproduces Fig. 5.6 with additions, OP is low. Society's institutions cause its members collectively to seek constantly to expand cattle numbers. But every increase in stock numbers beyond OS reduces the product of a society that is, at best, poor, and human and animal nutritional levels decline. Pressures grow irresistibly on owners to draw off excessive quantities of blood from emaciated cattle; to kill off older, less valuable cattle; and, especially, to increase the share of a smaller total milk output being consumed by humans, leaving still less for a larger stock of calves. The vitality and size of the herd are reduced in these various ways; it becomes more vulnerable to disease and parasitic infestation that further reduce numbers.

Increase of cattle stocks beyond OS reduces the product available for consumption by livestock owners and their dependants. This probably creates tensions within society and between neighbouring societies experiencing similar conditions. Pig keeping societies in New Guinea have been found to respond to similar though more acute conditions of stress by increased intergroup conflict, in the course of which large numbers of pigs are slaughtered and consumed. This has the doubly beneficial effect of providing food and of relieving the impossible burden of maintaining excessive pig stocks (Harris 1975 p.46–80). Presumably among notoriously warlike pastoralists similar occasional conflicts arose, for similar reasons, with broadly similar consequences.

Cattle products are valued, grazing land tenure is communal, and cattle are money for understandable reasons in traditional pastoral societies. Yet these conditions have an inherent tendency to destroy pastoral societies through the excessive build up o

---

7. Fielder 1973 p. 343. See also De Carvalho (1974), especially p. 209. David Livingstone recorded over a century ago that, while the Lozi traded oxen to the Mambali, they were forbidden to trade heifers "to bear calves elsewhere". Quoted by Gluckman (1963 p. 77).
8. Weight for weight, heifers in Ireland normally sell for about 8% less than oxen (see, for example, *Irish Statistical Bulletin*, December 1976, p. 298). Contrast this with the Upper Volta situation (Table 4.10).
9. A situation similar to the African one was created in Ireland in 1972 by a credit fed speculative boom in cattle breeding. "Farmers were so eager in 1972 to expand dairy herds that they bid up heifer calf prices to extremely high levels. These very high prices for Friesan heifer calves, caused by farmers' eagerness to expand dairy herds, thus became themselves an important factor in making dairying so attractive and increasing still further farmers' eagerness to expand herds". (Crotty 1974 p. 15.)

grazing stock to which they give rise. This build up of grazing stock is restricted by increased, unplanned mortality among livestock, as a result of withholding scarce milk from calves, of general malnutrition, of disease and parasitic infestation among malnourished cattle, and of intergroup conflict. These biological and political constraints operate so as to hold stock numbers in the vicinity of OS in Fig. 9.2. At stock levels below OS, conditions for man and beast are better than normal; milk is more than normally abundant; livestock have a better than normal resistance to disease etc. and are better able to reproduce themselves; intergroup conflict is less likely. The opposite conditions obtain when stock numbers increase beyond OS.

The system was efficient, of good order, in that production tended to the maximum with the given cattle technology, and its enjoyment was diffused. Conflict was minimised within and between groups.

Impact of Capitalist Colonialism on Cattle Production

Preventive medicine

Western influences on African cattle production have been technological and institutional. Overwhelmingly the most important technological influence has been the reduction of human mortality rates through the application of elementary preventive medicine techniques. These techniques originated in capitalist societies where, since the early 19th century, human birth rates have been declining. Transposed to Africa, where birth rates continue to tend towards a biological maximum, preventive medicine has led to rapid population growth.

Increased human population causes a diversion of the best grazing land to crop growing and, therefore, a reduced cattle production capacity. There is simultaneously an increased demand for cattle products that raises their price relative to the value of labour. That is to say, the price of meat, Pf, and the price of milk, Pm, tend to rise relative to the cost of variable inputs, Pv, of which the principal element under African conditions is family labour. These changes are illustrated in Fig. 9.2.

Here the perpendicular axis represents the value of output of milk (or beef) and the cost of keeping an animal in terms of labour units. The diversion of land from pasture to crop causes average output per head of stock to decline to zero at a lower stocking level, OB' instead of OB. The value of cattle products relative to labour rises from OA/OP to OA'/OP. The reduction in the grazing area and the increase in the value of milk and meat relative to labour cause the average return curve to change from AB to A'B' and the corresponding marginal return curve to change from AD to A'D'. The significance of this steepening of the average and marginal return curves is that overstocking (a) commences at a lower stock level, (OS' instead of OS), and (b) causes more loss, as indicated by the greater steepness of S'D'. Thus, at the new equilibrium stocking rate, the OK'th animal causes a loss of K'E', greater than the loss of KE caused by the OKth animal at the old equilibrium.

Preventive medicine applied to humans increases the pressures for, and the damage from, overstocking of communal pastures in Africa. The same principles of preventive medicine apply to livestock as to humans. Applied to livestock in capitalist societies, preventive medicine reduces unplanned livestock losses that are an economic cost. Applied to grazing livestock in traditional pastoral societies, preventive medicine also reduces unplanned stock losses, that are, however, the only means of preventing loss-creating overstocking. Preventive veterinary medicine in Africa, by reducing the nutritional level at which animals can survive, makes it easier for stockowners collectively to increase cattle stock (beyond OS' of Fig. 9.2); while, as noted, preventive medicine applied to humans increases the pressures for, and the losses from, overstocking.

Fig. 9.2   Effects of population and stock growth

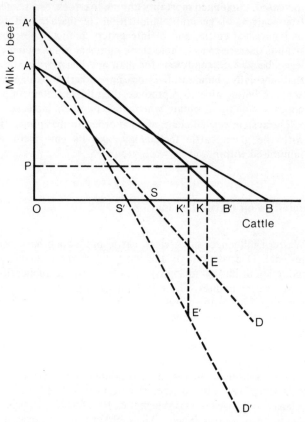

Preventive veterinary medicine, once introduced, creates its own demand. If some owners' animals receive medication, their mortality rate declines. The resulting increased pressure on communal grazing reduces all round nutritional levels, causing increased mortality among untreated animals. The owners of these, simply to maintain their position, have no option but to have them treated. Unsurprisingly, therefore, the demand for veterinary services in LDCs tends to be insatiable, and provides for aid-giving countries, who frequently have difficulty in identifying worthwhile projects for assistance, a major outlet for development aid. The situation is not dissimilar to using aid funds for arming hostile neighbours. The process, once initiated, has its own dynamic; as no party can afford to allow its military strength to fall seriously behind that of its competing neighbour, the armaments supplier has an insatiable demand for his products. For example, more than one half of the assistance given by the United Kingdom for the development of livestock in LDCs is for veterinary services (Evans 1977). This aid almost certainly causes loss in recipient countries that is borne by the poorest sections of the populations of those countries.

Drilling water holes has the same effects as preventive veterinary medicine. The water holes prevent the periodic thinning out of cattle stocks in dry seasons that was conductive to maintaining numbers at the level of maximum output (OS of Fig. 9.2).

Concepts of property   Capitalist colonialism has sought to impose capitalist concepts of property in livestock on traditional African society. African states, inheriting many of the values and manners of the colonial regimes, uphold similar concepts. Property rights in cattle on communal grazing lands are attributed the same absoluteness as property acquired in European capitalist crop growing society, with important consequences for cattle keeping.

First, cattle owners, assured by western type states of the produce of their cattle, have a greater incentive to increase that produce by owning more cattle than they had under traditional tribalism, when title to cattle and the produce of cattle was less definite and more diffused. Second, exclusive enjoyment of the produce of cattle keeping gives owners more resources from which they can more easily save and invest in more cattle, giving rise to larger cattle stocks but fewer owners. In particular, the critical constraint of the supply of milk for calf rearing breaks down under these circumstances. The value of milk is high for the decision maker when cattle ownership is diffused and when the choice is between milk for the cattle owner and his family and milk for his calves. The value of milk for the decision maker is low when cattle ownership is concentrated and when the alternatives for the cow owner are to allow his calves to suckle his cows, or to milk these for the benefit of a pauperised, cattleless people.

Finally, colonial and postcolonial governments have consistently curbed intergroup clashes that, as suggested above, have been part of the system of biological-political control of cattle stocks in Africa.

Quantity and quality of life

The effect of western intervention on traditional pastoralism is to increase the quantity, but lower the quality, of life. Control of epizootics and sinking water boreholes are easy ways of enabling cattle to survive that would have otherwise perished. Numbers of stock increase, but their productivity decreases. Malnutrition and general disability replace specific diseases, drought and theft as principal causes of cattle loss.

More cattle produce less meat and milk, but preventive medicine makes it possible for more people, less nourished, to survive. Strong, western-structured states deny the stockless the easy access that they formerly had to their neighbours' livestock, so the smaller cattle product is divided less equally among a larger population. The modern state makes it more difficult for pastoralists to live; preventive medicine makes it more difficult for them to die.

Many, even most, Africans may have benefited from capitalist colonialist influences, notwithstanding the disruption caused to traditional pastoralism. That is suggested by Table 9.2, which shows cattle production expanding, though less rapidly than population. Improvement is likely to have been achieved by developing the crop producing capability that, as noted in Chapter 3 and as illustrated by Fig. 3.1, many pastoralist societies have. Crop production, employing more productive land and governed by less complex, less fragile institutions, appears to be less vulnerable to disruption by capitalist colonial intrusion than is traditional, pasture based livestock husbandry. African cattle production, as a whole, by adopting to some extent capitalist type institutions as well as western technology, and especially by becoming more dependent on crop products — on lines examined more fully in Chapter 11 — can expand, despite the damage done to traditional pastoralism. But poorer pastoral societies, with a weak resource base and no crop growing capacity, like those in the Sahel, appear to have suffered a catastrophic breakdown in their husbandry system, finely attuned as that was to exploiting extensive areas of low capacity land. Elsewhere in Africa, states, supported by western type administrative, police and military systems, have succeeded so far in controlling communities in which there is evidence of widespread, increasing and worsening poverty.

Some Current Approaches to Increasing African Cattle Production

Though the nature and causes of maladjustment in African cattle production may be obscure, the consequences are clearcut and give rise to widespread concern. There is concern, as in the case of the Sahel region, that a delicately balanced system has been disrupted with the result that natural resources have been destroyed and an irreversible process of declining production and worsening poverty has been set in motion.[10] There is concern, as in densely settled parts of Kenya, to relieve the pressure of population on arable land by a more intensive exploitation of extensive grazing areas (Kenya 1974 p.8, Simpson 1973 p.6). More generally and positively, there is an awareness of the vast extent of Africa's grazing lands and of the great size of African cattle herds, and of the desirability of harnessing these more effectively so as to improve the grindingly poor living conditions of the continent's rapidly expanding population. These widespread concerns have given rise to numerous efforts to mobilise more effectively the continent's cattle producing capacity.

Three projects, or programmes, that appear to be representative of the type of effort being undertaken are examined here, in the light of the economic model and the analysis that have been developed. The purpose of the examination is threefold: first, to illustrate the model by reference to particular situations; second, to appraise the projects/programmes that are examined; and third, to identify possibly more effective ways of exploiting Africa's cattle potential. The projects/programmes examined are (a) an FAO/UNDP cattle fattening project in Kenya; (b) World Bank projects to establish cattle ranching in Kenya; and (c) the Botswana Government's national policy on tribal grazing land.

FAO/UNDP Kenyan Cattle Fattening Project

Extensive trials of fattening cattle in feedlots have been conducted by the FAO in collaboration with the Kenyan Ministry of Agriculture from 1968 onwards. The advantages of feedlot fattening of cattle were seen to be: ". . . a tremendous opportunity for increasing the volume of production from the existing national herd of Kenya. The key to understanding why cattle should be fed lies in the additional volume of meat which can be produced. Thus although the greatest profit per animal can be made by feeding an animal with low cash inputs on natural grazing, a profit can still be made by feeding a balanced ration to an animal in confinement. Although margins per head are small, a sufficient throughput of cattle can be handled to give a substantial overall profit to a large-scale operator. On a national scale the case is even more striking. The KMC receives only about 20% of the annual slaughter of beef cattle in Kenya. The total national offtake is usually estimated as between 10 and 12%. If all young stock were channelled through feedlots prior to slaughter it is probable that the offtake would be something of the order of 30% of the national herd. Assuming that the number of cattle slaughtered locally were to remain constant, while the additional cattle were processed at the KMC, this would indicate a sevenfold increase in throughput. In addition, heavier carcasses would increase the weight of meat handled still further. While this is an unrealistically high assumption for the immediate future, it points to the tremendous potential for increasing foreign earnings through the rational use of the country's beef herd" (FAO 1972a). A social return in the short term of 47% and in the long term of 25% on capital employed was predicted (Newberry 1976 p. 523).

10. See, for example, Massachusetts Institute of Technology (1974) and Picardi (1974). See also Australian National University, Department of Demography 1974a and b.

The project was conceived mainly as an appendix to the existing cattle industry. It did not attempt to alter institutional arrangements. It would, as an appendix, add to the value of cattle output by processing cattle in feedlots at a cost lower than the value added. Some external economies were expected: the feedlots could pay an attractive price for feeder cattle, which would induce breeders to sell, thus reduce stocks and so cause output from overstocked rangeland to increase. Reported costs and returns from feedlot fattening in Kenya are shown in Table 9.3.

Kenyan feedlotting of cattle differs in the following respects from American feedlotting, on which it is modelled:

USA	Kenya
1. Beef importer	Beef exporter
2. Grain exporter	Grain balance; exports approximately equal imports
3. Cattle/grain price ratio: 16.81[11]	Cattle/grain price ratio: 7.09[12]

These differences make Kenyan feedlotting of cattle vulnerable in three respects: (i) feeder cattle costs; (ii) feed costs; and (iii) cattle realisation price.

Table 9.3   Costs and returns from feedlot fattening in Kenya in US $

Average purchase price per head (393 kg)	114.00
Average feedlot cost ,, ,,	56.55
Average realisation price ,, (524 kg)	181.00
Average margin ,, ,,	10.45

See FAO 1973c p. 11.

African per caput grain production is half the world average (Table 9.1). Collectively, Kenya and its neighbours in East Africa constitute a major grain deficit world region. Kenya itself is a marginal exporter (Table 9.4), though the continued availability of a relatively small export surplus is questionable in view of the country's 3.4% annual population growth (Kenya 1974 p.5). Africa's tight grain supply is reflected in the wheat-relative price of beef (Table 4.1). The tightness of the situation in Kenya is shown above by the cattle/grain price ratios of 16.81:1 and 7.09:1 for the

Table 9.4   Production and net export of cereals, Kenya, 1967–1976.

	Production × 10³ tons	Net Exports × 10³ tons
1968	1924	128
1969	2007	234
1970	2078	76
1971	1985	−27
1972	2230	10
1973	2155	184
1974	2118	64
1975	2201	36
1976	2186	107
1977	2333	−52

See FAO 1972b p. 88, 1975a p. 41, 1978a p. 91, 1969 pp. 109, 111, 1975b pp. 117, 120, 1978b p. 106.

11. Ratio refers to year 1971. (USDA 1974 pp. 29, 307).
12. FAO 1971a p. 4.

USA and Kenya respectively. The significance of this scarcity of grain in Kenya for the economics of feedlot fattening cattle is illustrated as follows.

Feeder cattle and feed costs account for about 90% of the value of fat cattle. This, in the USA, is normally made up of about equal parts for the feeder animal and for the feed.[13] Given that the cost per unit weight of feeder cattle is 110% and 84% respectively of the value per unit weight of fat cattle in the USA and Kenya, the comparable cost of feeder cattle in Kenya will be 45×84/110=34% of the value of fat cattle. If the value of fat cattle is taken as 100UUA (USA units of account) in the USA and 100KUA (Kenyan units of account) in Kenya, the allocation of costs will be:

	USA (UUA)	Kenya (KUA)
Feeder cattle	45	34
Feed	45	56
Other costs and profits	10	10
Value of fat animal	100	100

One UUA in the USA, where the cattle/grain price ratio is 16.81, will buy 16.81 unit weights of grain; or the fattener can budget on buying 45×16.81=756.45 unit weights of feed to fatten an animal. One KUA buys 7.09 similar unit weights of grain in Kenya, so the fattener can only budget on buying 56×7.09=397.04 unit weights to fatten an animal. It would be impossible for the Kenyan feedlotter to fatten his cattle on half the feed required by American cattle fatteners.

Emphasis was placed by the FAO (FAO 1973a) on the use of molasses and other byproducts as supplementary feed. This reflects a widely held belief in the existence in LDCs of large amounts of byproducts whose feeding value is inadequately appreciated by livestock owners. However, the beef/molasses price ratio in Kenya appears to be not much more favourable than the beef/grain price ratio. A ton of beef in 1968 was worth 25 tons of molasses in Kenya and 30 tons in the United Kingdom.[14] The availability of low cost byproduct feeds is an illusion in Kenya as elsewhere.

The ratio of feeder to fat cattle prices in Kenya is low by normal US standards. The price per unit weight of feeder cattle as a percentage of the current price per unit weight of fat cattle in Kenya, as suggested by Table 9.3, is 84%. A comparable value for the USA is 110% (Table 4.8). The relatively low cost of feeder cattle made it possible to operate a feedlot in Kenya in 1972 with a 6% margin over operating costs despite a low cattle/grain price ratio (Table 9.3). However, given present institutions, especially those factors that make it attractive for African cattle owners to carry stocks of cattle, it is unlikely either that there will be an increase in the offtake of young cattle at a price per unit weight that is 84% of the price per unit weight of fat cattle; or that many young cattle will be forthcoming at a lower relative price for young cattle. In the unlikely event of store, or feeder, cattle becoming available on

13. See, for example, USDA, Economics, Statistics and Cooperative Services, *Livestock and Meat Situation*, (June 1978), p. 12.

14. For Kenya in 1968, see Newbery 1976 pp. 449, 485. The average c.i.f. price of molasses in Britain in that year was £11.77 per ton (UK 1969a p. 14). The average price received by British farmers for bullocks for slaughter in 1968 was 205 shillings per cwt, equivalent to £360 per ton of dressed carcase (UK 1969b p. 40).

more favourable terms relative to fat cattle values, feedlot fatteners would still have to compete with pasture fatteners who would force up store cattle prices.

The Kenya cattle feedlot project was conceived in the heady late 1960s and early 1970s when a worldwide cattle boom suggested the possibility of Kenyan beef being elevated to the level of a luxury, beyond the reach of most domestic consumers, and produced principally to earn foreign exchange. But even if the cattle boom had continued indefinitely, feedlot fattening would have been unprofitable in Kenya. This is because, on world markets, cattle and grain prices must move in fairly close unison over the medium term. If the value of Kenyan beef had continued to rise, so too would the cost of Kenyan grain, so that, in the medium term, the cattle/feed price ratio would not have changed (unless grain prices were held down to subsidise cattle feeders). That ratio could only be widened, to allow the feedlotting margins normal in the USA, by raising incomes towards the US level. Pending that, Kenya can only hope to export pasture produced beef.

FAO reported in 1973 that feedlotting cattle in Kenya gave a social return on capital of 44% and a private return of 28% (FAO 1973b p.28). That report, and a later publication based on the same study (Newberry 1976), assumed inter alia, that Kenyan beef would continue to have access to the high priced EEC markets, although it should have been clear in 1973 to any competent observer of the world cattle situation that the end of the boom was imminent (Crotty 1973a, b and c). The European Economic Community, the world's largest meat market, banned most beef imports, including those from Kenya, when the slump came, and EEC beef imports fell from 622 000 tons in 1973 to 88 000 tons in 1975 (UK 1974 Table 11, ECC Statistical Office 1974 and 1976).

Powerful beef producing lobbies in major importing countries make access to their markets normally difficult. The USA and Japan protect domestic producers by quantitative restrictions on beef imports and the EEC protects its producers through a system of variable import levies. Quality and disease consideration provide additional leverage to discriminate against and discourage imports of Kenyan beef.

The FAO-sponsored feedlot fattening of cattle in Kenya was ill conceived, without prospect of success. It epitomises in important ways the ineffectualness of present efforts to mobilise pastoral resources in LDCs. It involved a transfer of technology from a high income, technologically advanced country (the USA) to a low income, technologically retarded country (Kenya), without adequate consideration of the different circumstances in which the transferred technology was to be applied. It was inspired by the crude economic objective of "maximising value added", without reference to comparative advantage, the crucial consideration in trade issues. It assumed the ready availablity for feed of good quality byproducts, neglected by established producers. Finally it had resort to the somewhat esoteric and nebulous concepts of shadow prices and social benefits to give an appearance of promise to the project, while neglecting, or giving inadequate consideration to, such obviously crucial factors as the supply of feeder cattle and feed, and the demand for beef. Fattening cattle on grain in Africa, where per caput grain availability is half the world average and pastureland availability is two and a half times the world average (Table 9.1) lacked commonsense. It was a nonsense.

BRD Projects

Cattle projects accounted for 45% by value of all IBRD financed loans to the African agricultural sector approved in 1973–74 (IBRD 1974b pp.46–9). The total cost of these projects was estimated to be US$106.5 million of which the IBRD undertook to finance US$48.7 million. IBRD-financed cattle projects are now clearly an important element in the African cattle industry.

The Kenyan Livestock Development Project of 1968 was an early IBRD catt project in Africa, and was intended as a pilot project on which subsequent Bar projects would be based (Simpson 1973 p.4). Press statements issued by the Bank relation to subsequent African cattle projects do not suggest that these depart radical from the Kenyan prototype. It is appropriate therefore to consider the Kenyan proje in the light of the foregoing analysis of the African cattle industry; conclusio pertaining to this pilot Bank project are likely to have a broad relevance to oth IBRD African cattle projects. The Kenyan Cattle Project envisaged:

(i) apportioning communal grazing land to group, company or individual ranche and

(ii) providing these ranches with water holes and financing to acquire breeding stoc and feeder cattle for fattening.

The group ranches "are productive enterprises in which a group of people, joint have title to land, collectively maintain agreed stocking levels, market the surplus rotation, herd their livestock collectively yet continue to own the livestock a individuals" (Simpson 1973 p.12 quoting IBRD).

"Membership of the group in theory is based on kinship and traditional land right The people living at the time of the establishment of such ranches in the area a entitled to join. In practice the families in the locality are encouraged to form grou representative committees to parcel out the land into ranches. Once the boundari are decided, title to the land is registered and this can be charged as security fc loans. The representative committee then undertakes the management of the rancl employing paid managers if necessary. The original plan provided for the establishme of 19 group ranches ranging from 28 000 acres to 107 000 acres in size. Fluctuatior in size follow mainly from the desire to have geographical or other easily recognise boundaries in the absence of fences. ... A maximum figure for the total catt population was set for each ranch *but details have not yet been worked out how th quota should be enforced as regards a limit on the size of individual member herds"* (Simpson 1973) (Italics supplied).

The company ranches "are production enterprises in which land is leased fror Government by a number of shareholders who put up cattle or a cash equivalent t stock it. Animals are collectively owned and disposed of ... day to day directio ... is under the control of paid management" (Simpson 1973 p.11 quoting IBRD) "The type of company envisaged consists of African shareholders who are largel absentee" (Simpson 1973 p.11).

Individual ranches are "production enterprises in which an individual member c a tribal society may, with community consent and the authorization of the loca County Council, legally register communal land as private property. On that propert the individual runs his own livestock, with conscious intent to give his herd a market orientated rather than subsistence structure" (Simpson 1973).

"The owners of the individual ranches already allocated are all Masai but Masa with a difference. They include cattle traders, local storekeepers, government officials a local chief and an aspiring politician. Their holdings to the casual visitor appear t be as populated as the normal group ranch. The African extended family systen means that many people beside the owner regard these holdings as home. Whethe this attitude will change with increasing commercialization remains to be seen (Simpson 1973).

Most ranches receiving loans were individual, company or commercial ranches. The 1974–78 Development Plan of the Republic of Kenya reports: "The first phas

---

15. "Commercial ranches date back to the European settlers and many are still run b Europeans" (Simpson 1973 p. 16).

of a major livestock development programme for the range area was completed in 1973. A credit programme operated by A.F.C. forms an integral part of this overall development programme. During the first phase the A.F.C. lent about £2 million to 110 ranches. These include 11 group ranches and 45 smaller individually-owned ranches ... plus commercial and company ranches ... About 65% of the funds provided were used for purchasing immature stock and other short-term inputs, while the remaining 35% were invested in long-term improvements, especially water supplies". (Kenya 1974 part 1 para. 10.71).

An unfavourable public reaction against company ranches was reported: "People felt that the land was being alienated from the masses to the profit of a few rich men who might not be (from the area) anyway. Proposed ranch boundaries threatened squatters' shambas while the "unorganised" ranches and communal grazings also could vanish. ... Side by side with the opposition came a growing awareness of the difficulties in the operation of the existing company ranches. Lack of managerial ability, corruption and failure of shareholders to provide capital or stock generally inhibited development" (Simpson 1973 p.12).

The group ranches, in so far as no allocation of grazing rights to individual families takes place, imply no more than the registration of the rights of existing families to graze local pastures. The communal nature of land ownership is unaltered, except in that legal sanction is given to excluding the cattle of non-local pastoralists. The marginal return per animal to the individual grazier continues to be identical with the average return per animal to the community. Likewise, the marginal return to the individual's "other" inputs continues to be shared by all users of the grazing area. Meanwhile, the more intensive application of modern technology which is part of the project, especially the provision of more water holes, will exacerbate overstocking and accelerate the deterioration of grazing lands.

A system of grazing quotas with corresponding responsibilities for "other" inputs, could, conceptually, reduce stock numbers and increase "other" inputs to optimal levels. Strong and complex institutions would be required to administer arrangements of this nature, as individual families would profit from increasing their cattle stocks above their quotas and from reducing their "other" inputs below their ascribed levels. It is difficult to see how the institutional arrangements could operate without the group ranches evolving into company ranches. The company and individual ranches imply a straighforward transformation from communal to individual tenure of grazing land. This transformation will eliminate the conflicts generated by the impact of modern technology on a system of communal grazing where cattle are money. It is likely to do so, however, at the cost of creating the powerful, socially divisive forces associated with the individual ownership of grazing land, without achieving a substantial increase in output.

Consideration has been given in Chapter 3 to the very exceptional conditions required to make the individual tenure of pastoral land socially beneficial. The consequences of the individual appropriation of pastoral land for Latin America and for Ireland have been touched on in Chapter 8. They have been disastrous. Individual tenure of pastoral land is not incompatible with social wellbeing; they can be reconciled, but there is nothing in the IBRD proposals to indicate an awareness of the conflicts the proposals will create, much less to reconcile the conflicts. The IBRD proposals for individual and company ranches, and for group ranches in so far as these are likely to evolve into individual and company ranches, involve an institutional transformation in Africa which, while contributing little to increased output, will replace an integrated, egalitarian society with a peculiarly divisive one, dichotomised into landowning and landless classes. A multiplication of situations like the following seems an unavoidable consequence of the implementation of IBRD proposals for cattle ranches:

"Some fifty families of so-called 'illegal squatters' who graze their cattle (the only stock in the area) at the single watering point presently available, 'will have to be removed' " (Livingstone 1976 p. 75).

Projects based on the extinction of rights of access to land, essential for their existence, and held from the immemorial past by persons who are among the poorest in the world, are not conducive to social wellbeing and harmony.

The Botswana Government's "National Policy on Tribal Grazing Land" (Botswana, Central Statistics Office 1975).

The official statement of national policy on tribal grazing land is remarkably sensitive and percipient. It includes the following by the President of Botswana: "The time has come to tackle a subject about which there has been a lot of talk but not much action — the better use and development of our land. As our human population and the numbers of our cattle and other livestock increase there is a growing danger that grazing will be destroyed by uncontrolled use of communal grazing areas by ever growing numbers of animals. Once grazing has been destroyed it is extremely difficult to get grass re-established. And under our communal grazing system it is in no one individual's interest to limit the number of his animals. If one man takes his cattle off, someone else moves his own cattle in. Unless livestock numbers are somehow tied to specific grazing areas no one has an incentive to control grazing. . . . We are faced with a situation which demands action".

The profoundness of the changes that are proposed is recognized. The proposals mean changing "the Botswana way of life: (they) will affect, directly or indirectly, virtually every Motswana".[16]

The statement recognises the harm being done now: "Increased herds, under the system of uncontrolled grazing, have led to serious overgrazing around villages, surface water sources and boreholes. Overgrazing has led to sheet erosion and bush encroachment which reduces the amount of good grazing. This is worst for the small cattle owners, most of whose herds graze in the village areas".

Referring to the need for reform, it states: "We must alter the old system. If we go on as we are doing now, not only will production and profit per hectare go down every year, but the gap between rich and poor will grow bigger. If we can remove the limitations of the communal grazing system, everyone will benefit". Throughout, it emphasises the need "to ensure that land development helps the poor and does not make them worse off".

Basic Policy objectives are stated as:

"(a) To make grazing control, better range management and increased productivity possible. . . .
"(b) To safeguard the interests of those who own only few cattle or none at all".

To meet these objectives:
"Government will encourage Land Boards to divide the tribal grazing areas into three zones — Commercial Farming Areas, Communal Grazing Areas, and Reserved Areas. The terms of tenure and the type of development permitted will be different for each zone.

In [Commerical Farming Areas] groups and individuals will be given exclusive rights to specific areas of grazing land. A defined number of hectares of land will be allocated, not simply the use of a borehole as is now the case. Ranch development will be encouraged, including fencing and piping of water. Leases will be granted in Commercial Farming Areas, and land in these areas will cease to be held in the

---

16. A Motswana is a native of Botswana.

traditional way. Rents will be payable to the local authorities in return for the exclusive rights given in the lease.

Proposed rules for allocation and development in Commercial Farming Areas are set out in Part V. These areas are not meant only for the large individual cattle owners. First priority will be to help groups of smaller owners to run commercial ranches. Preference will be given to such groups in making allocations".

The official statement includes the following schematic presentation of the problems of the Botswana cattle industry and the Government's proposals for remedying these (Fig. 9.3).

The proposals, though sensitive and percipient, are nevertheless likely, if implemented, to give rise to difficulties which may be even more grave than those they seek to alleviate. The proposals will relieve pressures on communally grazed land near to existing villages by requiring owners of large herds, and by facilitating groups of owners of small herds, to transfer from the old, communal grazing to the new commercial grazing lands. The relief thus afforded to cattle on the old communal grazing will reduce the death rates, and increase the birth rates and make possible

Fig. 9.3   National policy for tribal grazing land

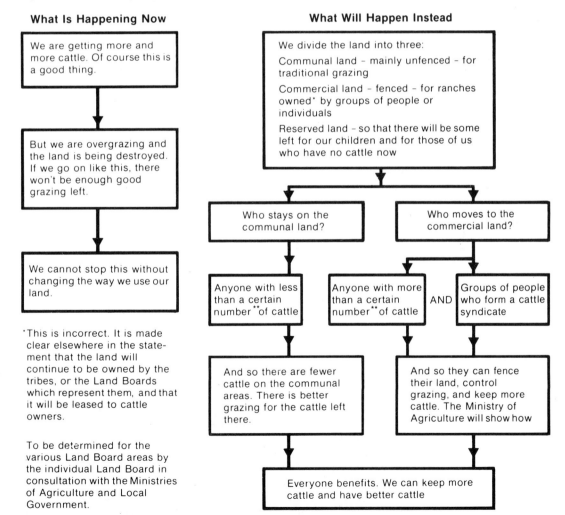

What Is Happening Now

We are getting more and more cattle. Of course this is a good thing.

But we are overgrazing and the land is being destroyed. If we go on like this, there won't be enough good grazing left.

We cannot stop this without changing the way we use our land.

*This is incorrect. It is made clear elsewhere in the statement that the land will continue to be owned by the tribes, or the Land Boards which represent them, and that it will be leased to cattle owners.

**To be determined for the various Land Board areas by the individual Land Board in consultation with the Ministries of Agriculture and Local Government.

What Will Happen Instead

We divide the land into three:

Communal land – mainly unfenced – for traditional grazing

Commercial land – fenced – for ranches owned* by groups of people or individuals

Reserved land – so that there will be some left for our children and for those of us who have no cattle now

Who stays on the communal land?

Who moves to the commercial land?

Anyone with less than a certain number **of cattle

Anyone with more than a certain number** of cattle

AND

Groups of people who form a cattle syndicate

And so there are fewer cattle on the communal areas. There is better grazing for the cattle left there.

And so they can fence their land, control grazing, and keep more cattle. The Ministry of Agriculture will show how

Everyone benefits. We can keep more cattle and have better cattle a rapid growth in cattle stocks. It will accentuate those processes that have recently characterised African cattle production and which result from the interaction of western technology with traditional cattle keeping. Cattle stocks on communal grazing, relieved of the pressures of density of stocking numbers, will expand rapidly, their surplus numbers being drawn away to stock newly developed commercial areas. A process akin to the swarmings of bees seems likely, as cattle stocks breed rapidly on the communal grazings and spread from there to occupy new commercial areas. Cattle, under good nutritional conditions are biologically capable of increasing numbers at about 30% annually. The old communal grazing areas could thus, in a relatively short time, generate foundation stock for all the country's grazing lands, extensive as these are. Serious pressure on land, which has been already experienced locally, would quite quickly become general (Chambers & Feldman 1973 p. 115–6).

Botswana would, under the proposals, move towards a situation where all its land will be communally grazed or will be enclosed in commercial ranches. The pace at which this situation is approached will depend (a) on the cost of establishing ranches in the commercial areas and (b) on the rent, or land tax, charged under the long term, renewable leases. The lower the cost of establishment and the land tax, the nearer to the biologically possible rate of growth of stock numbers will expansion in ranches approach. The higher establishment costs and land taxes are, the slower will expansion in ranches be and the more conditions on communal grazings will continue as at present. That is, the more relief the proposed conditions now give to communal graziers, the more rapidly will the situation be reached where all the country's land will have been expropriated and Botswana society will be dichotomized into landowners and landless.

The proposals specify that the land in commercial areas will be leased, so that "local authorities receive a return from those who acquire the privilege of exclusive use of tribal land". Leases are to be for "a period of fifty years, after which the lease will be renewable". If high rents or taxes are charged under the leases, change in the present situation, other than from the consequences of overstocking communal land, will occur slowly. If rents are low, change will be rapid and leases of land will soon acquire value. A Botswana landed property class will have been formed and this class can be expected to struggle to secure and enlarge its interests, by, for example, having land taxes reduced and having leases that are already long, lengthened. Already, as noted, enterprising individuals are hastening to establish claims on tribal grazing areas and have created "a land rush".

The advantages of individual tenure seem obvious when land is abundant and is held communally. But the individualisation of land tenure is possibly the most profound and far reaching institutional change that a society can undertake. Especially where land is used mainly for pastoral purposes, the individualization of tenure dichotomises society into landed and landless, with directly conflicting interests. It creates a vested interest that, experience suggests, however innocuous and amenable to political control it may now appear, is unlikely to remain so.

There are, in any case, circumstances in the Botswana situation that suggest that the problem will quite soon become acute. The human population is increasing at over 3% annually; domestic employment opportunities, understandably in a cattle dominated economy, are increasing much more slowly; the rapidly expanding workforce is, therefore, forced increasingly to seek employment as migratory labour in South Africa (Botswana, Central Statistics Office 1977 pp.17–8).

The benefits from Botswana's rapidly expanding cattle stocks, meanwhile, accrue to a remarkably small section of the population. The Report of the Rural Income Survey shows that 15% of the rural populations owns 75% of the cattle, and that 45% own no cattle (Botswana, Central Statistics Office 1976 p.111). This extreme concentration of wealth, characteristic of capitalist type pastoral situations, would have been inconceivable under Botswana's indigenous tribal institutions that would have been far too weak to contain the resulting social tensions. That it did not occur under the colonial regime may have been due to a concern for general wellbeing not greatly less than that of the sovereign Government, combined with a capacity to resist local vested interests greater than that of the Botswana Government. But even a Government able to call upon the administrative, police and military forces of the modern State, located as it is in the unstable cockpit of southern Africa, cannot indefinitely contain the social pressures that result from the interrelated facts of a population growth in excess of 3% annually, virtually no increase in employment, and the ownership of 75% of the society's cattle by 15% of its people. The democratic character of that State is likely to be an early casualty.

An Alternative Approach to Developing Africa's Cattle Potential

The representative projects and programmes for expanding African cattle production that have been examined seem likely to worsen a bad and dangerous situation. They appear to be based on a failure to appreciate the nature of the complex, socioeconomic-cultural relationships involved in traditional cattle production and, as a result of that failure, to attempt to impose capitalist type technologies and institutions where they are inappropriate. The purpose of the present work especially is, with the help of a model of cattle owners' decision-making, to gain insights into these relationships and, as a result of these insights, to identify means of restoring balance and good order at a recognisably superior level.

Social net revenue (SNR)

Individuals attempt to maximise their net benefits from cattle (NR) in the manner analysed in Chapter 5. Rational exploitation of cattle resources in the social interest requires similarly that society should maximize social net revenue (SNR) from communally owned lands. SNR has a meaning similar to that of net benefits as discussed and illustrated above. Maximising it implies that society will take all appropriate measures to increase the social benefits from communal land up to, but no further than, where the additional benefits equal the additional costs incurred. Maximizing SNR in this way is the necessary and sufficient condition for the efficient use of communal land.

A tax on livestock using communal grazing is the most important and appropriate mechanism for maximising SNR. Tax revenue, net of collection cost, must be maximized in order to maximize SNR. This is illustrated by Fig. 9.4.

AB is the social average return from cattle on a communal grazing. AD is the corresponding social marginal return. OG is the price of "other" inputs. Individuals will expand cattle numbers to GB, where marginal returns and marginal costs to the individual are equal. At this stocking level, returns equal costs (OGBH). Social marginal return per head of cattle is −BD, on the assumption that the social cost equals the individual cost of "other" inputs, OG. Stocking beyond ON causes a social loss, CBD, equal to the social gain, GCA of stocking up to GC, the socially optimum stocking level, and there is no producers' surplus.

A tax of EC per head of grazing stock will cause profit-maximizing cattle producers to reduce stock numbers until the individual's gross marginal return from cattle rises to OF, with a net of tax return of OG, the individual's marginal cost of keeping cattle. Any rate of tax other than EC will reduce tax revenue, GFEC. It can be shown, through the properties of similar triangles, that a tax rate E'C' reduces revenue by CC'N', and a tax rate E" C" reduces revenue by CC"N". The social return from cattle grazing is maximised by maximising cattle tax revenue.

Fig. 9.4   Cattle tax and pastoral efficiency

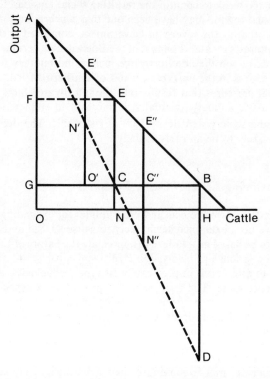

The need to maximise cattle tax revenue rules out taxes on cattle at point of sale as these could be avoided by reducing sales and consuming more cattle products; or by increasing stocking, which will cause further overstocking. Taxes on grazing cattle rather than on their sale or slaughter, are required.

Maximising cattle tax revenue implies minimising tax evasion. Evading cattle taxes is peculiarly easy unless those involved in their payment and collection have an incentive to maximise revenue. This incentive can be given by relating revenue disbursements to revenue collection as closely as possible, preferably on the basis of reasonably discrete grazing/taxing areas. If the revenue raised by a tax on the cattle grazing an area is disbursed among the inhabitants of the area in a manner acceptable to public opinion in the area, public opinion is likely to favour the tax and to oppose evasion.[17] Evasion can be further reduced by such devices as forfeiture of untaxed cattle, their value being divided between the taxing authority and the discoverer of the cattle.

Appropriate institutional arrangements might be as follows. Proprietorial rights in the communal grazing land would be vested collectively in the residents of a neighbourhood. Every adult resident would have an equal share in an Operating Company (OC). The shareholder residents would elect from time to time a land management board that would, in turn, employ executive staff. The OC would seek to maximise

17. The *jangali*, or traditional cattle tax levied on pastoralists by centralising rulers, including European colonialists, transfers resources from cattle owners to the centre. All pastoralists including stockless persons, are likely to lose from the transfer and have an incentive to evade, or to assist the evasion of, the *jangali*. For further information on traditional cattle taxes see, for example, Due 1963 pp. 61, 151; Perham 1937 pp. 51, 105–6. Methods of cattle tax evasion are described by St. Croix 1944 pp. 34–6.

the flow of SNR over time at a politically agreed discount rate. OC surpluses would be allocated in accordance with the wishes of the shareholders as expressed in periodic general meetings. Conceivably, they would be used to improve the grazing land; to provide for the shareholders public goods and services; or given in cash to the shareholders.

Not all resident shareholders would own cattle, and not all cattle on the grazing area would be owned by resident shareholders; conceivably some cattle owners would be from outside the area. The number of shareholder-residents would normally exceed the number of cattle owners, and as all resident shareholders would share in the profits, local opinion would favour the maximisation of SNR, the necessary and sufficient condition of efficient communal land use. The OC would seek to increase demand for grazing rights on its land. It would itself be free to graze cattle, but would be normally unlikely to do so. By grazing cattle, the OC would increase demand for grazing rights and would so increase cattle tax revenue. But the increase in cattle tax revenue would be likely to be less than the revenue the OC would earn from grazing cattle, so the net effect would be to reduce net revenue. (The OC would not normally be expected to make enough from grazing cattle to pay the cattle tax, because individual cattle owners, lavishing skill, care and attention to detail on their cattle would get more from their cattle than the employees of the OC would extract.) The OC is envisaged as a property-holding company, taking all the measures appropriate to such a company to maximize net revenue from its grazing lands over the long term. The cattle grazing the land would normally belong to individual cattle owners, resident in or outside the locality and paying revenue-maximising cattle taxes.

A wide range of activities would be appropriate to an OC, in as much as they would be likely to increase the flow of SNR discounted over time at rates acceptable to the majority of shareholders. There are major economies of scale in managing a grazing area which are not available to individual graziers. Fencing and watering for 10 paddocks for rotational grazing can be provided on 10 000 acres for far less than 100 times the cost of doing so on 100 acres. There are major economies of scale in providing cattle chutes, crushes, dipping baths, isolation pens, weighing scales. Most veterinary services, especially those of a prophylactic sort, can be provided at lowest cost on a large scale. Cattle herding can be done most effectively, at lowest cost, in large units. It is practical to maintain continuous watch over large herds of cattle in large, well fenced, heavily stocked paddocks, observing at an early stage cattle in difficulties from illness or from shortage of water or fodder and alerting the stockowners to the need for action. Individuals specialising in herding can acquire exceptionally acute perception.

OCs would be well circumstanced to exploit jointly wild life and cattle potential. They would be in a position to assess the benefits from wild life, in the form of harvested game, revenue from tourists attracted by the wild life, either collected directly or through hoteliers and others engaged in the tourist industry. The OCs could trade these gains from wild life against the losses caused by predators, damage done to fencing, and competition for grazing. The OCs would be in a position to maximise benefits, and to minimise losses, from a given wild life presence.

There are important economies of scale in preserving fodder during the growing season for use in the dormant season. The OC could make hay or silage at a lower cost per unit than on individually held holdings. It could buy and spread — including aerially — fertilizers, seeds, insecticides, and weedkillers more cheaply.

OCs would be particularly likely to achieve economies of scale in mobilizing resources for investment in increased cattle production. The retained earnings of the OC and the reinvested dividends of saving shareholders are important potential sources of funds. The OC, secure in its title to the community lands and the revenue deriving from these, would be well positioned to tap outside savings through the banking system, pension funds, or other repositories of savings. Central banks, acting on behalf of groupings of OCs, would be better positioned to secure foreign funds than when these funds are to be disbursed to individual cattle owners.

A major defect of African cattle production now is that inadequate "other" resources are used on land, while too much are used on cattle. It would be similarly wrong for an OC, with a good ability to mobilise savings, to use these exclusively on land improving projects. It would be surprising if it could not relend at greater profit to actual or potential graziers to enable these to increase the numbers, or improve the quality, of stock. The discarding, under capitalist-colonialist influence, of the traditional arrangement whereby stockless members of an African community had fairly ready access to the stock owned by others, has been noted. The discarding of this practice of *mafista* gives rise, as in Botswana, to extreme polarisation of cattle ownership. This polarisation of stock ownership would be unlikely where an OC sought to maximise cattle tax revenue. Owners of few stock normally get a higher output per head of stock than owners of many stock, and could therefore afford to pay a higher tax per head. It would be an appropriate concern of the OCs to replace the traditional *mafista* system by a rational system of lending to creditworthy persons with no, or few, stock.

Family responsibilities are a major factor determining creditworthiness. Generally persons with large families are illpositioned to service debts. Their having large families might also be taken as indicating a lack of prudence and forethought, and to that extent a lack of creditworthiness. Banking prudence would therefore suggest that an OC, concerned to maximise lending to stockowners while minimising losses from its lending operations, would not normally lend to parents of large families. This aspect of the OC's operations might be expected to reduce birth rates.

The OC could influence the quality and genetic composition of the cattle on its land in a number of ways. Animals infected with disease or infested with parasites could be excluded, or confined to restricted areas, while facilities for treating them could simultaneously be supplied. Likewise noncastrated males of an unacceptable quality could be excluded or restricted to special areas. Sires or semen of superior breeds or strains might also be introduced if it appeared that the productivity of their progeny would increase sufficiently to raise, by competitive forces, the revenue from the cattle tax by more than enough to cover the cost.

OCs would have an incentive, and would be well positioned, to direct research and extension services along profitable lines. The acid test of these services, which they rarely pass, is that their cost should be exceeded by the increased farming profit which they generate. Applying this test, OCs, singly or in federations, would have a incentive to undertake, or cause to have undertaken, research likely to result in better returns from cattle and so higher cattle taxes. They would have an incentive to see that relevant results of research were made available, at lowest cost, to their graziers. They would likewise have an incentive to see that graziers were not subjected to revenue-depressing advice.

OCs, concerned to maximise their net revenue, would wish to maximise the price received for their products by their graziers, especially for that part of the produce sold to third parties. This would require them, again probably in federations of OC to interest themselves in the marketing process, from grazing land to consumer including foreign consumer. Any paring of margins in the chain would further the OC's objective of maximising net revenue.

Similarly OCs would be concerned to minimise the cost of inputs to graziers, as the lower the cost of these, the larger would be the the profits from cattle and thus the higher would cattle tax revenue be. It would be appropriate therefore for OCs interest themselves, again probably in federations, in the supply system for grazing land inputs, possibly engaging directly in trade or manufacturing.

Allocating SNR

It is politically and economically expedient that all adults resident in an area with communal grazing should share equally in the ownership, control and profits of the OC. Equal, local sharing of the profits of the OC provides the best assurance of a public opinion favourable to economic efficiency, which, in this case, is synonymous with maximizing each resident's share in SNR.

Equal sharing of SNR by resident adults can also have important macroeconomic benefits. Periodic dividends from the OC to residents will increase the relative attractiveness of local residence, by comparison with residence in urban areas, where no OC dividend can be expected and where, frequently, migrant labour merely spreads a little more thinly the demand for labour in "the informal sector", without adding to total product. The more sparsely populated an area is, the greater should be the value of the residential dividend from the local OC, and the more effective should it be in countering the centripetal pull of the centre, which is normally strongest and socially most destructive in sparsely populated peripheral areas. The dividends should effect some redistribution of the supply of labour from urban centre to rural peripheries.

Maximizing SNR does not exclude the use of land for purposes other than grazing livestock and wild life. Specifically, its use for crop production on the principle discussed on p. 11, is not excluded. Efficient exploitation of communal land, especially if combined with measures to curb the birth rate, should result in substantial dividends for adult residents, thus lower the cost of labour, and increase the relative attractiveness

Fig. 9.5   Source of expansion in traditional pastoralism

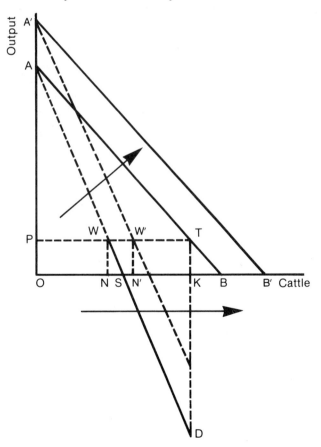

of labour intensive crop production. OCs could lease land to individuals for crop growing, or could themselves grow crops, if the rent paid, or the profit expected, equalled or exceeded the profits from the land under grass.

Marketing

The present proposals aim at increasing African cattle production by redirecting resources already used for that purpose. This redirection is to be brought about by institutional adaptations outlined above. Additional resources are unnecessary to increase output. Fig. 9.5, which is similar to Fig. 5.6, illustrates how this can be done.

Indigenous institutions cause resources in African cattle production to be used exclusively for expanding stock numbers, as indicated by the horizontal arrow, pointing eastwards (Fig.9.5). Western technology and capitalist type institutions facilitate this allocation, so that the amount of resources used for stock building tends towards OK, at a total cost OPTK. Resources beyond S reduce output by SKD (=PAW), when SNR is zero.

The proposed institutional changes would cause a redirection of N'K resources from stock building to increasing stock carrying capacity (or, from allocation in the horizontal, easterly direction, to allocation in the northeasterly direction represented by the second arrow). The effect would be to increase output by PA'W', partly as a result of increased grassland productivity (AA'W'W), and partly as a result of destocking (SKD=PAW).

There is no apparent reason why, with appropriate institutional restructuring, African grassland productivity should not rise to, say, the North American level, which is now about 10 times higher. Africa has the important advantages of a large pool of low cost labour, skilled in livestock husbandry, and a preference for cattle as assets to hold.

The principal justification for a costless increase in milk and meat output is to enable Africans to consume more of these products, that they value highly. "A marketing problem" does not arise in the sense that increased output/consumption is not constrained by the need to recover through sales, within or without Africa, the cost of increasing output, as this is zero. However, other things being equal, if Africans can increase their livestock production several times over, it is highly probable that they would prefer to use a major part of the real increase in incomes that this would imply for increased consumption of goods other than livestock products. Any trading of livestock products for non-livestock products to which this preference gave rise would add to the benefits that institutional restructuring can bring. These benefits are PA'W' (Fig. 9.5) without trading; they would be larger with trading.

Possibilities for Africans to trade in cattle products with non-Africans are discussed in Chapter 12.

The South East Asian Case: Cattle Communally Grazed; Calves Have Value

Introduction

Noncapitalist agricultural societies in the Old World ranged from a virtually complete dependence on pastoralism to a virtually complete dependence on crop growing. Extreme dependence on noncapitalist pastoralism was most closely associated with Africa. Dependence on noncapitalist crop production was most closely associated with East and South East Asia, where, in warm, well watered, fertile, alluvial soils, crops yielded well. Yields in selected areas of cultivated land in these favoured regions were sufficiently high to enable man, with little assistance from draft animals, to cultivate a sufficient area for his maintenance (Equation 3.2). Crop growing societies evolved with only a slight dependence on grazing livestock for which, in any case, there was little pastureland to graze (Table 10.1).

Table 10.1 Population, cropland and pastureland in the Far East[a] as a percentage of world totals.

	%
Population	32.33
Cropland	13.45
Pastureland	7.60

See FAO 1977a pp. 50–2, 65–6.
Note a: Japan, China (mainland), Formosa, North Vietnam, Laos, Burma, Cambodia, and South East Asia (see Note to Table 10.2).

The peoples of the Far East never acquired, or they lost, the genetic characteristic of lactose tolerance peculiar to the pastoralists who inhabited most of the Old World. The mass of China effectively excluded penetration by pastoralists from the north; the Himalayas barred penetration from the northwest; and India lay between the pastoralists of southwest Asia and the crop growers of the Far East. Far Easteners are, therefore, almost exclusively lactose intolerant (Simoons 1978). They use their very limited pastoral resources mainly to produce draft power and meat. Milk generally is an unwanted and economically unimportant product.

The cattle/buffalo economies of six South East Asian countries are examined here. The countries selected are in the rainforest tropics; relevant data on their cattle/buffalo economies have been fairly readily available; and, with the recent exception of South Vietnam, disposal of their pastoral resources has been determined by individual stock owners responding to market forces, rather than by central direction. The countries, together referred to hereinafter as "The Region", are Indonesia, Malaysia (West), Philippines, Sri Lanka, Thailand and South Vietnam. Apart from northern Thailand and northern Luzon (Philippines) they lie within 15 degrees of latitude of the equator.

Regional Characteristics

Characteristics that are important in the cattle/buffalo economy of the Region are given in Table 10.2. Average incomes in the Region are only half as high as those of

Asia as a whole and are one sixth the world's average. Total land per person is closely in line with the Asian average, but the Region's land allocation is very distinctive. Its total cropped area per person and the proportion of all land cropped are in line with the Asian pattern, though the proportion of the Region's area under crops other than tree crops and the area of these crops per head of population are low by Asian standards. The Region has almost two fifths of Asia's total tree crop area and nearly one third of its forests. The proportion of the Region's land under pasture is less than one quarter the world or Asian average. The proportion of cropland, other than tree crops, that is irrigated is in line with the Asian average.

Table 10.2   Percentages of world and Asian totals accounted for by South East Asia[a]

	World	Asian
Population	6.48	11.44
GNP	1.08	5.69
Total land	2.31	11.22
All crops	3.39	10.73
tree crops	n.a.	37.58
other crops	n.a.	8.62
Pasture	0.48	2.70
Forest and woodland	4.23	28.76
Other land	1.51	6.38
Irrigated land	4.42	6.17
Cereal and pulse production	4.45	11.44
Cattle and buffaloes	2.61	6.47
Beef and buffalo meat production	1.18	12.08
Total meat production	1.63	7.86
Milk production	0.09	1.24

See FAO 1977a.
Note a: Indonesia, Malaysia (West), Philippines, Sri Lanka,
        Thailand, South Vietnam.

Cereal and pulse production per person is at the Asian level, and is high relative to the cropped (other than trees) area. This appears to be due to the Region using its cropped land (other than trees) almost exclusively for rice growing. The Region, nevertheless, is one of the major grain deficit regions in the world, with annual net imports of about one and a half million tons.[1]

Cattle/buffalo stocks are low per head of population, though meat production is twice as high per head of stock as in Asia as a whole. Total meat production per person in the Region is, however, only two thirds the Asian average. The Region shares with China an extremely low output of milk, either per person or per head of cattle/buffalo.

These land use characteristics are consistent with the Region's location in the rainforest tropics. Continuous heat combined with heavy, fairly uniform rainfall favours tree crops. Land denuded of tree crops quickly loses its soil structure and its plant nutrients are leached from it. Heavy, uneconomic fertilising is necessary to sustain annual cropping, other than inundated rice growing. Pasture cannot easily compete with more lush growth; the nutritional content of the natural herbage is low (Camoens 1976 p. 121); and dense scrub and secondary jungle rapidly encroach. Cut off from the great rangelands of the world by India on the west and China on the north, the Region has many more buffalo than cattle, and it maintains these largely on crop byproducts, on grazing under tree crops or on waste areas.

Important social benefits accrue from the high incidence of lactose intolerance in the Orient and in the Region. Cattle/buffalo owners, because milk is unwanted, breed their stock only to produce calves. As calf gestation is competitive with draft work, unwanted calves are not produced complementarily with milk (Fig. 5.2) as in India

1. The Region's net cereal imports in 1977 were 3.4 million tons (FAO 1978b p. 107).

The very restricted pasturage of the Region and of the Orient as a whole is used to support only draft animals and necessary replacements for the herd, that in any case produces much of its own maintenance needs in the form of rice straw and postharvest grazing on rice-stubble land. None of the pasturage is used to support milch animals or surplus followers. Indeed, it is impossible to conceive how, under the conditions of communal grazing that were universal prior to the Tudor enclosures in England, restricted pasturage could have been used to make it possible for more people to subsist by crop growing.

Change in the Region

Table 10.3 records distinctive changes in the Region that bear on its cattle economy. Population has been growing one third more rapidly in the Region than in Asia generally; irrigation has been extended half as fast again as in Asia generally. The Region's cattle/buffalo stocks have been declining, and its supply of tractors has been increasing rapidly.

Table 10.3   Regional, Asian and world change, 1961–65 to 1975.

	Percentage increases		
	Region	Asia	World
Population[a]	35	26	23
Area irrigated	29	15	18
Cattle stocks[b]	−2[c]	5	12
Buffalo stocks[b]	−11[c]	12	13
Tractors	170	143[d]	36

See FAO 1970, 1976b.
Notes: a. Period 1964–1975.
b. Period 1965–1975.
c. Exclusive of Philippines, for which however it is noted "The Carabao population appears to have fallen markedly in recent years, from an estimated 4.6 million in 1970 to only 2.7 million in 1976". (Gwyer 1977).
d. Asia, exclusive of the Region, Japan, India and Turkey.

The equatorial belt, in which the Region is located, was a notoriously insalubrious location. The conditions favouring rank vegetative growth also favoured the propagation of infectious and parasitic diseases that resulted in high mortality rates and in the restriction of population to specially favoured areas. These for the most part were riverine, where the alluvial land was regularly fertilised and watered by flooding, or Java's rich volcanic soils. The introduction of elementary preventive medicine had a particularly pronounced impact on the Region, dramatically reducing death rates and causing a correspondingly dramatic growth in population. Thus, for example, the population of Malay race in Malaysia that in 1850 was "well below 500 000" (Kennedy 1962 p.188) rose to 1.6 million by 1921 (Malaya 1960 p. 3) and is now almost doubling every 20 years (Malaysia 1977 p.271).

The Region's exceptional poverty reinforces the effects of preventive medicine in reducing mortality and in raising population growth rates. Poor people, with a high rate of time discount, are compelled by circumstances to focus on gratifying immediate needs and pleasures (p. 48). The consequences in a distant future of present actions have no present significance when the future is discounted at the high rate of time discount of hungry people.[2]

2. Demographers have advanced the hypothesis that poor people have children to ensure the survival of some to assist in their work and to care for them in old age (Mueller 1977 and Nag et al 1977). The hypothesis conflicts with the universal perception that poor people are

More people necessitate the growing of more grain in a poor, grain deficit Region. That, under the circumstances, means increasing rice production. Extending rice growing from naturally inundated riverside padi fields calls for irrigation, and hence the coincidence of exceptionally rapid population growth and exceptionally rapid extension of the area irrigated in the Region.

Irrigation is a capital intensive means of increasing agricultural output. Irrigation for rice growing is, for example, much more capital intensive than clearing jungle for the growing of nonirrigated annual crops.[3] Irrigation, however, is unavoidable in the Region where, as noted, rapid structural breakdown of the soil and leaching of nutrients tightly circumscribe the possibilities for nonirrigated annual cropping. Irrigation in the Region is normally provided by the State, often financed by foreign borrowing.

The large capital required to extend rice growing beyond naturally inundated riverine areas is typical of the Region's agriculture, which is exceptionally capital intensive. Except for naturally inundated riverine rice growing, very heavy investment is required, either for irrigated rice growing, or to clear jungle land for replanting with tree crops that take many years to mature. Where farmers elsewhere wait months to get a return from their cultivations, the Region's tree croppers wait years.

There are many manifestations of the high incremental capital-output ratio (ICOR) of agriculture in the rainforest tropics. One is the early, general and continuous involvement of metropolitan capital in agricultural production in these regions. Plantation agriculture was practised in the Philippines, Sri Lanka and Indonesia from early in the colonial era. It continues to play a major role in Malaysia, as in West Africa and Central America. The readier access of plantations to metropolitan capital confers on this form of production advantages over the normally more efficient, selfemploying, smallholder form in enterprises that, like tree cropping, are exceptionally capital intensive.

The Federal Land Development Authority (FELDA) is a government agency that develops land for smallholder tree cropping in postcolonial Malaysia. The cost of development per acre is M$4320; or for the accepted size of settler rubber holding of 12 acres, M$51 845[4], which exceeds the capital employed per worker by Ford, the most capital intensive of the major USA automobile manufacturers (*Economist* 197: p. 99).

Large parts of the Region remain uncultivated forest (Table 10.2) "Even by the 1970s, only about one-fifth of the total area of Peninsular Malaysia had been alientated (for commercial exploitation)" (Barlow 1978 p. 201). A similar situation exists in other countries in the rainforest tropics; the largest, Brazil, has only 4% of its land under crop, compared to 11% for the world as a whole (FAO 1978a pp.45, 50). Capital, not land, is the effective constraint on output, as it was in western Europe and North America until quite recent years (Chapters 3 and 7).

The third distinctive change noted in Table 10.3, that of the decline of cattle/buffalo stocks, suggests a possible explanation of the high output of meat per animal noted

---

so preoccupied with immediate wants that they cannot contemplate more distant needs. The present discounted value of future benefits falls short of the present discounted cost of having children for any plausible rate of time discount by poor people. Planting a rubber tree would be, for the poor people of the Region, a less expensive but more secure way of providing for their future. But they cannot even afford that: see Crotty 1978a.

3. The cost of developing swamp forest for rice growing in South West Perak in 1975 was estimated at M$ 1500 per acre (2M$=1US$). (Crotty 1978b p. 29).

4. Based on Federal Land Development Authority (FELDA) memorandum, 24.6.1974, giving average development cost as M$ 2710.10 per acre and showing phasing of expenditure from year one to year nine, when current expenditure and income balance. Charging interest at 10% annually on outstanding investment raises cost per acre to M$ 4320.

in discussing Table 10.2. An output of beef and buffalo meat per head of stock that is twice the Asian average may have been achieved by stock depletion. If that is so, the Region's meat production may decline in coming years.

Decline in the Region's cattle/buffalo stocks is a source of widespread public concern and has given rise to various explanations. These usually include (i) the replacement of draft animals by tractors; (ii) the sale of animals in response to a strong demand for meat; (iii) the relaxation of restrictions on cattle/buffalo slaughter; and (iv) the incidence of diseases affecting animals' reproductive capacity (Gwyer 1977 p.3, FAO/IBRD 1970 pp.10–23). These phenomena certainly occur in the Region; but they also occur, occasionally in more pronounced form, where cattle/buffalo numbers are nevertheless increasing. Other considerations further weaken the phenomena's explanatory force. A strong demand is usually regarded as necessary to evoke an expanding supply; it is not self-evident why, in the Region, it leads to a reduced supply. Relaxation of controls on animal slaughter may contribute to decline in stocks, but the need for the restrictions in the first instance is left unexplained; as is also the fact that cattle/buffalo stocks elsewhere increase in the absence of restrictions on slaughter. Finally, if diseases now reduce stocks that formerly increased, the question arises as to why this should occur now, notwithstanding increased expenditure on veterinary services in the Region; and why disease should reduce stock numbers in the Region, but not in Africa or India, where conditions for cattle/buffaloes are not noticeably better. The listed phenomena might be more appropriately seen as associated with, rather than causes of, the reduction in stock numbers.

Plate 5 A Malay farmer cultivating land for rice with a water buffalo (reproduced by permission of the Malaysian Ministry of Information and Broadcasting)

ecline in Cattle/Buffalo Stocks: a Hypothesis

Decline in the Region's cattle/buffalo stocks is here perceived as an effect of rapid population growth and the associated rapid extension of irrigation, and as being structurally related to these phenomena through the distinctive characteristics of the

Region's agriculture. Analysis of this relationship is revealing of the Region's cattle/buffalo economy, and can be useful for policy appraisal.

Capital scarcity

The Region has been witnessing exceptionally rapid growth of an exceptionally poor population, practising an exceptionally capital intensive agriculture. Even if irrigation works have been supplied by the State, the working capital for extended rice growing and all the capital for the tree crops, that are the principal enterprises of smallholders in the Region, has had to come from smallholders' own resources.

Rapid population growth, set off by the application of preventive medicine that reduces death rates, is manifested in an increase in the average number of surviving children per family. The proportion of productive to dependent persons in families increases, and poor producers are forced to reallocate their limited resources away from activities with slow returns and towards those with quicker, even if lower long run, returns. Smallholders come under pressure to withdraw resources from tree cropping activities like replanting, weeding and fertilising, and to focus on harvesting and even "slaughter tapping" in the case of rubber trees; or to focus on rice growing or to sell their labour to plantations with better command over capital. Resources are shifted from physical capital maintenance or formation, to human capital formation; the capital/labour ratio declines; and the rate of time discount, I, increases.

This situation must worsen over time as smallholder capital is depleted, population grows, and plantation employment declines (Crotty 1978a). Without outside intervention of comparable potency to the introduction of preventive medicine that disrupted a traditional society, equilibrium may be reached by a return to former high death rates, though caused by malnutrition instead of disease. Husbandry standards decline and land, notwithstanding — indeed, because of — rapid population growth reverts to jungle (Crotty 1978a).

Economic models of the Lewis type (Lewis 1966 pp.55–67) perceive poor agriculturists in these situations using their surplus labour for capital formation, by planting and tending tree crops. Paradoxically, the Lewis model has most relevance when incomes are highest and least when they are lowest. Well nourished, high income agriculturists may benefit by employing otherwise leisure time for work that adds to future income; but if poor, ill nourished people are to "undertake the hard physical work of clearing and maintenance" (Barlow 1978 p.40) for rubber growing, they must have additional nourishment to sustain the effort; and they must have it now, rather than seven years later when a rubber tree commences to produce.

The Region's agriculture is capital intensive. Its people are poor. Rapid population growth under these circumstances creates intractable problems, manifested especially in capital saving expedients that must worsen the situation in the long run. The withholding of inputs that give a slow return from tree crops is one manifestation of this process, and leads to the situation, common in the Region, of a low standard of smallholder, capital intensive, tree crop husbandry. The liquidation of cattle/buffalo stocks is another manifestation of the process. The liquidation, encouraged by the reduced value of animal draft power under double cropping and by the increased value of meat (see below), relieves the pressing needs of a poor people but at the cost of exacerbating their wants in the longer run. Extreme poverty sometimes gives rise to the tragedy of "eating the seed-corn". The exceptional poverty of the Region's smallholders forces them to eat their draft animals.

Double cropping and technological change

Extending the rice growing area by irrigation virtually necessitates double cropping. Rice double cropping is necessary to justify the heavy capital expenditure on irrigation. Double cropping in turn requires virtually a revolution in the Region's rice growing methods.

The most distinctive climatic characteristic of the Region is that, being located in the equatorial belt, seasonal climatic variations are minimal. Hours of sunlight, rainfall and temperatures vary little from season to season. These climatic conditions relaxed for the Region's traditional rice growers the normal seasonal constraints to which rice growers are subject, and allowed them to cultivate more extensively with their limited draft power, supported on a limited acreage of poor grassland. The various operations of ploughing, cultivating, planting and harvesting were protracted over extended, overlapping periods. Thus, for example, rice harvesting in Tanjong Karang in Malaysia, traditionally extended from February to May, the other production stages being correspondingly protracted (Crotty 1978b).

Protracted cultivations made it possible to use buffaloes for ploughing and cultivating over prolonged periods so that, even if output per animal per day was small, output per season of many ploughing and cultivating days could be substantial. Further, because the land was first ploughed and subsequently harvested over protracted periods, the time during any year when all the land was ploughed and unharvested was brief, normally not more than a couple of months. Stubble land was therefore available for all but a couple of critical months each year, between the end of ploughing and the commencement of harvesting; and, in the Region where growth is continuous throughout the year, it provided valuable grazing of succulent weeds, grasses and rice plants from shed grain. The Region's limited area of poor natural pasture could support the draft animals and their followers through the brief period when all padi land was under crop and when, in any case, the animals were resting.

Double cropping requires in any year, on a given area, twice as much work to be executed in a much briefer time. Harvesting of the main crop in Tanjong Karang must now be completed between February and March, and the off season crop must be harvested in October, a month with one of the highest average rainfalls (Crotty 1978b). The small seasonal climatic variations that were a strength in single cropping become a disadvantage in double cropping. It is more difficult to breed quick maturing rice varieties for double cropping in equatorial conditions of uniform day length and temperature, and with continuous rainfall to discourage ripening and to delay harvesting. Varieties that ripen quickly enough can be bred, but at greater cost than elsewhere in terms of other desirable characteristics like yield, resistance to disease and palatability that must be foregone.

These problems make it exceptionally difficult to adhere to a tight rice double cropping schedule in the rainforest tropics. They create pressures to concentrate cultural operations, that formerly extended over several months, into the shortest possible time. One aspect of these difficulties is an acute labour shortage during the harvest season that results, for example, in Malaysia in harvest workers commonly being paid 20% and occasionally 30%, of the crop for their harvesting services. The contractual cost of harvesting cereals mechanically in temperate countries, by contrast, normally does not exceed 5% of the crop's value.[5]

The Region's draft animals are a less efficient source of draft power under double cropping than under traditional single cropping conditions. They cannot plough in one month what they formerly had five months to plough. The double cropped rice land, being under crop for most of the year, the draft animals are confined to the Region's limited, poor quality natural grassland for most of the year.

Pressure to switch to mechanical power sources, that can be utilised more intensively in season for timely ploughing and cultivating and that are not dependent on reduced grazing resources, are therefore greater in the Region as a result of double cropping than elsewhere. Although the Region has almost half as many more people per acre

5. Crotty 1978b. The normal contract charge of combine-harvesting grain in Sussex, England, in 1978 was £10 per acre, grossing about £200 for wheat.

of crop, other than tree crops, as Asia as a whole (Table 10.2) its rate of tractorisation is exceptionally rapid (Table 10.3).

The price of beef and buffalo meat

National prices of agricultural products not entering international trade are difficult to obtain, especially on a basis suitable for international comparison. An indication only of the trend of beef and buffalo meat prices in the Region is, therefore, attempted.

An expanding demand for a high quality food, meat, that causes its price to rise relative to that of rice, a lower quality food, is not inconsistent with conditions of widespread income decline. Modern type states established in traditional societies appear characteristically to give rise to increased economic inequalities. Several examples of this phenomenon have been noted in earlier chapters. Incomes of less privileged landless or smallholder agriculturists decline even though average per caput income rises. Thus, the pauperisation of Malay smallholders has proceeded contemporaneously with substantial increases in the real incomes of persons in the public service, in protected manufacturing, in subsidised land development schemes, and of members of trade unions employed on estates.[6] The favoured classes are willing and able to pay more for cattle/buffalo meat at the same time as the animals have become less valuable to smallholders for draft purposes.

A large proportion of the Region's population are Muslims and do not eat pigmeat, so their demand centres on beef, sheep and goat and poultry meat. The Region being one of the major grain deficit areas of the world, poultrymeat production has to be based on imported feedgrains and is therefore costly. The limited sheep and goat meat production affords little competition to beef, which is much the most important meat produced from local resources. Beef is also generally preferred to other meats and local beef is preferred to imported beef (Malaysia 1975 p.54). Cattle that would be regarded in developed countries as of inferior beefing quality and inadequately fattened were worth in Malaysia in 1975 M$1 per lb liveweight,[7] which was as much as top quality beef cattle were currently worth in the EEC, the highest priced major meat market in the world.

Demand for cattle/buffalo meat has also been firm in at least two other countries. Imports to the Philippines have been increasing rapidly, (FAO 1978b p.53) and prices have been high in Thailand.[8]

Summary

Rapid extension of rice double cropping has reduced the current net value of draft animals (a) because of their inability to plough and cultivate land expeditiously, that is especially important for adherence to a double cropping regime in the rainforest tropics; and (b) because of the reduced stubble-grazing available to them. Simultaneously, the pauperisation of a people already poor and dependent on a capital intensive agriculture, by rapid population growth, has raised their rate of time discount, I, which, for any current net value of draft animals, reduces their capital value. Simultaneously also, as the capital value of animals for draft purposes declines their value for meat increases with the rise of the incomes of privileged non cattle/buffalo owning sections. These circumstances put pressures on cattle/buffalo

6. Malaysian average real incomes have been increasing by about 2% annually (Malaysia. Department of Statistics 1973 p. 38), while incomes on smallholdings have been declining (Crotty 1978a p. 231).
7. Author's field observations.
8. Thailand, Ministry of Commerce, 1978, p. 4. The price of beef is controlled by government in Sri Lanka (*Sri Lanka Yearbook,* 1977, p. 70) but visitors report that beef can only be bought on the free market at prices well above the controlled level.

owners to liquidate their stocks, even though doing so exacerbates their long term impoverishment.

Model of Decline

Recognising that, in the Region, cows and female buffaloes are kept for draft services and are bred to produce calves (but not milk for a lactose intolerant people), the net revenue equation (Equation 5.24) needs to be reformulated as:

$$NR = PdD + PcC - (PcI^t + PvV_2 . I^{t/2})K/n - Pv . V_3 \qquad (10.1)$$

where Pd is the price of draft services and D is the amount of these produced by the cows in the herd.

Bearing in mind that, grazing being communal, the marginal return from cows to the individual owner is the average return (pp. 55–60), and that an equilibrium condition is

$$\frac{\partial NR}{\partial K} = 0 \text{ (Equation 5.25), then}$$

$$\frac{\partial NR}{\partial K} = PdD^* + PcC^* - (PcI^t + PvV_2^{t/2})/n - PvV_3^* = 0 \qquad (10.2)$$

where D^* and C^* are the output of milk and calves, and V_3^* is the variable input, per cow/buffalo per annum.

Breeding at all stages competes with working. There are no complementary stages, as in MK or RC of Fig. 5.2, where calves and milk are complementary products of cows. Calves must therefore always have a value equal to the value of the draft services foregone while the dam produces the calf. This value may be denoted as:

$$Pc = W . PdD^* \qquad (10.3)$$
where $0 < W < 1$.

The more cows/buffaloes are bred, the more their productive capacity is channelled into this activity and away from draft production. At the limit, PdD^* declines to zero and W increases to 1. As C^* (Equation 10.2) increases, W (Equation 10.3) must also increase.

If cows/buffaloes are bred to maintain a stable draft herd, average annual calf production per breeding animal must be twice the average annual rate of breeding cow/buffalo replacement (the calves being half female), or:

$$C^* = 2/n \qquad (10.4)$$

Equation 10.2 may therefore be restated as:

$$PdD^* + W . PdD^* . C^* - \tfrac{1}{2}C^*(W . PdD^*I^t + PvV_2 . I^{t/2}) - PvV_3^* = 0 \qquad (10.5)$$

VDA, the value of a draft animal, is the value of the flow of its future products net of maintenance costs, discounted to the present at the appropriate rate of time discount, I (Fig. 5.5). The annual value of draft cow/buffalo outputs, net of maintenance costs, is:

$$AV = PdD^* + W . PdD^* . C^* - PvV_3^* \qquad (10.6)$$

VDA may be derived from AV as:

$$VDA = (PdD^* + W \cdot PdD^*C^* - PvV_3^*)R/I \qquad (10.7)$$

where R/I is a function that expresses the present discounted value of future net outputs of draft services and calves.

The value of calves, Pc, is derived from the value of draft cattle VDA, in the same way as from the value of slaughter animals, VFA (Equation 5.16). The animals in this case, however, are used for breeding, so t instead of θ is the appropriate age. That is:

$$Pc = VDA/I^t - PvV_2/I^{t/2} \qquad (10.8)$$

From Equations 10.3, 10.7 and 10.8

$$W \cdot PdD^* \cdot I^{t+1} = R(PdD^* + W \cdot PdD^* \cdot C^* - PvV_3^*) - I^{t/2+1}PvV_2 \qquad (10.9)$$

and

$$Pd \cdot D^* = (PvV_3^* + I^{t/2+1} PvV_2/R)/(I + W \cdot C^* - W \cdot I^{t+1}/R) \qquad (10.10)$$

Taking PdD* as the dependent variable, the following tabulation shows how PdD* changes with the independent variables to maintain equilibrium.

PdD*	:PvV$_2$	PvV$_3$*	I	t	R	W	C*
22.21	: 10	20	1.1	3	6	0.1	0.2
21.79	: 8	20	1.1	3	6	0.1	0.2
17.19	: 10	15	1.1	3	6	0.1	0.2
22.96	: 10	20	1.2	3	6	0.1	0.2
22.37	: 10	20	1.1	4	6	0.1	0.2
22.75	: 10	20	1.1	3	5	0.1	0.2
22.26	: 10	20	1.1	3	6	0.15	0.2
21.99	: 10	20	1.1	3	6	0.1	0.3

As suggested in the preceding discussion:

(i) reduced availability of stubble-grazing raises PvV_2 and PvV_3*;
(ii) the need, created by the rapid extension of irrigation and double cropping, to expedite cultivations, lowers the value of animal draft power, PdD*; and
(iii) impoverishment, caused by the exceptionally rapid growth of an exceptionally poor population dependent on an exceptionally capital intensive agriculture raises I.

Disequilibrium arises from the simultaneous decrease in the value of the left hand side and increases in the value of the right hand side of Equation 10.10. This disequilibrium implies for cattle/buffalo owners a situation where the benefits of keeping draft animals has declined below the cost of keeping them. Owners benefit by reducing stock numbers, which simultaneously:

(i) reduces PvV_2 and PvV_3*, because fewer animals graze the communal land and less supplementary food is necessary;
(ii) reduces I, through the conversion into cash of some cattle/buffalo stocks; and
(iii) raises PdD* for the remaining draft animals as their services are restricted to more crucial, productive work.

The declining value and the increasing cost of draft animals are one perceived cause of reduction in numbers. The increase in the value of these animals for slaughter (VFH) is another. The need for the value of breeding cattle/buffaloes (VDA in the present case) to equal or exceed their value for slaughter (VFH) has been considered on pp. 98–100 and need not be reconsidered here.

An Appraisal of Malaysian Government Policy on Cattle/Buffaloes

An appraisal of official policy with respect to cattle/buffaloes in the Region as a whole is beyond the scope of this work. Attention is limited to the cattle/buffalo policy of Malaysia, that appears to have elements that are common in policies in the Region. It is understandable that Malaysia's policy on cattle/buffaloes should have features common to the policies of other countries in the Region, where the problems and opportunities confronting cattle/buffalo enterprises are similar and tend therefore to give rise to similar policies.

The Malaysian Government seeks to expand cattle/buffalo production as a source of meat that is less dependent on imported feedstuffs than pig and poultry meat, and as a means of improving the low incomes of Malay cattle/buffalo owners. The principal methods used to expand production are, in sequence of their introduction, the "pawah" system, cattle multiplication centres and beef ranches.

The "pawah" system is a development of an indigenous institution under which maiden heifers are allocated to individual smallholders on the understanding that the recipients will return the animal's first female progeny, reared and fit for mating. The allottee has the use of the original animal throughout and acquires ownership on the return to the donor of the first mature female progeny. The system has been operated by the veterinary/livestock authorities of the individual States for several years.

The cattle multiplication schemes were introduced as part of the Second Malaysian Plan. "A major constraint on rapid expansion of the ruminant livestock industry in Malaysia is the shortage of productive breeding stock. To alleviate this difficulty and following the recommendation of an FAO/IBRD livestock project identification mission in 1970, three cattle multiplication units will be established in West Malaysia and multiplication facilities at the Kluang Station will be expanded. These units will help propagate improved stock in large numbers for the development of a large-scale cattle and dairy industry. They will also provide useful opportunities to test under commercial conditions research results relating to animal health and management, pasture and forage production" (Malaysia, Economic Planning Unit 1971 para. 451).

Greater emphasis has been given subsequently to projects aimed at directly expanding cattle production. The Mid-Term Review of the Second Malaysia Plan notes: "The period under review witnessed the establishment of MAJUTERNAK, a corporation whose basic objective is to promote the commercialisation and rapid development of the livestock industry. MAJUTERNAK has undertaken the implementation of beef and dairy projects in Pahang, Perak, Trengganu, Johore and Sarawak. For the remaining years of the Plan, two additional projects are planned for Johore and Pahang. The implementation of these projects will increase domestic supplies of meat and dairy products" (Malaysia, Economic Planning Unit 1973 para. 388).

The long established, State-supported "pawah" scheme has had little success. A high proportion of the animals allocated to smallholders have been reported lost, stolen or dead, and no females have been recovered in respect to these. The scheme, while absorbing public funds, has not increased stocks of cattle/buffaloes owned by Malay smallholders.

The scheme, when operated according to regulations, makes possible an increase in consumption by participating smallholders only several years later, when the second calf matures. Given the existing conditions of low fertility and slow maturation, this is unlikely to be for five or more years after the receipt of maiden heifers. The recipients might expect thereafter to have a mature animal for sale in alternate years until the sale of the last of the progeny in the 13th year after the receipt of the heifer. Assuming that heifers are mated at three years of age, that cows calve in alternate years, and that three year old cattle of both sexes are of value VFA, the present discounted value of the progeny of the "pawah" heifer which the recipient can expect to sell is:

$$\text{VFA} \,(1/I^5 + 1/I^7 + 1/I^9 + 1/I^{11} + 1/I^{13}) = \text{VFA} \,.\, \text{M} \qquad (10.11)$$
$$\text{where } M = 1/I^5 + 1/I^7 + \ldots + 1/I^{13}$$

If, optimistically, the value of the cow's draft services covers both the cow's maintenance costs and the cost of rearing its progeny, the participant's net present discounted benefit from the scheme would be VFA.M. This, for values of I greater than 1.22 is less than VFA.

Participants in the "pawah" scheme who discounted the future at a higher rate than 22% annually could expect to get less than VFA from it by operating according to the regulations. They could get VFA from the scheme by disposing of the animal on receipt and reporting it lost, stolen or dead. It is likely that for most Malay smallholders and participants in the "pawah" scheme I > 1.22.[9] These profit by evading the regulations and selling for slaughter the heifers they receive for breeding. It is, therefore, not surprising the "pawah" scheme has had no success in increasing Malay cattle/buffalo stocks and that many of the heifers issued under the scheme have disappeared, "lost", "stolen" or "dead".

The cattle multiplication centres stem from the proposition that cattle breeding stocks are at too low a level to sustain the national herd and simultaneously to permit its expansion. The view is also held that the introduction, through the multiplication centres, of cattle crossed with exotic breeds will increase the productivity of the indigenous stock. It is implicit in this view that stock numbers are declining because calf production, for pathological reasons, is inadequate to compensate for the normal attrition of the breeding herd. There is an implicit rejection of the view that cattle/buffalo stocks are being depleted because it is more profitable to produce draft services rather than calves, or to slaughter rather than to breed females.

Increasing the national herd through cattle multiplication centres will require substantial public sector involvement. Assuming that the average breeding life is 10 years and that the cattle multiplication centres achieve a high level of cow fertility and successfully rear virtually all calves bred, they might, optimistically, rear annually 80 calves per 100 breeding cows. That is, the calving rate for the multiplication centres, (denoted as $C_c{}^*$) might be as high as 0.8. Given that the national herd is declining because $nC^* < 2$ — which is the implication of multiplication centres to expand the herd — and that $n = 10$, C^* for the national herd must be less than 0.2.

If the national herd is taken as 100x, and C^* as 0.2, in order to raise C^* to 0.3 the breeding herd at the cattle multiplication centres will need to be Y, where:

Total national breeding
  herd (including cattle
  multiplication centres) = 100x + Y   (10.12)

9. Huang 1971. The author quotes estimates of interest rates paid by smallholders that range from 400% annually (by the Division of Cooperatives) to 30–40% (by an IBRD team).

$$\text{Annual calf output} \quad = 20x + 0.8Y \tag{10.13}$$
$$= 30x + 0.3Y$$
$$(\text{where } C^* = 0.3)$$
$$\text{From which:} \quad Y = 20x \tag{10.14}$$

That is, to rasie C^* from 0.2 to 0.3, for the country as a whole, the breeding herds at the cattle multiplication centres would need to be 20% of the national breeding herd. Further, to maintain C^* at 0.3, the cattle multiplication herds would need to grow *pari passu* with the national breeding herd. To raise and maintain C^* at 0.4, the breeding herds at the cattle multiplication centres would need to be 50% of the national herd. Financial provision has not been made for these levels of involvement (Malaysia, Economic Planning Unit 1973 para. 401).

The cattle multiplication centres might trigger off sustained expansion of the national herd by improving the level of technical performance. They could do so if, by genetic improvement, they made it possible with given inputs to produce more milk, draft services or calves, or to fatten or rear cattle more quickly. Improvements of this nature are conceivable, though there is no evidence in Malaysia, except possibly in the case of milk, that the introduction of exotic cattle breeds into a very difficult, tropical rainforest environment can, at smallholding level, increase the value of cattle output over and above the cost of the additional inputs.

Substantially higher milk yields have been obtained by Indian cow keepers in Malaysia using crossbred cows, and this is reflected in premium prices for crossbred heifers. But scope for expanding Malaysian milk production is limited. A substantial increase in milk production would cause the price of milk, now sold on a narrow, high priced liquid milk market, to drop to the level at which it could be processed to substitute for low cost imported milk products. Thus, for example, butter imports to Malaysia in 1973 cost 72 cents per lb, the equivalent of 30 cents per gallon of milk, or about one tenth the price received by Malaysian milk producers (Malaysia, Dept. of Statistics 1973 p.10). There is no possibility that the use of crossbred cows will reduce milk production costs to enable local production to compete with imported dairy products.

An increase in cattle supplies from the multiplication centres, by reducing the price of beef, Pf, and the value of cattle for slaughter, VFA, conceivably could cause an expansion in cattle stocks. This would occur if $nC^* > 2$, and cattle/buffalo stocks are being reduced because, at the margin, heifers are worth more for eating than breeding. This outcome appears unlikely, however, (a) because a substantial increase in cattle/buffalo production would be necessary to reduce Pf and VFA, given beef's relatively small contribution to Malaysia's total meat supplies, and (b) because if a substantial increase in cattle stocks occurred, there would be offsetting increases in Pv, the cost of "other" inputs, as well as reductions in Pd, the value of draft services.

Ranch beef and milk

The main thrust of public policy in relation to cattle has more recently been, in Malaysia, towards the development of large ranches producing milk and fat cattle for sale, and surplus crossbred heifers for distribution on favourable terms to Malay smallholders. These ranches have been established by MAJUTERNAK, the State owned livestock corporation, or by MAJUTERNAK in conjunction with aid-donating agencies, including the UK Commonwealth Development Corporation.

Most Malaysian land is still under tropical rainforest (Barlow 1978 p.201). Land of itself is therefore not a constraint. However, the most fertile and most accessible land has been developed. Undeveloped land is, for the most part, less fertile or less accessible.

Land developments costs in Malaysia are substantial. FELDA recently reported the cost of felling and burning rainforest as in excess of M$200 per acre, over a three year period (Malaysia, FELDA 1974). The indicated cost of pasture establishment, including fencing, is a further M$200–300 per acre.[10] If the site is located in an undeveloped, unsettled area, additional costs will be incurred for housing, roads and other amenities. FELDA reports its costs in respect of these items to be 64% of agricultural development costs (Malaysia, FELDA 1974). Thus, although there is an abundance of uncleared, unused land in Malaysia, its development cost is substantial.

Tropical rainforest land is severely leached and is therefore usually of low fertility. Unfertilised, cultivated pasture on cleared land of low fertility in the tropics is unproductive and quickly reverts to scrub and jungle. Attempts to date to develop mixed grass-legume pastures, which require less fertilising, have so far been unsuccessful in Malaysia. Repeated, heavy fertilising is necessary to maintain pastures in productive condition, even on land that has been developed expensively. Similar problems have been experienced in attempting to establish extensive pastures on clearances from the Amazonian jungle (*Financial Times* 1978).

Milk production in Malaysia on land that is costly to clear and costly to maintain in production will itself be costly. As long as output is small, it may be possible to sell this milk profitably on the local, small, high priced liquid milk market. If milk production is expanded, however, the value of milk will be forced down for processing in competition with low cost, imported dairy products. Further, given the lactose intolerance of the Malays and Chinese, who account for 89% of the population (Malaysia, Dept. of Statistics 1977 p.291), demand prospects for milk are, in any case, poor. Any substantial expansion of ranch cattle production must, therefore, be beef oriented.

Ranch beef production involves keeping cows to gestate and suckle calves, the weaned calves being subsequently fattened on the ranch grazing land. Feed conversion rates are very low; very many units of feed are required to produce one unit of meat. The system is justified where feed costs are very low, conditions that obtain in the ranching areas of Australia and South America, where land costs are negligible and ranch operating costs are also very low. Feed costs are not low in Malaysia, where, as noted, both establishment and maintenance costs of ranches are high.

High feed costs obtain in beef production in North America and western Europe where, as in Malaysia, the capital and operating costs of land are high. But high cost feed is normally used there only at the final, fattening stage of production, when feed conversion rates are much better. Feeder cattle are, or have in the past been, produced at relatively low cost by cows grazing poor quality, low cost range land, or as a byproduct of the dairy industry. It has been noted in Chapter 7 that beef production costs in North America and western Europe have risen sharply since the Second World War because the supply of feeder cattle from these sources is no longer adequate. Increasingly expensive land and feed is being used to produce feeder cattle in North America and western Europe, with the result that young cattle costs have risen sharply in relation to the price of fat cattle and young cattle costs are forcing up beef prices.

Present proposals for beef production in Malaysia imply the use of high cost land and fodder throughout, as is becoming increasingly necessary in North America and western Europe. This implies that the cost of production of ranch beef in Malaysia will be high, though possibly not higher than the present very high price paid for the small amount of beef now produced in Malaysia. The proposed ranches may, to that extent, provide an acceptable return to the resources invested.

The ranches, however, are unlikely to reduce the price of local beef to Malaysian consumers. Neither are they likely to replace with lower cost, locally produced beef the pig and poultry meat that is produced for the most part with imported feedstuff and that now constitutes the major portion of Malaysian meat supplies.

10. See Appendix B below.

The cattle ranches are unlikely to have an impact on Malay smallholding cattle production. The price of beef, Pf, or VFA, is unlikely to decline. The value to smallholders of heifers for breeding, VBH, will be unaffected by the ranches. If smallholders are supplied with heifers for breeding at a reduced price by the ranches, they will dispose of them, as they have disposed of heifers received under the "pawah" scheme, because, at the margin, VFA will continue to be higher than VBH. The more heifers are supplied by the ranches to the smallholders and the lower the price at which they are supplied, the larger will be the windfall gains of the smallholders from selling the heifers for slaughter. The ranches, apart from this possible role of supplying low cost heifers to Malay smallholders to be subsequently slaughtered for immediate consumption, will be enclaves of new technology, of questionable economic value.

An Alternative Approach

Decline in cattle/buffalo stocks implies
$nC^* < 2$, or VDA $<$ VFH, or both.
That is, either cattle/buffalo owners are unwilling to forego some of the draft services of their female stock while these are gestating and suckling calves; or owners find they can get more from selling their stock for slaughter than these are worth when retained as working and breeding animals; or both. In any case, the reduction in stock numbers is almost certainly the result of choice by the owners, and not the result of pathological disorders forcing nC^* below two. The explanation of the decline in stock numbers in the Region is perceived to be that, at the margin, the value of draft service, PdD, is less than their cost, and the value of an animal for draft/breeding purposes, VDA, is less than its value for slaughter, VFH. Increasing PdD or decreasing PvV_2, PvV_3 or I does not appear to be realistically attainable. There are, however, possibilities of exogenously increasing the value of calves, Pc, and therefore making their production more profitable, and of raising the value of an animal for draft and breeding (VDA) above its value for slaughter (VFA).

Raising Pc

Prices of young cattle/buffaloes in Malaysia are low relative to prices of mature cattle/buffaloes. There are no published statistics, but observations by the writer at abattoirs in 1975 showed that the price per lb of cattle was normally higher for stock in good condition than for cattle in poorer condition. Cattle/buffaloes are normally slaughtered in Malaysia, as in South America (Chapter 8) in what would be considered, in North America and western Europe, unfinished condition. The current price of cattle for slaughter of around 600 lb was observed to be about $1 per lb. The price per lb of cattle of lighter weight, or in poorer condition, was less. Discussions with cattle dealers in north Malaysia suggested that store cattle/buffaloes of around 300 lb liveweight were freely available at 85 cents per lb. This contrasts with the situation in North America and western Europe where the price per unit weight is normally considerably higher for young cattle than for mature ones (see Table 4.8). The low price per unit weight of young cattle, relative to the price per unit weight of mature cattle in Malaysia, corresponds to the normal relationship between prices per unit weight of young and mature cattle in South America. The explanation is seen in terms of a slow fattening rate (i.e. θ is high; Equation 5.8) and a high rate of time discount, I. Though the value of fat animals, VFA, tends to be higher than the value of animals for breeding/draft, VDA, the value of calves, $Pc = VDA/I^\theta - PvV_1/I^{\theta/2}$, tends to be low. For a given price of beef, Pf, the value of calves, Pc, can be raised:

(i) by increasing the rate of fattening and/or reducing the fattening period without causing an excessive increase in fattening costs; and/or

(ii) by reducing I.

I can be reduced by transferring the cost of financing the fattening operation from capital starved smallholders to others, better endowed with capital.

Recent developments in tropical grassland technology suggest that it may be possible to increase the rate of fattening substantially with a less than commensurate increase in variable costs, PvV_1. These hinge on the capacity to produce in the rainforest tropics, from heavily fertilised, cultivated pastures, annual yields of around 15 tons per acre dry matter with a crude protein content of 10–12% and to convert this fodder into beef at reasonable conversion rates.[11]   Tan Hong Tong and Pillai report yields of 16 tons of dry matter per acre per annum on a commercial scale at Labu Estate, Seremban, Malaysia, the grass being cut and dried for export to Japan (Tan & Pillai 1974). The grass was harvested every 6–8 weeks. Annual fertilising per acre was N.914 lb, P_2O_5 290 lb, and K_2O 806 lb.

Experimental work in Malaysia suggests that the indigenous Kedah-Kelantan cattle have the capacity to gain 1 lb liveweight daily, with a feed conversion rate of 9 lb of dry matter per 1 lb liveweight gain. Devendra reports conversion rates with unselected Kedah-Kelantan heifers of 1 lb liveweight gain per 9.15 lb of dry matter on all-grass diets.[12] Dalzell reports daily liveweight gains with unselected Kedah-Kelantan heifers in excess of 1 lb on diets using waste palm oil sludge.[13] Feed conversion rates and daily liveweight gains should be better feeding young, noncastrated males. These normally have daily liveweight gains some 20% greater than females and have 15–20% better feed conversion rates. That is, Kedah-Kelantan young, noncastrated bulls may be expected to gain up to 1.20 lb daily with a feed conversion rate as high as 8 lb of dry matter of grass per 1 lb liveweight gain. Young buffalo bulls may be expected to perform even better.

Cattle fattening, using methods of intensive grass production proven on a commercial scale in Malaysia, feeding the grass to young, local cattle/buffaloes, and getting results from these cattle/buffaloes in line with those reported by Devendra and Dalzell promises to be highly profitable at 1975 prices. Cattle fattening on similar lines may also be profitable in other parts of the Region and in other tropical rainforest areas in West Africa and South America. Input-output particulars for a hypothetical Malaysian project are developed in Appendix B for illustrative purposes.

The effect on the profitability of cattle/buffalo keeping of an exogenous rise in the price of calves, Pc, can be seen through Equation 10.15 (from Equation 10.5) taken to describe the present situation, and Equation 10.16, to represent the new one.

$$NR = PdD^* + W \cdot PdD^* \cdot C^* - \tfrac{1}{2}C^* \cdot WPdD^*I^t - \tfrac{1}{2}C^*PvV_2 \cdot I^{t/2} - PvV_3^* \quad (10.15)$$
$$NR_1 = PdD^* + PcC^* - \tfrac{1}{2}C^*Pc \cdot I^t - \tfrac{1}{2}C^*PvV_2 \cdot I^{t/2} - PvV_3^* \quad (10.16)$$
$$NR_1 - NR = PcC^* - W \cdot PdD^*C^* - \tfrac{1}{2}C^*PcI^t + \tfrac{1}{2}C^*W \cdot PdD^* \cdot I^t \quad (10.17)$$
$$= C^* \left[(Pc - W \cdot PdD^*)(1 - \tfrac{1}{2}I^t) \right] \quad (10.18)$$

Taking t = 3, for values of I $\geqslant$ 1.26,
$$NR_1 - NR < 0.$$

11. (a) R. J. McIlroy, An Introduction to Tropical Grassland Husbandry, p. 65.
    (b) N. Williams, Univ. of Malaysia, (personal communication 2.2.75) reports annual yields in excess of 20 tons of dry matter per acre with Napier grass.
    (c) Ajit Singh Sidhu, Field Crop Research Branch, MARDI, Malaysia, (personal communication 14.2.75) reports yields of 32.7 tons of dry matter per ha p.a. from Napier grass.
12. C. Devendra, MARDI, Malaysia, "Livestock Production and the Food Crisis" (unpublished paper read at the Seminar on the Food Crisis at Kuala Lumpur, January 1975).
13. R. Dalzell of Dalzell and Associates, in experimental work at Unilever's oil palm estate Kluang, Malaysia, on the feeding of oil palm sludge, reported (February 1975) average daily liveweight gains from Kedah-Kelantan heifers in excess of 1 lb.

That is, cattle/buffalo keeping will be less profitable, and owners will wish to reduce stocks. This occurs because, although gross revenue is increased by $(Pc-W.PdD^*)$, cost is increased more, by the increased capital cost resulting from the rise in calf prices. Probably for most cattle/buffalo owners $I > 1.26$, so that an increase in calf prices would encourage them to sell off their young cattle for fattening, accelerating the decline in stock numbers.

It would, however, be simple to restrict buying for fattening to male animals. The net revenue in that case would be:

$$NR_2 = PdD^* + \tfrac{1}{2}C^*(Pc + W.PdD^*) - \tfrac{1}{2}C^*W.PdD^*I^t - \tfrac{1}{2}C^*PvV_2.I^{t/2} - PvV_3 \tag{10.19}$$

and

$$Nr_2 - NR = \tfrac{1}{2}C^*(Pc - W.PdD^*) \tag{10.20}$$

which is positive.

An increase in cow numbers caused by raising the value of young male cattle/buffaloes would simultaneously increase the supply of animal draft power and, to that extent, facilitate rice production. Fattening male cattle/buffaloes on intensively produced grass in the rainforest tropics thus offers a means to increase the very small amount of meat produced from indigenous sources in these areas while simultaneously making possible increased rice production. Intensive grass production may be the key to more meat and more rice in the rainforest tropics.

The Indian Case: Cattle Grazed Communally; Milk Has Value

Introduction

India, with 240 million cattle and buffaloes, has 18% of the world's total stocks. It has as many cattle and buffaloes as Europe and the USSR combined. Its grassland, by comparison, is very restricted (Tables 11.1 and 11.2).

Table 11.1   Land use (ha) in India, 1972.

Total area	328 048 000
Arable land and land under permanent crops	164 980 000
(Including irrigated land	31 590 000)
Permanent meadows and pastures	13 130 000
Forest and woodland	65 760 000
Other land	84 178 000
(Includes unused but potentially productive land, waste land, barren land, and land not listed elsewhere)	

See FAO 1975a pp. 5, 73.

Cattle normally graze freely over nonirrigated cropland during the dry season, after harvesting and when pasture growth is poorest. "Other" land, where suitable and accessible, and some forest and woodland are grazed. Grass may also be cut from "other" land and from forest and woodland for feeding to cattle.

Table 11.2   Percentage of world's total accounted for by India

Population	15.2
GNP	1.5
Cropland	11.2
Grassland	0.4
Cattle and buffaloes	18.3
Beef and buffalo meat	0.4
Total meat	0.7
Milk	5.9
Cereals and pulses	8.5

See Appendix A.

Indian incomes are extremely low, only one tenth of the world's average. They are only two fifths of African incomes, one seventh of average incomes in South America, and one quarter of the average level of incomes in Asia exclusive of India (Table 2.1).

India's cropland and cereal/pulse production is less than proportionate to population. However, the shortfall in relation to grassland and to cattle products is much greater: though with 11% of the world's cropland, India has less than 0.5% of the world's grassland; with 8.5% of the world's cereal/pulse production, India has only 0.4% of the world's beef and 5.9% of the world's milk production.

India's population, though among the world's poorest, is well endowed with cattle/buffaloes. Per head of population, it has 0.41, compared to 0.33 in Europe, 0.38 in Africa, 0.57 in North and Central America, and 0.34 in the world as a whole. Indian cattle, however, are among the world's least productive in terms of meat and milk. They produce virtually no meat and their milk output per head is one third of the world's average. They are, however, a major source of draft power.

Milk production per ha of grassland in India is extraordinarily high at 1.85 tons, compared to 0.137 tons per ha of grassland for the world as a whole. The EEC is the only major land area with as high an output of milk per ha of grassland as India has. However, as will be seen presently, much Indian cattle production is attributable to produce from land other than its grassland.

Production of milk per person in India is only two fifths of the world average, while meat production per person is only 5% of the world average. Taking eight tons of milk as equivalent to one ton of meat, India's meat-equivalent production per person is only 15% of the world average. Its cereal/pulse production per person, on the other hand, is nearly 60% of the world average.

Cattle, as well as being virtually the only source of animal protein, are also the principal form of agricultural draft power. Over 40% of India's 176 million cattle are working oxen, three years of age and over (Table 11.5).

Cattle are regarded as sacrosanct in India. Many Indian states prohibit the slaughter of cattle and the Hindu majority of the population oppose the eating of beef on religious and aesthetic grounds.

Table 11.3 World and Indian growth rates, %, 1961–65 to 1974.

	World	India
Population	21	24
Cattle/buffalo stock	18	5
Beef/buffalo meat production	35	13
Milk production	20	24
Total meat production	40	19

See FAO 1966, 1977a.

India's population is increasing more rapidly than the world's as a whole (Table 11.3). Its cattle/buffalo stock is growing much more slowly than world stocks. While the growth of Indian milk production is abreast of world milk production and of Indian population growth, Indian production of meat is growing at only half the world rate and less rapidly than the Indian population. Production of meat-equivalent per person, already extremely low, is declining in India.

Historico-Cultural Background

India's position among the noncapitalist agricultural societies of the Old World was the product of a unique blend of crop growing and pastoralist cultures. A warm climate, the Indus and Ganges rivers, and the monsoons that watered most of the subcontinent made India preeminently suited for crop growing. India, however, was not as insulated from pastoral influence as China, the other great crop growing culture of the Old World. China could more easily repulse the sparse, and therefore primitive pastoralists of Mongolia, and remain more insulated from their influence. India's history has been largely that of successive invasions by the pastoralist crop growers of South West Asia and Asia Minor, drawn by the subcontinent's richer natural resources and wealth. Pastoralist influences percolated through and permeated the predominantly crop growing Indian culture.

Pastoral influences gave rise to a moderately lactose tolerant population that valued milk as a food (Simoons 1978 p. 967). The extensive use of draft animals made possible the more effective exploitation of India's topography, allowing cultivation to spread beyond the fertile alluvial valleys, where yields were high, to less favoured areas where yields were lower. More land was cultivated and, though average yields were lower, more grain was produced. The point is illustrated by a comparison of Indian and Chinese land use (Table 11.4).

Table 11.4   Land, grain and pulse production, India and China.

	India	China
Total land area ($\times 10^3$ ha)	328 048	959 696
Cultivated area ($\times 10^3$ ha)	165 070	130 000
Grain and pulse production ($\times 10^3$ tons)	134 208	250 649
Production per ha of cultivated land (tons)	0.81	1.93
Production per 100 ha of land area (tons)	40.91	26.12

See FAO 1976b.

Yield per cropped ha is more than twice as high in China. But only 14% of China's total area is cropped, compared to 50% of India's. Output of grain and pulse averaged over the entire area of each country is much higher in India than in China.

Cultivators on India's less favoured land had to supplement human muscle power with animal power if the conditions necessary for crop growing were to be met (Equation 3.1). The same influence apparently continues to operate; there was a negative correlation between yield of grain and pulses per acre, and draft oxen per 100 acres of cropland, by state in India in 1961.[1] ($r^2 = 0.3212$.)

The diffusion of cultivation in India made it more difficult than in other riverine cultures for a monolithic despot to emerge. Indian despotism was characterised by numerous, usually warring, petty despots, rather than by a single despot, as in China, Egypt, or Mezzo-America. Fragmentation of despotism reduced India's power to resist pastoralist invaders, and successive waves caused further fragmentation and made still more difficult the emergence of a dominant despot, capable of resisting invaders. There was much commingling of the crop growing culture based on the Indus-Ganges with the pastoralist influences introduced by invaders from South West Asia.

These environmental conditions resulted in five characteristics of Indian cattle husbandry that are central to the process of decision making. First, as an indigenous, noncapitalist society, India retains and practises communal grazing (Chapters 9 and 10). Second, Indians, being predominantly lactose tolerant, value milk as a food. Third, as a predominantly crop growing, urbanised society, India has long used coins for money. They were "in use as early as the beginning of the sixth century BC" (Carson 1970 p. 499), half a millenium before the conquest by Caesar of the pastoral Gauls and Britons, for whom cattle continued to be money. Cattle in India, therefore, have traditionally been a nonliquid asset, to be held instead of money, the liquid asset. This implies that I in India had a higher value than one; and a higher value than in Africa, where cattle were cash.

Further, individual capital not being a barrier to population growth in riverine Indian society, as it was in Europe (Chapter 3), birth rates have tended to the biological limit, and many survived. The society's institutions were characteristically riverine, despotic, and did not include those peculiarly western European features that facilitated private capital formation (Chapter 3). Capital formation was, therefore

1. Crop yields are the average of three years, 1962/63 to 1964/65 (India, Ministry of Agriculture, Directorate of Economics and Statistics, 1967 and 1969).

slow. The ratio between population and the stock of private capital has been high people have been poor. I has therefore been very high. (Evidence of the present high value of I in India is introduced later.)

It is difficult for poor people to accumulate capital in any form, including cattle It is, as noted in Chapters 5 and 10, especially difficult for poor people to retain for breeding female cattle/buffaloe that will bring them benefits over a protracted future instead of slaughtering them to get substantial immediate benefits. Pressures t slaughter cattle are less, other things being equal, when the cattle are communall grazed than when they are individually grazed (Chapter 8). But other things are no equal; a high population/capital ratio implies also a very high value for I, an therefore pressure to dispose of cattle. These pressures could have precluded th growth of cattle stocks and held Indian society tightly to the courses of the grea rivers, as Chinese and Egyptian societies were held tight to the rivers on which the were based.

The apotheosis of Indian cattle, that allowed cultivation to spread beyond the rive valleys, appears to have taken place during the first millenium of the Christian er (Lal 1967). This was the same time that the accumulation of cattle stocks in wester Europe made possible the clearance of forests and the extension of cultivation.

It is speculated that only a people holding the eating of beef to be taboo could hav carried cultivation far beyond the river valleys. Muslims, without this taboo, settle in those parts of the Indian subcontinent, the Indus valley and the Ganges delta where crop yields are highest and the need for cattle as draft animals is least.

The principle of social evolution that caused some ethnic groups to acquire th genetic aberration of lactose tolerance, that caused African pastoralists to allocat land between crop and pasture, that caused the rise and collapse of Rome, that gav birth to capitalism among the forests of Dark Age Europe, appears also to hav resulted in Indian cows becoming sacred. The principle advanced in Chapter 3, tha more densely force out less densely settled societies, suggests that a society able t resist pressures to dispose of cattle would have dominated a society without tha resistance. A cattle owning society, able to cultivate the monsoon watered Decc plateau, could spread out and away from the main rivers, to become more numerou and more efficient, and therefore able to dominate a less adaptable, cattleless society The only way a riverine crop growing society, in which cattle are not money, coul acquire large numbers of cattle was by making their consumption culturally taboo The effect of this was, in terms of the model of Chapter 5, to make the price of bee equal to zero, which is the fourth of the distinctive characteristics of Indian cattl husbandry referred to.

If cattle are not eaten in India, there is no temptation to slaughter, instead o breeding, heifers. Heifers, when bred, produce milk, for which Indians, being lactos tolerant, have a strong liking. The price of milk in India, Pm, is high; it is the highe because the price of beef, Pf, $=0$. If the price of milk is very high, a poor people wil not willingly feed it to calves, and without milk, calves perish. Cattle populations ca decline through calf mortality as quickly as through heifer slaughter. Given very hig values of I and Pm, cattle can only survive if calves are assured of sufficient milk fo their survival. This is the fifth distinctive characteristic of Indian cattle husbandry indigenous cows, of the variety *bos indicus*, only lactate if their calves are alive an at foot. Keen judgment is exercised by Indian cow keepers to allow calves to drav sufficient milk from their dams to enable them to remain alive, but not a drop more The significance of this, in terms of the model developed in Chapter 5, is that few variable inputs are needed for rearing heifers, V_2, or for rearing cattle for draft, V The calves must, in any case, be kept alive during their dams' lactation, when thei nutritional needs are most costly. They can, thereafter, be set loose to survive, o perish, on the communal grazing.

The distinctive characteristics of Indian cattle husbandry are, therefore, seen as adjustments to India's location and topography. A buffer zone between the pastoral west and the crop growing east, its population is largely genetically lactose tolerant and therefore values milk. Its semitropical river valleys imply that India's, like China's, would be a riverine, urbanised society, with a specialist money form, coins. This further implies a very high value for I. A people with a very high value for I could acquire the cattle necessary to cultivate lands away from the immediate vicinity of the rivers, and which, unlike in China, was not mountainous, or unlike in Egypt was not desert, only if beef consumption were taboo for them. Even then, these cattle could only survive by the calves' survival being a condition of the dams' continued lactation.

India and Europe

It is easy to see how geographical conditions resulted in India in cattle playing a much greater social role than in China, and in crop growing being a much more important activity than in Africa. Less readily perceptible are the reasons for the very different paths of social development followed in India and Europe from a common base of a dual reliance on cattle and crops. The point, however cursorily and speculatively it must be considered in the present context, gives insights into the differences in the cattle economies of the two societies.

Three factors are identified as likely to have given rise to divergent lines of development. First, the influence of the Indus-Ganges was overwhelming in India. Crop growing in their basins resulted in a surplus that appears to have been half the total product. Thus, quite typically, "The share of gross produce shared by the State was very high, usually about one half" (Gupta 1964 p. 108). This imposed an essentially riverine, despotic character on Indian society. No similar influence dominated the European scene, where natural resources were far poorer and where, without the surplus of a riverine economy, state power was weaker.

Second, and related, crop growing in Europe was more capital dependent than in even the least favoured parts of India. That is, in terms of equations 3.5 and 3.6, s was considerably higher for Europe than for India. The advantages gained by societies favouring capital formation were more overwhelming in Europe than in India, and they became dominant in Europe more readily. Power was more evenly distributed between poor European states and European cultivators with relatively large capitals.

I, the cost of capital for the cattle owner was, for these reasons, probably much lower in Europe even in the Dark Ages, than in India. Cattle stocks could accumulate without a taboo on beef eating — except at the most critical season of the year. (The Church's prohibition on meat eating during Lent reinforced economic considerations to dissuade hard pressed, ill nourished European peasants from slaughtering and eating their oxen during springtime, when they were most needed, for draft power and for meat.)

The cattle/man ratio had to be higher in Europe, for reasons discussed in Chapter 3. Further, cattle, like people, ceased to be productive in Europe at a higher level of nutrition than they did under India's more congenial climate, so that it was profitable in Europe to dispose of breeding and working stock while they retained some edible muscle, whereas cattle in similar condition continued to be productive in India. A general taboo on beef eating would, therefore, have been wasteful in Europe, where larger quantities of beef per person became available from a relatively larger cattle herd, culled at a better nourished level.

The price of milk, Pm, was probably relatively lower in Europe than in India, because of the additional animal protein available from beef in Europe and because of the higher cattle/people ratio there. A lower Pm and a lower I (for reasons already discussed) reduced the temptation in Europe to starve calves of milk. Breeds of cattle could survive without developing the *bos indicus* characteristic of lactating only with a calf at foot.

The third factor suggested as causing the divergence in social development in Europe and India, from a common base of dual reliance on cattle and crops, was that cattle were indigenous to Europe's forests but not to India's jungle. Cattle and their owners could exist in the forest clearings of Europe; they existed only outside the jungle in India. Expansion in Europe was from the forest outwards; it was from the plain inwards in India. Differentiation and experimentation were possible in the former case; the overwhelming power of wealthy, riverine, despotic states was exercised up to the jungle's edge and compelled compliance with an undifferentiated subsistence existence in the latter case.

Plate 6   Malnourished Indian cattle returning in the evening from overused communal grazing land (Photo: Ardea)

The Economics of Indian Cattle Husbandry

India is unique among the great noncapitalist cultures of the world in combining a predominantly crop growing economy with a very substantial cattle producing element. This combination has imparted five characteristics, already noted, that form the context for decision making by Indian cattle owners. The decision making process is examined here.

Exogenous variables: price of beef (Pf); price of milk (Pm); cost of inputs (Pv); and rate of time discount (I):

Orders of value for three of these variables have been suggested above, together with reasons: Pf=0; Pm and I are very high. The cost of variable inputs, Pv, is low in so far as the principal element is family labour. It will also be recalled that, because of the need to keep calves alive while their dams lactate, the amount of the variable inputs, V_1 or V_2, needed to carry the calves on to the productive period, as cows or draft cattle, is small.

A taboo, that causes the price of beef, Pf, to be zero, makes it easier for poor people to have cattle for draft work. Because Pf is zero, the value of an animal fo slaughter, VFA, is also zero (Equation 5.18). But, though VFA=0, the value of a draft animal, VDA, can be high. The significance of this point is considered further below.

Endogenous variables: milk (M); calves (C) and weight gain (WG):

Reasoning and conclusions similar to those in the African case (pp. 122–3) obtain here and need not be repeated.

Commentators frequently refer to the importance of cattle dung for fuel and manure in the Indian economy. It can be incorporated into the analysis without designating it a separate output by imputing a higher level to milk output, M, than otherwise.

The sanctity of cattle and the price of calves (Pc):

Bovines, under favourable circumstances, commence to breed at around three years of age and produce 20 calves in as many years. As cows are kept in India primarily to produce milk, they are encouraged to calve frequently, preferably annually, thus producing considerably more calves than are required simply for reproduction. Given a breeding herd size that is constant, or expanding slowly, this implies a surplus of heifer calves. Draft cattle have a working life of about 15 years. Replacement requirements for a stable, or slightly expanding draft herd will, therefore, also be far less than the number of young male cattle supplied by the breeding herd.

The peculiarity of *bos indicus*, that requires calves to be at foot to induce dams to milk, has been noted. Calves must therefore be kept alive, consuming valuable milk, even though, at the end of the dam's lactation, they are not required as replacements for the breeding or work herds. Neither are they required for slaughter, because of the unwillingness of most Indians to eat beef. They are, therefore, valueless (supporting evidence follows).

If young cattle are valueless, so also are calves. That is, Pc, in India as in pre-Second World War Europe and the USA, is zero.

The role of young cattle mortality:

The usual means of disposing of calves surplus to replacement needs is by withholding milk, or slaughter at birth (Chapter 6) or when fattened (Chapter 7). None of these means of disposal is available in India, where cows lactate only if their calves are at foot and beef eating is taboo. Herd stability is instead achieved by the starvation of reared cattle.

Indian cows have an apparently 38% calving rate, 21 million cows producing annually a similar number of calves, all of which are reared (Table 11.5). Almost half of the calves that are reared for the first year perish during the following two years so that the number of both males and females aged between one and three years is only slightly larger than the numbers less than one year. Every year, therefore, approximately five million males join the working oxen herd, of some 73 million aged three years and over, while a similar number aged between one and three years dies; and five million heifers join the breeding herd, of some 55 million cows aged three years and over, while another five million heifers aged between one and three years die. This implies that the average working life of an ox is 15 years and the average breeding life of a cow is around 10 years.

It also implies that of the 20 million calves that India's cows annually produce, only half are required to maintain the breeding and working herds. The other surplus half, after being kept alive during the period of the cows' lactation, are allowed to perish.

Table 11.5   Composition of the Indian cattle herd, by states, 1966, and nationally in 1966, 1961 and 1956 (thousands).

	Males over 3 years	Males 1–3 years	Males <1 year	Females over 3 years				Females 1–3 years	Females <1 year
				Milking	Dry	Not yet calved	Total*		
India	73 329	12 105	11 150	20 974	25 803	4994	54 683	13 583	11 149
A. Pradesh	5407	659	684	1292	1916	622	3830	740	698
Assam	2510	435	561	1089	603	131	1823	490	523
Bihar	6931	1134	927	1395	2253	166	3814	1185	875
Gujarat	3101	471	339	813	813	136	1762	448	405
Haryana	918	142	189	352	235	24	611	191	172
J. & Kashmir	558	146	134	255	346	45	646	169	130
Kerala	520	162	231	483	593	134	1210	394	331
M. Pradesh	9203	2308	1467	2622	4289	224	7135	2834	1473
Maharashtra	6550	981	819	1607	2318	556	4481	1037	808
Mysore	2666	565	633	1220	1486	412	3118	625	624
Nagaland	19	na	na	10	10	2	22	na	na
Orissa	4397	694	707	1137	1559	463	3159	727	684
Punjab	1290	270	254	485	301	39	825	254	230
Rajasthan	4092	961	967	1825	2549	405	4779	1387	917
T. Nadu	4947	523	574	1198	1267	390	2852	530	574
U. Pradesh	13 231	1615	1594	2669	3354	687	6710	1351	1578
W. Bengal	4909	775	862	2125	1486	472	4083	936	921

India, 1961 and 1956

	Males over 3 years	Males 1–3 years	Males <1 year	Females over 3 years				Females 1–3 years	Females <1 year
				Milking	Dry	Not yet calved	Total*		
1961	72 528	11 808	10 850	20 667	25 016	5319	54 204	13 133	10 801
1956	64 874	11 232	10 528	20 099	21 485	5675	49 903	11 776	10 270

*Includes small numbers of work animals.
Note: Provisional figures for India 1972 are:
    Males over 3 years 74.6 million.
    Females over 3 years 56.8 million (of which milking 22.2 million).
    Cattle less than 3 years, male and female, 47.5 million.
See India, Ministry of Agriculture 1969, 1971b, and India, Planning Commission 1975.

Weaned calves graze the communal grazing land where half of them perish during the two years following weaning. Cattle mortalities during this period of life are, under other circumstances, normally minimal. For example, these are believed to be 8% and 5% respectively in Colombia and Venezuela, where cattle mortality rates are considered to be exceptionally high (ECLA/FAO 1962 pp. 20, 79).

The heavy mortality rate among Indian cattle aged between one and three years implies that young cattle are valueless. The minimal inputs are not provided to prevent very heavy mortalities at a stage of cattle growth where these are otherwise minimal, because the young cattle are valueless and do not warrant the inputs. Heavy mortalities at the calf stage, when cattle are most vulnerable and require the most expensive feeding, do not occur because the calves must receive sufficient nourishment to maintain them alive as a condition of their dams continuing to lactate.

Calves in India, as in Northeast America and Northwest Europe prior to the Second World War, are a free, valueless good. They are produced complementarily to milk in the segment MK of the production possibility curve MKRC of Fig. 5.2. Calves surplus to the needs of the breeding herd — and of the draft oxen herd in some European countries — were normally slaughtered at birth in Northeast America and Northwest Europe. The need to have calves at foot to induce *bos indicus* cows to lactate makes it necessary for Indian cattle owners to keep calves alive during the first vulnerable six months or so of the calves' lives. This precludes their slaughter at birth or the withholding of milk, without which pre-weaned calves would die.

Once the dam has ceased to lactate, the calf owner no longer has an incentive to feed the calf. Religious scruples then preclude the humane slaughter of surplus stock, and the absence of a market for young cattle precludes their sale. Economic self-interest requires the cattle owner to withhold "other" inputs from the valueless, weaned calves, but this withholding of "other" inputs — including milk — which would have been fatal at the preweaning stage, is not fatal in the post-weaning stage. Half the weaned calves survive the following two years on communal grazing land, in accordance with religious precept and at no cost to the individual. All of the cost of abiding by religious precepts and refraining from slaughtering surplus cattle falls on society by way of additional cattle, fated to perish of starvation before producing, grazing the communal land, and reducing the grazing left for others.

Religious conviction coincides with the cow owner's self-interest in ensuring the survival of calves during their most vulnerable, preweaning stage. Religious convictions preclude the humane slaughter of surplus weaned calves, but adherence to religious precepts costs the individual calf owner nothing; there is no market on which to sell the weaned calves and allowing them to graze the communal grazing land is effectively free for the individual.

A broadly similar pattern obtains in the case of buffaloes (Table 11.6). About half the cows calve in any year. Most of the female calves are kept alive but half the males perish in the first year. Nearly half the females surviving the first year perish during the following two years, and two thirds of the yearling males die in the following two years.

Table 11.6   Indian buffalo herd, 1966 (thousands).

	Over 3 years	1–3 years	Under 1 year
Males	8191	2437	3966
Females (of which milking 12 924)	26 145	6286	5893

See India, Ministry of Agriculture 1971b p. 4.

The "scarcity" and high cost of work oxen, which prevents many smallholders from owning them, is not due to an inadequate supply of calves. It is due to the difficulty which poor people have in investing resources to rear calves and in waiting to get a return on these resources over the 18 or so years of an ox's life. Hence the apparent paradox of five million weaned male calves annually being allowed to perish while smallholders' cultivations are frequently limited by the nonavailability of oxen at peak work periods. Though the need of smallholders for work oxen is acute — VDA is high — their rate of time discount, I, is also high; at the margin, when half the available calves are reared,

$$VDA/I^\theta - PvV_1/I^{\theta/2} = Pc = 0 \tag{5.16}$$

Net revenue from cattle (NR):

Recalling that:

$$NR = PmM + PcC - (I^tPc + I^{t/2} . Pv . V_2)K/n - Pv . V_3 \tag{5.24}$$

If $Pc = 0$, Equation 5.24 may be rewritten for India as:

$$NR_1 = PmM - I^{t/2}PvV_2 . K/n - PvV_3 \tag{11.1}$$

Indian cattle keepers will wish to increase the number of cows they keep, K, until the increase in net revenue, NR_I, with respect to K is zero. That is, until

$$\frac{\delta NR_I}{\delta K} = 0.$$

Recalling that cow owners, under conditions of communal grazing, get the average return to cows as cow numbers are increased (pp. 55–60), so that

$$\frac{\delta M}{\delta K} = M/K, \text{ then}$$

$$\frac{\delta NR}{\delta K} = Pm . M/K - I^{t/2} . PvV_2/n - Pv . V_3^* \tag{11.2}$$

where PvV_3^* is the variable input per cow.

In equilibrium, therefore,

$$Pm . M . /K - I^{t/2} . PvV_2/n - PvV_3^* = 0 \tag{11.3}$$

This system is inherently stable, or homeostatic, in a traditional Indian society, where most incomes are at the subsistence level. If incomes decline:

(i) the price people are able to pay for milk, Pm, declines;

(ii) the rate of time discount, I, increases;

(iii) the first term of equation 11.3 decreases in value and the second term increases in value;

(iv) the expression will tend to become negative, implying a loss from cattle keeping, and so induce people to keep fewer cows;

(v) fewer cows, or a lower value for K, will raise the value of the first term and tend to restore equilibrium.

A similar equilibrating process is set in motion, *mutatis mutandi*, if the source of disequilibrium is an increase in incomes.

If the number of cows, K, increases exogenously, beyond the level of OS of Fig. 5.6, real incomes decline, because the supply of milk, M, declines. The effect of this on the first term, Pm.M. K cannot be predicted a priori. The decline in the supply of milk will tend to raise its price; but the decline in the incomes of people as a result of the decline in milk production will modify the increase in milk price, Pm. Meanwhile, M/K is assumed to have declined. The reduction in real incomes causes I, and therefore $I^{t/2}.PvV_2/n$, to increase. This reduces the profitability of cow keeping, and leads to a reduction in the number of cows, K.

Efficiency of system:

The system, as defined, appears to be efficient in relation to the available technology and the institutions of a riverine society. As observed, the number of cows tends to be held at the point where total milk production, M, is a maximum. Draft oxen are available at lowest cost, because the price of calves, Pc, is zero; the variable inputs, V_1, are minimal; and the rearing time, θ, is low because there is no overstocking. The supply of animal protein and fats, and the supply of draft power for grain production are maximised.

The Impact of Capitalist Colonialism

Reduced mortality:

The effects on cattle keeping of reduced human and bovine mortality appear to be the same in India as in Africa, for where they have already been analysed, in Chapter 9

The riverine surplus:

One of the principal, if not the principal, effects of the British Raj in India has been the substitution of capitalist concepts of law and property for a riverine despotism. "The conception of law which (the British raj) brought with it was at once more definite and more comprehensive than either the Hindu law, which had been largely a matter of fluctuating and variable custom, or the Muslim law which, though definite in character, had been narrowly limited in scope" (Dodwell 1934 p. 856).

Slowly but persistently, since Plassey, that half of total output that was surplus to the cultivators' full maintenance needs and that was formerly appropriated by despotic rulers, has been redirected towards the new class of bourgeoisie and petite bourgeoisie. A substantial proportion of India's population now have above subsistence incomes. That proportion includes owners of land and those with a claim to land as tenants, who now have a valuable asset. This is different from the traditional, preBritish position, when all above full maintenance was taken from the cultivator. "If then the revenue imposed did not actually exceed the surplus produced, this was only because such a course would have reduced, not increased, the total revenue and thus defeated its own purpose" (Habib 1963 p. 190).

The process usually termed "land reform" has secured for some cultivators some, at least, of the surplus from land that formerly accrued to despots. But it has had, as a corollary, the effect of excluding others from access to land. Security of possession of land for some implies firmness of exclusion for others. When the despot appropriated all the surplus, land was equally available to all who could get from it a maintenance and the despot's surplus. When the State secures for some title to land, the landless are excluded from the land, or have access to it on the landed's terms. The creation of a rural proletariat has been the corollary of the creation of a rural bourgeoisie.

Towards a new equilibrium

The effects of capitalist colonialism on Indian cattle keeping are considered in terms of the equilibrium condition, repeated here:

$$Pm \cdot M/K - I^{t/2} \cdot PvV_2/n - Pv \cdot V_3{}^* = 0 \qquad (11.3)$$

Reduced human and bovine mortality causes milk output, M, to decline, and cow numbers, K, to increase (pp. 127–8), on both accounts reducing average yield per cow on communal grazing. The decline in milk supply causes its price, Pm, to rise. Bourgeois incomes being over subsistence, the scope for Pm to rise is greater than when the mass of the population merely subsisted. Conceivably, the value of the term Pm.M./K could increase as M declined and K increased; the rise in milk price could be more than sufficient to offset the decline in average yield per cow on communal grazing, so increasing the gross revenue per cow. Real incomes of the new class of rural proletariat may be lower than rural incomes in the past; preventive medicine keeps people alive now who in the past would have died from malnutrition and the diseases associated with it. The rate of time discount, I, for the proletariatised owners of cows on communal grazing is therefore likely to be higher than it was for cow owners in the past.

A rise in I for proletariat cow owners increases pressures to reduce variable inputs, V_2, used for heifers being reared. Improved veterinary services and measures of a similar nature, that reduce bovine mortality, make it possible to reduce V_2 while maintaining, or even increasing the herd. Recalling that:

$$CC \text{ (the cost of a cow)} = I^t \cdot Pc + 1^{t/2} \cdot Pv \cdot V_2 \qquad (5.21)$$

that in India, Pc=0; and that V_2 is in any case low (p. 166), even if I is very high, CC can continue to be very low.

The cost of Indian cows is, in fact, low. The reported unweighted average price of young cows in Bihar in Andhra Pradesh in 1974/5 was Rs.550, which was approximately equal to the current value of 50 gal of milk (India, Ministry of Agriculture 1975 p. 295-7). Comparably, a downcalving cow in Ireland, where the price of milk is 30 pence per gal, is around £300, or the value equivalent of 1000 gal of milk.

A buoyant milk price, Pm, and a low cost of cows, CC, encourages cattle owners to increase their cow herds, K. More cows on communal grazing imply less milk, and therefore still further increases in Pm, giving rise to a backward sloping supply curve. All of the adjustment, therefore, falls on the term, Pv.V_3*, of Equation 11.3.

The creation of a rural proletariat and its increase in size tends to reduce the labour element of PvV$_3$* variable inputs, especially in relation to the price of milk, Pm. This helps to make it attractive to increase the non-labour components of the variable inputs, V_3, especially in the form of supplementary feed. A high relative price of milk

Table 11.7   Value of milk in Europe, USA and India 1971–72.

| | Value of 100 kg milk | | |
	Wheat (kg)	N in Nitrogenous fertilizers (kg)	Value of average GNP/ caput (1972) in units of 100 kg milk
Europe[a]	114	48	187
USA	132	56	370
India	182	64	5

See ECE/FAO 1976, India, Ministry of Agriculture 1972, India, Fertiliser Association of India 1972; USDA, Agricultural Statistics, 1974.
Note a: Unweighted average of 15 European countries.

(Table 11.7), a heavy reliance on concentrate feeds (Table 11.8) and a chronic shortage of fodder are remarkable features of the Indian cattle economy. The shortfall of fodder has been measured for Karnataka in 1971/2; the supply of dry fodder was 45% and of green fodder was 22% of requirements (Rajapurohit 1975).

A high milk/feed price ratio makes attractive the use of feeds supplementary to grazing. Landless cow owners reach the equilibrium condition specified in Equation 11.3 by buying large quantities of these supplementary feeds and, in doing so, force their price up to remarkably high levels.

Table 11.8   Annual cost of milch cow, Punjab 1969–70, and Ireland 1970.

	Punjab Rs/Cow	Ireland £/Cow
Concentrates	227.60	8.00
Other feed	325.01	9.00
Other variable costs	3.27	5.00
Total	555.88	22
Milk yield (gals/cow)	150.00	555.00
Variable costs per gallon Rs.	3.71	0.63
Pence	23.16	3.96

See: India, Ministry of Agriculture 1973b pp. 252–3, Kearney 1975 p. 127.

Farmyard Cattle Keeping

Increased cattle numbers depress output from communal grazing and tend to raise the price of both milk and draft services. The situation, though having points of semblance with what exists in Africa, differs in at least one important respect: Africa's agriculture is predominantly pastoral while India's is predominantly crop producing. Long before average returns declined to zero on Africa's communal grazing, society would be so impoverished that it could not further increase cattle stocks to depress output further. It is conceivable that average returns on communal grazing could be reduced to zero in India while crop growers continued to offer a high price for milk and draft services, so making further expansion in cattle stocks profitable.

As cattle numbers on communal grazing expand towards OK with average output declining along AB (Fig. 5.6), and the price of milk and draft services rising once stocks increase beyond OS, it is open to individual cattle owners to adopt "farmyard" methods of cattle production. This is characterised by the provision by the owner of supplementary feed for his cattle. The returns which the individual gets from farm-yarding his cattle depends on the state of the communal grazing. The point is illustrated by Fig. 11.1.

Points K, L and M on OY correspond to varying stocking densities on communal grazing. At a low stocking density, K, returns to supplementary feeding are zero, because the cattle are so well nourished on the communal land that the supplementary feeding is wasted. Stocking density is higher at point L and nutritional levels are lower. Yields can be raised along LNR to the cow's genetic potential by using increasing quantities of feed. At a still higher stocking density, corresponding to M, yields on the communal grazing are reduced almost to zero, or OM. Bigger returns to supplementary feeding are obtained as output rises to the cow's potential at R', partly because of the more undernourished condition of the cattle on the very overstocked communal grazing, and partly because of a higher price for milk (OQ/OK) as production on overstocked communal grazing land declines. The return to supplementary feeding at any point along the LNR and MTR' curves is the distance

Fig. 11.1   Returns to yard-feeding cattle

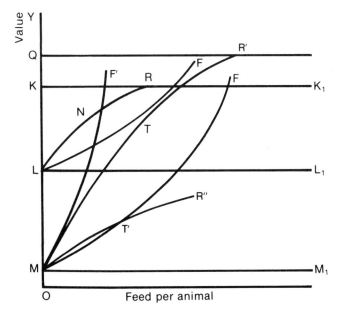

between the curves and a line drawn from the origin of the curve parallel to the base (i.e. LL_1 for LNR and MM_1 for MTR').

The return to supplementary feeding will depend, in addition to the state of the communal grazing, on the cow's potential. Thus, at a stocking density corresponding to M, Fig. 11.1, the return to the supplementary feeding of a poor cow is represented by MT'R'', compared to MTR' for a good cow. The milk-producing quality of a cow depends on V_2. If V_2 inputs are held low, cows with a good survival capacity but a poor milk potential will survive. Rearing cows with a good milk potential requires higher V_2 inputs. Again, bearing in mind the components of the cost of a cow (CC), Equation 5.21, it is clear that poor cow keepers, with a high rate of time discount, I, are unlikely to have good cows. The return to them from supplementary feeding their poor cows is likely to be MT'R'', while the return to wealthier cow keepers is likely to be MTR'.

The low average yield of Indian cows has been noted. There is abundant evidence that, within India, the quality of cows and their yields vary directly with size of farm. Thus, farm management studies report depreciation costs for cows and buffaloes increasing with size of farm in Kerala, 1962/63; Punjab, 1968/69; and Uttar Pradesh, 1968/69.[2] Pant & Karanjkar (1965) and Garg & Azad (1975) observe similarly.

The supply of supplementary feed is limited, both in total and as to the amount individuals have. Small amounts are likely to be available as otherwise waste by-products of crop production. As more is required to feed more cattle, the supply becomes competitive with crop products, and at the limit all land may be used to produce supplementary feed for cattle.

The curve LF represents the cost of supplementary feed to an individual cattle keeper at different levels of feeding per head of stock, with a given number of cattle in his farmyard. MF is identical with LF except that it is drawn LM lower. Costs like returns, are measured by the distance from the cost curves, LF, MF, etc., to the line drawn from the origin of the curve and parallel to the base. Because of increasing costs, the more feed per animal that is given, the higher the unit cost of the feed causing the total cost curve, LF, MF etc., to be confex to the origin. Every cattle keeper has a family of feed costs, each curve in the family representing a different number of cattle in his farmyard. For any number of cattle held, the level of feed costs is lower for large than for small farms. Thus, MF' may represent the cost of supplementary feed to a landless person wishing to farmyard a single animal. Supplementary feeding in this case is unprofitable even when yields on the communal grazing are very low, because supplementary feed costs at all times exceed the value of the additional milk produced.

The milk production function for farmyard cow-keeping is of the nature:

$$M = K \cdot V_3{}^{\beta i} \cdot V_2{}^{vi} \cdot r/ACC \tag{11.4}$$

r/ACC is a measure of the change in the response to farmyard inputs as stocking levels on communal grazing change. ACC is the annual cost of a cow on communal grazing (corresponding to OK, OL and OM in Fig. 11.1.) The lower ACC is, the more densely stocked communal grazing land will be, the more poorly nourished the cattle on it will be, and hence the greater will be the return to supplementary feeding.

Cows are kept to produce milk (M). Provided V_3 and V_2 are increased proportionately, M increases in proportion to the number of cows kept. The cows do not, as in grazing, compete with one another for the available grass. V_3 represents current supplementary feed inputs to cows, to which they respond at a diminishing rate. V represents supplementary feed given to heifers. V_2 affects cow production in two ways

2. See India, Ministry of Agriculture 1971a pp. 143, 267, 1973b pp. 208–9, 1973a pp. 208–9

first, the more supplementary feed a heifer receives, the better she will milk once she commences to breed; second, the more supplementary feed given to heifers, the less likely is selection of heifers to be on the basis of survival capacity and the more likely is it that heifers will be selected for their milking capacity. V_2 is also subject to diminishing returns.

The appropriate production function for farmyard bullock keeping is:

$$D_r = F . V_2{}^{vo} . V_3{}^{wo} r/CC \tag{11.5}$$

where F is the number of work oxen, V_2 is supplementary feed given to them in the course of rearing, and V_3 is the supplementary feed given during their working life.

If P_v is taken as the price of "other" inputs, consisting mainly of supplementary feed given to farmyard managed cattle, P_v will vary for the individual as:

$$P_v = aK (V_3 + V_2) \tag{11.6}$$

The more V_3 (mainly supplementary feed for cows and work oxen) and V_2 (mainly supplementary feed for heifers) are used by an individual, the higher will the cost of supplementary feed, P_v, be for him. The cost of supplementary feed will vary from individual to individual according to his circumstances. Generally for large farmers with abundant crop byproducts and land on which to grow fodder, the cost of supplementary feed will be low; the coefficient, a, will have a low value.

The net returns from farmyard cow keeping are:

$$NR = P_m M - K . W . P_v V_2 - K . P_v V_3 - K . ACC \tag{11.7}$$

where M is the additional milk produced by farmyarding, ACC is the net cost of cows to the farmyard enterprise, and $W = I^2/n$ Substituting for values of M and P_v gives:

$$NR = Pm . K . V_3{}^{\beta i} . V_2{}^{vi} . r/ACC - aK^2 . W . V_3 V_2 - aK^2 . W . V_2{}^2 \\ - aK^2 V_3{}^2 - aK^2 . V_3 V_2 - K . ACC \tag{11.8}$$

Net revenue from farmyard cow keeping is maximised by adjusting K, V_3 and V_2 so that:

$$\frac{\delta NR}{\delta K} = \frac{\delta NR}{\delta V_3} = \frac{\delta NR}{\delta V_2} = 0 \tag{11.9}$$

These conditions are satisfied by the values of K, V_3 and V_2 which satisfy the following non-linear simultaneous equations:

$$\frac{\delta NR}{\delta K} = Pm . V_3{}^{\beta i} . V_2{}^{vi} . r/ACC - 2aK(V_3 + V_2)(WV_2 + V_3) - ACC = 0 \tag{11.10}$$

$$\frac{\delta NR}{\delta V_3} = \beta iPmKV_3{}^{\beta i}V_2{}^{vi} . rACC/V_3 - aK^2 [V_2(W + 1) + 2V_3] = 0 \tag{11.11}$$

$$\frac{\delta NR}{\delta V_2} = viPmKV_3{}^{\beta i}V_2{}^{v} . rACC/V_2 - aK^2 [W(V_3 + 2V_2) + V_3] = 0 \tag{11.12}$$

**he price of straw
nd the supply of
rain**

Most Indian cattle production now appears to be farmyard based. Little milk or draft services come from the overstocked communal grazing. The growth of farmyard cattle production has led to an increase in demand for feed and fodder for cattle. A World Food Programme mission "was much impressed with the fact that when travelling in areas of Gujarat where dairy farming is best organised, a plot of green fodder is seen on almost every land holding" (Indian Dairy Corporation 1976 p. 65). This mission, in 1975, also found the price of straw normally to be from Rs.40 to Rs.160 per ton, but "owing to the recent drought", the price had risen to Rs.240 per ton.

The price of milk, Pm, affects the value of straw, of other crop byproducts, and of catch-crops suitable for cattle feed. The price of straw, in turn, affects the production of the main product, grain. Likewise, growing and feeding a catch-crop on land that would be otherwise fallow affects the yield of the following crop. The relationship between the demand for cattle feed and the production of foodgrains can conveniently be analysed by considering the effects of demand for straw; similar reasoning and conclusions apply to other byproducts and to catch-crops.

A high Pm raises the value of straw, encouraging increased production of it for feeding and, incidentally, causes more grain to be produced. But a high Pm also makes it profitable to feed grain to cows. If straw is worth Rs.100 a ton for feeding, then wheat, at Rs.1250 a ton (India, Ministry of Agriculture 1975 p. 293) is normally better value as feed. It cannot be stated *a priori* if the additional grain produced, as a result of the high value of straw, will be more or less than the additional grain fed to cows as a result of the high price of milk. It is, however, clear that if straw is used as manure, rather than fed — or if a catch crop is ploughed in rather than grazed — the following crop will be bigger.

A low Pm, on the other hand, implies under Indian conditions that the landless continue to get their traditional milk supply. Their real income will, in that case be higher, and they can afford to pay more for grain. A low Pm, therefore, implies a reduced demand for straw for cows and an increased demand for grain for people. Bearing in mind the possibilities of substitution between grain and straw — by choosing, for example, between long and short strawed varieties — a high grain price is more likely than a high straw price to induce a large grain production. A high grain price and a low milk price would preclude the conditions indicated in Tables 11.7 and 11.8; they would result in more of the grain being produced being available for human consumption, and less of it being fed to cows. A low Pm would also cause more straw to be used for manure and less for feed. Combined with a higher grain price, a low milk price would result in more plots "of green fodder ... seen on almost every land holding" (Indian Dairy Corporation 1976) being ploughed in as green manure. Though less straw and less green fodder might be produced, its manurial value would be greater.

The conclusion is that a normal average price of around Rs.100/ton for straw, as well as reflecting a situation where milk, the traditional and sole source of animal protein for India's rural masses, has been placed outside their reach, implies also the diversion of cropland from the production of foodgrains for the proletariat to the production of milk for the bourgeoisie.

Status of Indian cattle keeping

India's cattle industry is clearly no longer a scavenging operation, as livestock enterprises normally are in low income countries (Chapter 4). Cattle consume large quantities of expensive feed (Table 11.8). The industry, in this respect, bears superficial resemblance to livestock production in economies where average incomes are considerably higher; economies that, in terms of Chapter 4, are at stage three rather than stage two, much less stage one, as, in view of average incomes, India might be categorised.

The superficial resemblance between India's cattle industry and livestock production in countries with much higher average incomes may mislead as to the appropriateness to Indian circumstances of policies and technologies associated with cattle production in higher income countries. This does not, of course, imply that India, or any country, must adhere to the path of livestock development that has been followed in countries now classed as developed; the principal purpose of the present exercise is, from a better understanding of the processes involved, to identify ways by which livestock development that took two centuries in DCs can be telescoped into as many decades in LDCs. The point rather is to emphasise that, notwithstanding the superficial similarity of its no longer being mainly a scavenging operation, India's cattle keeping is entirely different in status from livestock production in DCs now, or as it was in the 19th century. If a non-scavenging status implied that Indian cattle keeping had progressed to a more advanced stage of development, comparable to stage two of Chapter 4, then indeed the preoccupation in Indian dairying circles with such attributes of an advanced dairying technology as milk dispensers and sophisticated milk processing plants might well be justified.[3]

The high price of milk, Pm, in India that warrants the use of costly inputs is not, as in DCs, the result of a growth of demand. It is the result of a failure of supply. This is clear from the very high price of milk relative to incomes (Table 11.7). A high price of milk relative to average incomes does not indicate progress; declining real costs of food have been central to economic development in most, if not all, countries.

India's high Pm is at once both result and cause of income differentiation. Considerable segments of the population have achieved above subsistence incomes, largely through a less inegalitarian distribution of the surplus of a tropical riverine agriculture. They have been enabled to pay a high price for small amounts of milk. A high Pm places a traditional food outside the reach of those landless Indians whom security of tenure for some now excludes from land to which all rural Indians traditionally had access. Competition from the landeds' cattle forces the landless to abandon cattle keeping (only a relatively small proportion of the large landless class now keep cows);[4] or forces the landless to keep cattle on the landeds' terms for the fodder they must buy. That India's rural poor, who earn Rs.4 a day,[5] must work 25 days to buy a ton of straw, that is valueless elsewhere but costs Rs.100 a ton in India, to feed their cows, that traditionally fed on the public domain, denotes grave retrogression for the country's largest, poorest social class. It is a situation that would seem to presage red revolution rather than "white revolution", as the envisaged explosion in milk production is referred to, somewhat glibly it might appear under the circumstances.

Communal Grazing and Overstocking

Capitalist influences have led, in Africa's traditional pastoralism and in India's peculiar adaptation of traditional pastoralism, to chronic overstocking of communal pastures. Yet, as the South East Asian experience shows, overstocking is not a necessary consequence of the interaction of capitalism with communal pastoralism. Other factors also affect the outcome. Overstocking in the African situation results

---

3. This preoccupation was shared by the FAO/WFP mission referred to above, pp. 177–8: FAO 1976a pp. 21–4.
4. The landless account for about 40% of the agricultural population (India, Register General and Census Commissioners of India 1972 p. 3), but for only 6 to 17% of cow keepers (India, National Commission on Agriculture 1971 para. 3.2). See also Indian Dairy Corporation 1976 p. 107.
5. India, Ministry of Agriculture 1975 p. 291. The value of a ton of straw, Rs. 100, exceeded the value of 15 months' consumption per person in South Indian households in 1970 (Epstein 1973 p. 170).

from the combination of (a) a high regard for pastoral products and (b) a preferenc
for cattle as assets to hold. Overstocking of India's communal grazing occur
notwithstanding a high rate of time discount, I, because of (a) the high value of mil
Pm; (b) the low value of beef, Pf; and (c) the characteristic of *bos indicus* th:
requires calves to be at foot to induce lactation. Communal grazing in South Ea
Asia is not overstocked because of (a) the low value of milk, Pm; (b) the high valu
of beef, Pf; and (c) the high rate of time discount, I.

Indian Cattle Policy

Objectives and means

India's cattle, accounting for nearly 20% of the world's total, are a major factor i
Indian society. Government is concerned to harness this resource in the nation:
interest and indicates in the Draft Fifth Five Year Plan how it proposes to do s
(India, Planning Commission 1974). The Draft Plan states: "It is intended to develc
animal husbandry as an important economic occupation for the small and margin:
farmers and agricultural labourers. As with proper investments the commerci:
programmes of animal husbandry can be quite remunerative, there is a temptatic
for the richer classes to enter into these occupations to the detriment of the tradition:
classes dependent on animal husbandry. It will be a major aim of the Fifth Plan 1
ensure that the traditional classes get a lion's share of the new programmes of anim:
husbandry development. For this purpose, provision has been made in the State ar
Central Plans for giving assistance to small farmers and agricultural labourers f(
rearing cross-bred heifers and for raising poultry, sheep and pigs" (para. 1.202).

A public sector outlay on animal husbandry and dairying, exclusive of provision f(
Indian Council of Agricultural Research schemes relating to animal husbandry, (
Rs.522.40 crores is proposed for the duration of the Plan period. This is 11% (
planned public sector expenditure on agriculture and 1.4% of total planned publi
sector outlay under the Plan (para. 7.2).

A fuller statement of policy is contained in the Interim Report of the Nation:
Commission on Agriculture on Milk Production through Small and Marginal Farme:
and Agricultural Labourers referred to in the Plan (India, National Commission o
Agriculture 1971). There are two major policy objectives. The first is to increase tr
supply of animal protein for India's rapidly growing, poorly nourished populatior
The second is to do so through an expansion of milk production by small farmers ar
landless labourers, thereby increasing the incomes of these, the poorest, large class i
the country. Much emphasis is placed on dairying as a means of increasing the ver
low incomes of small farmers and landless labourers partly because it is recognise
that the benefits of recent agricultural progress in India, popularly referred to as "tr
Green Revolution", for the most part "flowed towards progressive farmers who als
happened to be those with larger holdings having irrigation facilities. Farmers wi1
smaller holdings and poorer means have, by and large, had to be left out. This resulte
in one kind of major imbalance in the rural areas. As a large proportion of rur:
population could not share the economic benefits resulting from this new strategy (
agricultural development, a strong feeling of dissatisfaction developed among the le:
affluent farmers giving rise to social tension in the rural areas. Social justice deman(
avoidance of such imbalances. It is not desirable to have growth without social justi(
and this points to the need for an integrated development of all sections of people
the rural areas by reducing the present widespread poverty, unemployment and unde
employment. In our efforts to achieve this objective in the rural areas, intensificatic
of cattle rearing and milk production programmes can play a vital role" (para. 3.1
Dairying as a means of raising the lowest rural incomes is emphasised because sm:
farmers and landless rural labourers are especially heavily engaged in this enterpris

The key means of implementing policy is the supply of better quality cattle stock to small farmers and landless labourers. "As indicated . . . the economic foundation of small producers in dairying can only be built around high producing milch animals" (para. 8.1). This is to be achieved principally by artificially inseminating local cows with imported bulls of dairy breeds, especially Jerseys, and assisting owners to rear the resulting heifer calves. "It is recommended that the small and marginal farmers who have produced crossbred heifers be extended financial assistance in the form of half subsidy and half loan and agricultural labourers two-thirds subsidy and one-third loan for the purchase of concentrates. This would mean that each farmer would get Rs.480 as a subsidy and Rs.480 as loan. A labourer will get Rs.640 as subsidy and Rs.320 as loan."

This approach will supplement other schemes under which small farmers get 25% and landless persons get 33⅓% of the cost as a subsidy in buying young cows that are the progeny of a cross with exotic dairy type bulls.

"Operation Flood" is an important element in Indian cattle policy that involves:

"(a) major increases in the capacity and throughput of dairy processing facilities;
  (b) competitive transfer of the bulk of the urban markets for the supplies of raw milk to the modern dairies;
  (c) resettlement in rural areas of cattle in the cities, which at present serve a large part of these city markets;
  (d) development of the basic transportation and storage network to facilitate regional and seasonal balancing of milk supply and demand;
  (e) development of milk procurement systems in appropriate rural areas in order to provide for raw milk a channel which is more remunerative than the traditional channel; and
  (f) improvement in standards of dairy farming by programmes of animal breeding, veterinary services, feedstuff supplies and management, thereby increasing milk yields per animal."

Operation Flood has received assistance valued at US$153 million from the World Food Programme (WFP) from 1970 to 1975. The assistance has been in the form of butter oil and skim milk powder (smp) that are part of the EEC's dairy surplus. The butter oil and smp are reconstituted into milk and sold in major Indian cities by the Indian Dairy Corporation (IDC). This addition to urban milk supplies helps to moderate the price of milk to urban consumers, while the realisations from sales are used to finance Operation Flood. Assistance to Operation Flood has also been provided by "UNDP, UNICEF and a number of governments and national agencies for development cooperation. . . . The World Bank has recently agreed to participate in the financing of three comprehensive dairy development projects" (Indian Dairy Corporation 1976 p. 12). The total cost of the World Bank projects is estimated to be US$147 million.

Policy and model

The policy variables on which Government proposes to operate are:

(i) P_m (Price of Milk); This is to be raised with funds realised from the sale of reconstituted milk.
(ii) vi (the parameter measuring the effectiveness of V_2 inputs used in rearing heifers in equation 11.4); this is to be raised by the provision of artificial insemination facilities.
(iii) CC (Cost of cows); This will continue to be held down and possibly lowered by improved veterinary services provided at public expense.
(iv) I (Capital cost) and P_v (Cost of "other" inputs); to be reduced by subsidies to small farmers and landless persons for rearing crossbred heifers.

Subsidies in respect of I and P_v are to be given on a "once off" basis. "The farmers who are able to obtain a heifer calf through the first round of artificial insemination could be encouraged to keep their local cows and further breed for another round to try for a second crossbred heifer the rearing of which need not be subsidized by the project" (India, National Commission Agriculture 1971 para. 8.5).

Crossbred heifers

Empirical evidence based on small farm and landless conditions of production has not been provided to support the view that crossbred cows are more efficient milk producers than local ones. They are, no doubt, technically superior, in having a genetically greater milking capacity, and probably better feed conversion rates at high levels of nutrition.

It has been suggested here that the genetically low productive capacity of Indian cattle for milk and draft services is due to the minimization of V_2 "other" inputs because of the high value of I in a poor society. It would have been possible, by rearing the progeny of selected dams, to improve milking and breeding capacity within the local breeds. Instead, the progeny reared have been selected naturally, by their capacity to survive on minimal V_2 inputs. High I values make naturally selected progeny more profitable than performance selected progeny. The technological change of introducing exotic breeds may alter this situation and may make it profitable to select heifers for their productive capacity rather than naturally for their ability to survive on minimum V_2 inputs. Though, as observed, supporting empirical evidence based on small farmer experience does not appear to have been forthcoming, it can be assumed, for discussion purposes, that the introduction by artificial insemination of exotic cattle breeds does make it profitable to reverse the traditional Indian system of natural selection of cows and choose heifers for their genetic quality.

If it is profitable to incur the additional cost of rearing crossbred heifers and feeding crossbred cows better to get higher yields, the point will be manifested in crossbred heifer calves acquiring value. The more profitable crossbred cows become the higher will be the price of crossbred heifer calves, or P_{cf}. If heifer calves acquire value, the net revenue from cattle changes from equation (11.7) to:

$$NR = P_m M + \tfrac{1}{2}P_{cf}C - (I^t P_{cf} + I^{t/2} . PvV_2)K/n - K . P_v V_3 - KACC \qquad (11.13$$

From equations 11.7 and 11.13, the net effect on NR of P_{cf} acquiring value

$$= \tfrac{1}{2}P_{cf} . C - I^t P_{cf} K/n \qquad (11.1$$

$$= P_{cf} . K(ch - I^t/n) \qquad (11.1$$

where "ch" is the annual rate at which cows produce heifer calves (i.e. half the normally understood calving rate). A calving rate of 40% (Table 11.5), gives a value of $ch=0.20$. The average breeding life may be taken as 10 years, or $n=10$ (Table 11.5) and the maturation age four years (Srivastava 1970 p. 4). The net effect on income from cattle of heifer calves acquiring value is, then, positive for values of I less than 1.19. That is, if cattle owners discount the future at over 19% per annum it will pay them to sell their heifer calves for cash rather than retain them for breeding except when they are subsidised to do so. It is virtually certain that the value of I for most small farmers and labourers is greater than 1.19.[6] If heifer calves acquire value it will pay all these people to sell them; only relatively wealthy persons, for whom I is equal to, or less than, 1.19, or small farmers and landless labourers in receipt of subsidies, will retain, or buy, crossbred heifer calves.

---

6. Crotty (1979b) indicates that I for Indian grain-growers exceeds 1.40.

The likely impact of exotic breeds on the performance of Indian cows has probably been exaggerated. These breeds could indeed dramatically improve the genetic potential of Indian cows to produce milk, as indeed would any form of selection from the indigenous herd, other than natural selection for low capital cost, have done in the past. The realisation of this potential may now be profitable for larger farmers, using large amounts of valuable feed, with relatively abundant capital to produce high priced milk; it is unlikely to be profitable for the landless using ever more costly feed, with little capital (Fig. 11.1).

If crossbreeding with exotic sires results in a technological breakthrough that reduces the cost of milk production on larger farms, this will be reflected in the price of crossbred heifer calves. The greater the technological advance, the higher will be Pcf, the price of crossbred heifer calves. Small farmers without capital and landless labourers will be unable to participate, unless their capital costs are subsidised continuously — and that is not envisaged. Once the subsidies for cow rearing cease, herd replacement will revert to natural selection, as at present and in the past. Public resources will meanwhile have been used to subsidise the rearing of more cows to add to the 180 million cattle India already has, and further to depress output from its overstocked communal grazing lands.

Other elements of cattle policy

Increased public expenditure on veterinary services reduces the cost of keeping cattle and therefore tends to still further overstocking of communal grazing (Fig. 5.6). Artificial insemination services facilitate the improvement of cattle by larger farmers, making it easier for them to keep more and better cows to compete with the cows of the landless on the communal grazing, and for inadequate fodder supplies.

The effects of dairy policy

The creation of a market for high cost, "farmyard produced" milk has been seen to be a consequence of the impact of capitalist colonialism on India's cattle culture and institutions. Operation Flood, seeking to exploit this market, is understandably attracted to areas where capitalist colonialism has made most impact; where "a large proportion of the rural population could not share the economic benefits resulting from ... agricultural development (and where) a strong feeling of dissatisfaction developed among the less affluent." (above p. 180). Farmyard milk production is likely to be most advanced in those areas because: (i) the landless are most pauperised and therefore compelled to market more milk; (ii) the price is higher as a result of demand from the local landed; and (iii) communal grazing is most overstocked.

Table 11.9 gives average yields of foodgrains, other than "small millets" and "other pulses", by District and State for those Districts classed as in "milk shed areas" (Indian Dairy Corporation 1976 p. 128). Foodgrain yield was above the State yield in 18 of the 22 Districts listed as milk shed areas. Operation Flood seems to locate within States in those Districts where the land is better and commercialization has progressed furthest.

Table 11.10 is reproduced from the report of a study of "the impact of ... milk cooperatives in rural areas. The study was confined to Kaira, Mehsana and Banaskantha milk unions of Gujarat State. ... The data (was) collected from 100 milk producers of 6 dairy villages, served by the world famous Amul dairy and 50 milk producers of 2 control villages of Kaira district" (Patel & Pandey 1976 p. 2).

The final column 5 of Table 11.10 shows that, in the surveyed area, dairy villages are located in areas of higher yields, in accordance with the general trend noted in Table 11.9. Column 4 shows that in the dairy villages, where crop yields are higher, the poor are poorer and the rich are richer than in the control villages; incomes of big

Table 11.9   Foodgrain yields in districts in milk shed areas.

		Foodgrain[a] yield per ha (1973–74) Tons
All India		0.94
State Andhra Pradesh	District	1.07
	Krishna	1.47
	Guntur	1.54
	W. Godavari	1.95
	E. Godavari	1.54
Gujarat		0.81
	Sabarkantha	0.85
	Baroda	0.91
	Kaira	0.88
	Ahmedabad	0.67
	Mehsana	0.94
	Banoskantha	0.95
Haryana		0.98
	Gurgaon	0.87
	Karnal	1.67
	Rohtak	0.81
Maharashtra		0.56
	Jaigaon	0.64
	Kolhapur	1.44
Punjab		1.91
	Ferezpur	2.02
	Jullunder	2.01
	Bhattinda	1.48
	Ludhiana	2.53
	Gurdaspur	1.75
Uttar Pradesh		0.84
	Muzaffar-Magar	1.02
	Buland-Shahar	1.02

Source: Indian Dairy Corporation 1976 p. 128; India, Ministry of
          Agriculture Directorate of Economics and Statistics 1975.
Note a: Excludes "small millets" and "other pulses".

farmers are 9.3 times those of the landless in the dairy villages compared to 2.6 time
in the control villages. This is precisely the situation that gives rise to widesprea
concern in India of the nature expressed by the National Commission on Agricultur
and already quoted here.

Columns 2 and 4 show that milk contributed a much larger proportion of the tota
income of the cow keeping landless[7] in dairy villages than in control villages. This i
partly due to the higher income from higher priced milk in the dairy than in th
control villages; but it is mainly due to the much lower incomes of the landless fro
other sources in the dairy villages.

The incomes from dairying recorded in Table 11.10 are gross. The cost of feed
be netted from the gross dairy income by the landless must be very high (Table 11.8
so that the contribution to family income of dairying must be much less than t
gross figure. The cost of feed is likely to be especially high in the dairy villages, whe
increased milk production creates more pressure on communal grazing, giving rise
an increased demand and higher prices for fodder. An additional expenditure f
cattle feed of Rs.360 per landless family in the dairy villages would leave the n
family income from dairying no higher than in the control villages, and of cour

7. Though many milk producers are landless, not all landless are milk producers. Between
quarter and a half of the landless appear to keep cows (Above p. 179 note 4).

Table 11.10   Average annual income per household from different occupations.

Group	Average annual income per household from various occupations (Rs)				Farm income per ha of land
	Crop farming	Dairy farming	Other sources	Total income	
Dairy villages					
Weaker Section					
A. Landless		2042	1080	3122	
		(65.41)	(34.59)	(100.00)	
B. Small farmers	2759	1834	645	5238	2469
	(52.67)	(35.01)	(12.32)	(100.00)	
Farmers					
C. Medium	7196	2250	185	9631	2222
	(74.72)	(23.36)	(1.92)	(100.00)	
D. Big	24 306	3938	833	29 077	3999
	(83.59)	(13.54)	(2.87)	(100.00)	
Overall	5315	2186	703	8204	3050
	(64.78)	(26.65)	(8.57)	(100.00)	
Control villages					
Weaker Section					
A. Landless		1683	2475	4158	
		(40.48)	(59.52)	(100.00)	
B. Small farmers	1508	1113	1588	4209	1650
	(35.83)	(26.44)	(37.73)	(100.00)	
Farmers					
C. Medium	4051	1537	292	5880	1313
	(68.89)	(26.14)	(4.97)	(100.00)	
D. Big	8256	1225	1238	10 719	1380
	(77.02)	(11.43)	(11.55)	(100.00)	
Overall	3262	1375	1207	5844	1382
	(55.82)	(23.53)	(20.65)	(100.00)	

Note: Figures in parantheses indicate % share of various occupations in total income.
See Patel & Pandey, 1976.

total family income of the landless in the dairy villages much lower than in the control villages.

Big farmers, though having more cows per family than the landless, hold few relative to the extent of the land they farm, and are therefore in a position to sell fodder and cattle feed to the landless. This may partly account for the very high income per ha of land obtained by big farmers in dairy villages; some of the high income may be due to their selling straw and other crop products at high prices to the landless for cattle feeding.

The results ascribed to Operation Flood obtain generally, though not necessarily universally. There could be quite different results in selected villages to which exceptional resources are directed. Additional resources would make possible an exceptionally good milk collection service that accepted small quantities of milk at frequent intervals to suit producers' convenience, weighed and graded the milk liberally, and paid frequently and at a high price for it. Additional resources would make possible abundant credit on favourable terms, especially for the landless, enabling these to participate to an exceptional extent in milk production with exceptionally high quality cows. These specially favourable milk procuring and credit conditions would be expected to result in an exceptional development of milk production in the selected villages, raising the demand there for cattle feed and attracting it in from other, nonselected areas. This process could be facilitated by subsidising the procurement of feed by the selected villages from other areas.

Selectiveness of this sort would add to the profits of favoured producers at the cost of increasing difficulties for poor consumers and landless milk producers in non-selected areas. It might be warranted to create "show" villages to impress influential but uncritical visitors and induce these to support the continued, or increased, flow of funds to Operation Flood. See Note 8 p. 187.

Losers and gainers

The principal effects of Indian dairy policy and of Operation Flood, financed in large part by the World Food Programme, by the World Bank, and by various national aid agencies are, then, seen to be:

(i) to raise further the price of milk in rural areas and to reduce further the amount of milk, the only available animal protein, consumed by the rural poor;

(ii) to increase milk production by the landed, forcing the landless either to abandon production, or to rely more on high cost fodder bought from the landed;

(iii) to reduce the amount of foodgrain available for human consumption by causing more grain to be fed to cattle and/or more land to be diverted to growing fodder crops;

(iv) to reduce the price of milk to the urban wealthy.

These results are diametrically opposite to the stated objectives of Indian dairy policy. Dairy policy, so far from alleviating the inequalities and the dissatisfaction developed among the less affluent in the rural areas that has been associated with the Green Revolution, aggravates the inequalities and must exacerbate the dissatisfaction. Rarely have the implements of policy been so ill designed to achieve the stated ends.

The explanation for the choice of instruments so incompatible with the ends of policy may lie partly in failure to appreciate how similar causes can have different effects under different circumstances; how the combination of western technology and a high milk price can have very different consequences in a tropical, riverine, crop growing society with a major cattle interest from those that would ensue in a temperate capitalist society. Similar causes have effects in India contrary to those expected in the West because of the combination of (i) communal grazing, (ii) the very high cost of capital, (iii) the unwillingness of Indians to eat beef, and (iv) the need for the presence of a live calf at foot to stimulate *bos indicus* to lactate. However, in part the choice of policy instruments peculiarly inappropriate to policy objectives may not be unrelated to the fact that, harmful as the implementation of policy may be to the interests identified, it brings very substantial benefits to others. Interests inside and outside India benefit from the implementation of dairy policy.

Operation Flood benefits wealthier urban consumers by providing more, better and cheaper milk. Urban prices are, nevertheless, too high to permit the urban poor to drink milk, which the World Food Programme considers desirable as the poor are thus forced to limit consumption to cheaper vegetable proteins (Indian Dairy Corporation 1976 p. 89).

Operation Flood benefits those with land within the milk shed areas, by paying a price for milk that makes its production more profitable than the alternative of growing grains for human consumption. The landed also benefit by selling to landless cowkeepers otherwise valueless products at prices like Rs.100 per ton of straw. They may also benefit from the further impoverishment of the landless by Operation Flood to the extent that impoverishment forces down farm wages (Table 11.10).

Finally within India, Operation Flood benefits those who administer and implement it. These include those involved in distributing milk from village producers to urban consumers; and those involved in providing goods — such as compounded cattle feed — and services — such as artificial insemination for cows — to the milk producer.

Only US$140 millions of the total of US$153 millions of the World Food Programme's contribution to Operation Flood was in the form of dairy surpluses. The balance consisted of administration costs. The recipients of these administrative salaries benefited directly from Operation Flood. The World Food Programme benefited also indirectly, in that the food aid given to Operation Flood appears to be ideal and therefore helps to rebut criticisms levelled at food aid generally, and at the World Food Programme in particular (Maxwell & Singer 1979). The dairy produce disbursed in India does not, like grain aid, depress prices to local producers; on the contrary, raises these. The counterpart funds realised by the disposal of the aid are used to develop a local dairy industry, apparently offering hope of India eventually becoming independent of dairy aid. Finally, given the major participation of landless and small farmers, aid to developing Indian milk production appears likely to benefit a most deserving section of the population. That these appearances are the opposite to reality does not take from the kudos that has accrued to the World Food Programme from its involvement in Operation Flood.

Aid-giving countries are usually under pressure to identify enough aidable projects in LDCs to absorb voted aid funds. Aidable projects must be deemed by the governments of the recipient countries sufficiently worthy to incur obligations of gratitude, at least, on their behalf; and they must be deemed by the authorities in the donor countries at least to appear sufficiently meritorious to silence critics. The significance attributed to Operation Flood by the Indian authorities has been noted. Its appeal for donor countries as a project worthy of aid may be gauged by the prominent featuring on television of the prime minister of one donor country, the United Kingdom, visiting a dairy cooperative aided by Operation Flood during an official visit to India.[8]

Operation Flood has a double attraction for governments of EEC countries. It provides them with a politically acceptable outlet for aid funds that are frequently embarrassingly difficult to dispose of; and it enables them to relieve the Commission of the EEC of embarrassing dairy surpluses. Sales of EEC dairy surpluses on the market gives rise to intense, hostile criticism.[9] The EEC public cannot easily be persuaded of the appropriateness of butter and skimmed milk powder (smp) being exported at a small fraction of their cost to local consumers. It is extremely important politically, therefore, to minimise commercial sales of dairy surpluses that create an acute public awareness of defects in the EEC's dairy policy. But dairy produce is perishable and expensive to store. If stocks accumulate, storage costs become excessive, or the quality of the stocks deteriorates, severe public criticism being incurred in either case. Destruction of the surpluses would probably be the least expensive way of disposing of them, but this again would provoke criticism by EEC dairy produce consumers. Operation Flood, under these circumstances, has been a boon to otherwise hard pressed politicians and officials. Dairy produce disposed of through this channel escapes criticism. The EEC media and public have been willing to trust their respective aid ministries, in collaboration with the World Food Programme, to use the dairy surpluses in a manner beneficial to the poor of the LDCs.

Operation Flood, therefore, in an important way facilitates the retention of the EEC's dairy policy. To that extent, it confers very great benefits on probably the wealthiest and politically most powerful farming interest in the world — western Europe's cattle farmers. These, without the EEC dairy policy that Operation Flood helps to preserve and for reasons developed in Chapter 7, would experience a very great decline in income, from a collapse in milk prices and from a smaller decline in other farm product prices.

Operation Flood, through these wider ranging influences, injures interests other than those noted above (p. 186). Restrictions on vegetable oil imports, designed to secure a better domestic market for butter fat, are an aspect of the EEC's dairy policy. These import restrictions impede the efforts of India and of other LDCs to export oilseeds and vegetable oils. Operation Flood, by helping to preserve the EEC's dairy policy, depresses Indian and other LDC exports.

If India rejected EEC surplus dairy produce, EEC aid in other forms might not

8. BBC television news, 10.1.1978. *The Times* (London), 11.1.1978 carried a story and a picture of the British Prime Minister visiting an Operation Flood dairy farm.
9. See, for example, *The Times* (London), 22.11.1978.

increase by US$153 millions, the value attributed by the World Food Programme to dairy aid. But public opinion within the EEC favourable to more and better aid would be reinforced, and India's prospects, at least, of getting useful aid would be improved.

There are, finally, the losses caused to EEC taxpayers and consumers by Operation Flood. The smaller part of these losses is the supply to India of butter oil and smp produced at great cost in Europe. The greater loss, to the EEC in the first instance and to the world generally, is that which results from the continuing allocation of large amounts of valuable resources for the production of unwanted, valueless milk under an EEC dairy policy sustained, in part, by Operation Flood.

The losers from Operation Flood, comprised of India's rural landless and lower income foodgrain consumers and of EEC consumers and taxpayers, far outweigh the gainers numerically, and their losses are likely to be many times greater in value than the gains of the gainers. But the losers, in India and Europe, are diffused and without a common vested interest. Those in India are pitifully weak and inarticulate; those in Europe are affluent and, for the most part, uncritical. The gainers, in India, in Europe and in the international agencies, are, on the other hand, close knit, wealthy, powerful and articulate.

Adapting India's Cattle Husbandry to Changed Circumstances

The analysis suggests ways in which Indian cattle husbandry could be adjusted better to realise what are understood to be the objectives of policy makers. These objectives, for present purposes, are taken to be:

 (i) to produce more milk and draft services, using resources that have little alternative value and including labour, communal grazing, straw, etc.;
(ii) to do so without worsening, but if possible alleviating, conditions for the rural poor, and especially for the rural landless.

A cattle tax, operated on the lines indicated in Chapter 9, is, as noted there, the necessary and sufficient condition for the efficient use of communal grazing land. I would, therefore, further objective (i) above. It should also further objective (ii). A tax on all cattle, and the disbursement of the proceeds in equal per caput payment to adults resident in the fiscal area, would redistribute income from landowners, of whom a high proportion have cattle, to the landless, relatively few of whom have cattle.

But maximising net cattle tax revenue, by affecting cattle inputs and outputs, would also have redistributive effects that merit consideration. It is assumed initially, for purposes of this consideration, that Operation Flood, or some other mechanism, is retained so that the price offered for milk in villages in the city milk shed area remains unchanged when cattle tax revenue is maximized.

If the price of milk to producers, Pm, and the price of draft services, Pd, remain unchanged when cattle are taxed, owners will wish to keep fewer and cattle numbers will decline. Fewer cattle on the overstocked communal grazing will result in more output from that source (Fig. 5.6). Fewer farmyarded cattle will lower the price of straw and other fodders; it will cause a diversion of resources towards grain production and it will result in less grain being consumed by cattle. Landless cattlekeepers will benefit from higher output from communal grazing and from lower fodder costs; and landless will benefit from greater supplies of grains for human consumption.

An Indian operating company (OC), on the lines suggested in Chapter 9, would have opportunities for increasing net cattle tax revenue principally through (a) using abundant, low cost labour for increasing the stock carrying capacity of communal grazing (including traditional communal grazing rights on postharvest cropped land

and (b) through raising the productivity of cattle so as to get more cattle product per unit of feed consumed. A very high rate of time discount, I, compels poor cattle owners to minimise variable inputs, V_2, in the rearing of breeding stock. The result is a continuous process of natural selection of cattle stocks for their ability to survive under worsening conditions of overgrazing and underfeeding. Maximising net cattle tax revenue would require an OC, able to borrow funds at relatively low rates — possibly from local large farmers — to re-lend to landless cow rearers to finance the rearing of more productive cattle. The selection for rearing as replacement stock of the progeny of, say, the most productive quartile of the cow herd, instead of the natural selection practised until now, would of itself transform the genetic quality of the Indian cattle herd in a relatively few years. Whether complementing this selection with the introduction of exotic breeds, or expediting it with artificial insemination would be worthwhile are issues for cattle breeding experts. The point here is that OCs, by borrowing funds at relatively low cost and relending these to landless cow rearers, can end the natural selection of India's cattle herd and raise very greatly, very rapidly, its productivity. This, as well as increasing output, would also increase net cattle tax revenue, as more productive cattle can bear a higher tax.

A cattle tax would encourage people to keep fewer draft oxen and to employ more fully those retained. It would make it attractive for people to hire, rather than to keep their own, oxen. It would put pressure on those with underemployed oxen to get additional employment for them through hire work. An effective credit system, operated by the OC, would make it possible for the landless to acquire good draft oxen for hire work. They would be able, through the low cost of their labour, to offer ox hire services more cheaply than others. They should be able to offer these services at a sufficiently low level to induce landed persons to keep fewer oxen.

The considerations mentioned on p. 142 governing the allocation of finance by the OCs would, of course, operate also in India. The rural landless, with virtually costless, high quality family labour, if they had access to finance at relatively low cost, could normally get better returns from cattle than the landed, who have alternative uses for their labour and who frequently rely on hired labour that is particularly inefficient for cattle husbandry. The landless would, therefore, find it profitable to pay higher cattle taxes than the landed could normally pay. Cattle husbandry under this pressure would move out of the hands of the landed into the hands of the landless. But, as in Africa, not all landless persons would be creditworthy. An OC, trading off gains from increased cattle tax revenue against losses from defaulting borrowers of cattle financing funds, would avoid lending to parents of large families, whom lack of forethought and extreme poverty made uncreditworthy. This consideration should reduce the birth rate among the rural poor.

The suggested measures seem likely to advance both objectives (i) and (ii), p. 188. The redirection of resources, now used for overstocking communal grazing, to increasing the productivity of that grazing would increase cattle output, as shown on p. 144. Output would be further increased by using unemployed or underemployed labour to increase the stock carrying capacity of the communal grazing. The transfer of funds from wealthier persons, with a low rate of time discount, I, and relatively little labour suitable for cattle husbandry, to poor persons, with a high value of I and abundant suitable labour, would raise the productivity of cattle stocks and make it possible to convert the larger output of fodder made available by the other measures into more cattle products.

The landless would benefit in at least four ways. First, they would share in the net cattle tax revenue. Most of this revenue would come from the landed initially, but in time would come increasingly from landless cattleowners, as the landed were forced out of cattlekeeping. Some of the benefits accruing to the landless when their cattle stocks per person exceeded those of the landed would revert to the landed through their share of the net cattle tax revenue. But most of the additional revenue would remain with the landless. The landless would benefit, second, by obtaining finance to rear productive cattle that would allow them to participate in cattle keeping, less seriously disadvantaged than by having only naturally selected animals. Third, the landless would benefit from the greater demand for their labour to increase the productivity of communal grazing. Finally, the landless would benefit from the production of more grain, of which a smaller proportion would be used for cattle feed.

It seems impossible to predict *a priori* how these changes would affect the supply of milk to cities. More milk would be produced. But rural incomes would increase. Given the assumption of no change in the price of milk, Pm, the rural landless would consume more. Only if the increase in consumption by the rural landless were less than the increase in their output of milk would there be an increase in the supply of milk to the cities.

Dropping now the assumption of a constant price of milk, Pm, the effects of the suggested changes can be examined in a situation where Pm declines. This could be brought about, for example, by abandoning Operation Flood. A lower milk price, Pm, would reduce the cattle tax revenue that could be raised and so the benefits from its disbursement. The transfer of cattle tax revenue from landless to landed, that would occur when cattle keeping became predominantly an activity of the landless, would be reduced if Pm were lower. A lower Pm would reinforce a cattle tax in reducing the number of farmyard cattle, which would mean a lower demand for fodder and for grain for feeding. This would cause more grain to be produced and a smaller proportion of it to be fed. It would also reduce the cost of fodder to the landless. There would, however, be less demand for the landless's labour to increase the productivity of communal grazing. Finally, the cost of milk to rural consumers would decline. Overall, the effects of a reduction in the price of milk, coupled with the introduction of the suggested changes, would appear to be beneficial to the landless. However, the benefits likely to accrue appear to be of a lower order of importance to those that would result from maximising net cattle tax revenue. This suggests that if net cattle tax revenue is maximised and disbursed in the indicated manner, the effect of the price of milk, Pm, on the landless would cease to be important. But as matters are, a high milk price has the most seriously adverse effects on the real incomes of the rural landless.

Implications for aid

The United Nations' World Food Programme, the operations of the World Bank and of the various foreign government and international agencies referred to above, p. 181, in so far as they assist Operation Flood, raise the price of milk, Pm, in rural areas (p. 181). Raising the price of milk in rural areas:

(i) reduces milk consumption by the rural poor;
(ii) diverts resources from grain production for the poor to milk production for the rich; and
(iii) reduces the net income from milk production of the rural landless by reducing production from communal grazing and by raising the cost of fodder.

Operation Flood is the primary responsibility of the Indian Government. However outside agencies, insofar as they contribute to the financing of Operation Flood, share responsibility for its consequences. They can free themselves from this responsibility by withholding further assistance to Operation Flood as this is now conceived.

More positively, the World Food Programme could, if permitted by the Indian authorities, by a different approach bring substantial benefits to India's rural poor The harm done to India's poor now by the WFP's aid to Operation Flood derive from the raising of the price of milk, Pm, to producers, in the manner described or p. 186. India's poor would benefit if the WFP used its resources instead to reduce the price of milk, Pm, to producers. This could be done by disposing of the EEC's dairy surpluses, not to the urban rich, but to the rural poor. Distributing the EEC's surplus dairy produce to the rural poor would reduce Pm in two ways. First, it would reduce the local, rural demand for milk. Second, by diverting funds from Operation Flood, it would reduce the demand of the urban rich for milk produced in rural areas. A reduction in the producers' price, Pm, for milk would have effects opposite to those that have resulted from raising Pm. Reducing Pm would:

(i) reduce the incentive to keep cows in farmyards and on communal grazing;
(ii) reduce the value of straw, etc., causing more grain to be produced and less of it to be fed to cows;
(iii) reduce overstocking of communal grazing and raise production from it;
(iv) reduce the cost of grain to rural and urban consumers;
(v) reduce the cost of straw and other fodder to landless cowkeepers;
(vi) increase consumption by the rural poor of milk (a) produced at less cost by themselves, and (b) reconstituted from EEC dairy surpluses.

Use of the EEC's dairy surpluses on these lines would be a move to rectify some of the harm done to India's rural landless by their exclusion, through "tenure reform", from access to land; by the creation of an Indian petite bourgeoisie that has raised the price of milk, Pm, to a level that causes foodgrains, and foodgrain producing resources, to be used for the production of milk at a price beyond the reach of the rural landless consumers; and by veterinary activities that cause overstocking of communal grazing to the point where this has ceased to be of benefit to the landless.

Surplus young cattle　A 50% mortality rate among cattle aged between one and three years, when mortality rates are normally minimal, is an effective way of stabilising the cattle population when (a) cows lactate only with calves at foot; (b) beef eating is taboo; and (c) veterinary services have reduced replacement needs for the breeding and draft herds. This crucial equilibrating mechanism in the Indian cattle economy poses difficulties for any programme of rational adjustment of Indian cattle husbandry to modern technology and to capitalist colonial intervention.

A cattle tax would result immediately in the Operating Companies being swamped with young cattle that people did not want, were unwilling to pay tax on, and were unwilling to slaughter. The unwanted young cattle would be capable of devouring any conceivable increase in fodder output. To the extent that they consumed more fodder, more would survive, adding in due course to breeding and draft herds that are already excessively large. Coping with India's surplus young cattle is clearly a precondition for the rational development of the cattle industry.

Two compelling considerations exclude the obvious remedy of slaughtering the unwanted cattle. First, to do so would outrage Indian religious tenets. Second, this analysis suggests that Indian religious attitudes towards cattle have, on the whole, been socially more constructive than western interventions, like raising the price of milk to producers and veterinary services that prevent high mortality rates from holding cattle numbers to a productive level. It would be imprudent, under the circumstances, to advise Indians to alter their religious beliefs or to act contrary to them. A more appropriate approach would seem to be to create conditions where individual cattle owners have an inducement, which they do not now have, to reduce numbers of young cattle, and to leave the matter thereafter to them.

There appear to be three approaches. Two of these are longer run and relate to reducing the supply of, and to increasing the demand for, young cattle that are now unwanted. More immediately, holding operations are envisaged that would permit action to increase the supply of fodder from communal grazing. These might take the form of fencing in communal grazing areas chosen by the OCs for the production of fodder for milch cows and draft oxen. An alternative approach might be for the OCs to remove surplus young cattle to remoter, less populated areas, where the cattle would be free to scavenge, and ultimately to die, on unimproved grazing. The task is to ensure that additional fodder is not consumed by unwanted young cattle; it is not to reduce the amount of fodder now consumed by them. Suffering to cattle will, of course, occur on a vast, but no greater, scale than now, as half of India's crop of 20 million young cattle starve to death every year. Some improvement in the condition of people may, however, be expected.

India's present vast supply of unwanted young cattle, it has been suggested here, is the result of a natural evolutionary process that has produced breeds of cattle that lactate only with calves at foot. It is of the highest importance, once production has departed from traditional lines, and especially once publicly provided veterinary services reduce cattle mortality rates, to alter this characteristic of Indian cattle. It should be possible quickly and inexpensively for India's cattle authorities to introduce genetic lines of cattle that lactate without calves at foot. No other livestock breeding innovation would be likely to bring such large benefits to hundreds of millions of the world's poorest. The benefits would accrue from withholding valuable milk at birth from unneeded calves, allowing these to die, with minimal suffering, without affront to religious scruple, and without consuming the milk and fodder that now keeps them alive for a year. The supply of young Indian cattle would then quickly adjust downwards to the effective demand for them and the problem of India's "sacred cows" would disappear.

One year old cattle are worth in western Europe about US$400 for further fattening. The demand prospects for no other major commodity look as good as that for young cattle (Chapter 7). Ten million cattle, aged between one and three years, die in India annually. None of the Indian cattle that dies of starvation would realize anything approximating to US$400. There are, however, grounds for believing that, through appropriate action by the Indian authorities, an external demand could be developed for young Indian cattle that would raise their value considerably above its present zero level, and that might make it profitable to breed calves of appropriate conformation, and to feed milk and fodder to them. This topic is developed in Chapter 12.

Towards a Rational Exploitation of Pastoral Resources

The Situation and its Causes

The central chapters of this book attempt to explain the poor use made of the world's pastoral resources that are crudely measured in Chapter 2 and Appendix A. Consideration of the matter generates an acute awareness of human inability to exploit effectively available physical resources with available technology for man's wellbeing. Neither natural resources nor technical knowledge limit pastoral production. Production instead is limited because society has bound and handicapped itself in innumerable ways that prevent the rational, efficient use of available resources. It is the misuse, not the paucity, of resources that limits pastoral production. Responsibility for the misuse rests with those who determine who the users are and their conditions of usage, rather than with the actual or prospective users.

Misuse of resources   Gross misuse of pastoral resources is widespread. The EEC creates mountains of dairy surpluses that are disposed of in India with the consequences considered in Chapter 11, and disposed of elsewhere to cause digestive disorders when fed to lactose intolerant poor people. Cattle, however poor their return, yield a higher profit to Latin American latifundia owners than alternative, more productive, but more labour intensive land uses. If Latin America were restored to its preColumbian cattleless condition, agricultural output would almost certainly increase greatly, as it did in Ireland between the Restoration of Charles II and the Battle of Waterloo, a period of 160 years during which cattle production was static but total agricultural output and the overall economy expanded rapidly (Crotty 1966). Cattle numbers are excessive in Africa and India in relation to the carrying capacity of grazing lands; output would be greater if there were fewer cattle. Breeding cattle are imported to South East Asia, making the breeding of cattle/buffaloes there by smallholders still less attractive, and causing fewer animals to be bred and more to be slaughtered.

Intervention by development agencies is often harmful. Reference is again made to the harm done in India and to lactose intolerant poor consumers elsewhere by the disposal of surplus dairy produce by the EEC and by the United Nations' World Food Programme. Much of the World Bank's cattle investment is to increase the production of young cattle, of which there is a chronic surplus in LDCs. The larger part of the United Kingdom's aid for livestock development and the principal thrust of the FAO's livestock effort in LDCs are in the form of veterinary services that aggravate overstocking and depress output.

A malevolent providence confounds man in his use of pastoral resources and technical knowledge, turning their abundance into dearth. It would be difficult to design a chain of circumstances more effectively to deny mankind the beneficial use of its pastoral resources. If it is true that those whom the gods would destroy they first make mad, pastoral man appears ripe for destruction.

An explosion of change

Particular explanations of particular cattle resource misuses have been offered in preceding chapters. A general explanation of the general, grave misuse of pastoral resources would seem to lie in the rapid change now affecting world pastoral production. Domesticated grazing animals have been intimately and ubiquitously linked with man since they made possible his evolution from the hunter-gatherer stage. Man, as well as adapting species to his needs, has himself adapted genetically to his grazing animals, by acquiring lactoce tolerance where appropriate. Pastoralism has permitted denser human settlement that in turn permitted evolution to superior settlement. Society, in adapting cattle to its needs, has made them money in Africa and gods in India. In Europe, in conjunction with forests, they provided the slender causeway that allowed man to escape from endless primitiveness, to establish a bridgehead of accumulation that grows with time and holds the promise of permitting man to realise his rational nature.

Time was of the essence of the relationship. Aeons were needed for the domestication of wild species and for the evolution of lactose tolerant ethnic groups able to subsist on their cattle. Only immemorial custom could secure for cattle their status as money or as gods. Medieval Europe is characterised as, above all, a time of changelessness and stability, especially in contrast to the subsequent Renaissance. But western European man had, by the end of the first millenium, already become a capitalist crop grower, with a secure bridgehead of accumulation to support further relatively rapid growth. The process of first accumulation that transformed the western European pastoralist into a crop grower must necessarily have been slower and more gradual.

An explosion of change, by contrast, now affects pastoralism. The human population dependent on grazing animals is now doubling in each generation in extensive areas; it has increased by as much in 25 years as it previously grew in the 12 millenia since man domesticated grazing livestock. Complex, delicate relationships between man and his grazing animals, that evolved through millenia, are strained or shattered by this explosion of change.

The political context

Rapid change occurs within a particular politico-institutional framework. It is the framework of the western type state that itself evolved in western Europe through millenia but has been widely adopted elsewhere in little over a half century. It is a form of government that, by comparison with traditional forms, is powerful but insensitive. It is powerful to initiate change; and it is powerful to contain, and insensitive to, the social unrest that may be occasioned by change. Major changes can therefore be accommodated without the political repercussions that would have rent traditional politics. A modern Botswana State, for example, can uphold a situation where 15% of the rural population have 75% of the cattle and 45% have none. A modern Indian State can exclude tens of millions of virile men from access to the land, on which they are absolutely dependent, except on the terms of the legal owners which include payment of 25 days labour for a ton of straw.

Failure of comprehension

The impact of change as it affects grazing livestock is most immediate and forceful on those in closest contact. The Irish peasant of 150 years ago, forced from the land because rising cattle and falling wheat prices made it profitable to expand labour extensive cattle grazing and to contract labour intensive wheat growing, was made immediately and painfully aware of change. The African who no longer has the use of his neighbour's cattle on "mafista", or the landless Indian whose cow no longer produces on overstocked communal grazing unless he feeds it straw and more expensive feeds bought from landowners, and the South East Asian whose buffalo canno cultivate his paddy fields quickly enough to adhere to a double cropping irrigation timetable, are all aware of change that worsens circumstances already poor. But apart from pathetic protests, like the Tudor peasants' "sheep do eat up men", or the evicted 19th century Irish peasants' "the land for the people, the road for the bullock", those most affected are inarticulate. Unable to articulate their suffering, they are even less capable of analysing and identifying its cause; or to trace their suffering to sudden change in complex relationships that from immemorial time have determined the condition of their class. Those who suffer from change may strike back blindly, wildly, savagely, by maiming stock or killing their owners, but their protests are ineffectual and easily contained by modern police and military.

Livestock technologists observing the scene can identify much to account for the yawning gap between the conditions of the starving livestock owners and tenders of traditional societies and their fellows in DCs. The husbandry of the landless Indian who extracts a few gallons of milk from his cow differs in a thousand ways from that of the North American or western European farmer producing embarrassing milk surpluses. It is a truism that the husbandry differences account for the production differences. But at a more profound level, often beyond the technologist's ken, it is the production level, determined by price, caste and institutions that determine the husbandry. Starving cows produce little milk. But it is not, as technologists tend to see it, because cows are starved that they produce little milk; it is nearer the mark that, because little milk is produced as a result of rapid change in circumstances that had been immemoriably stable, cows now starve.

The changes being experienced are essentially sociological, political and economic in nature, though having also a technological dimension. Their study is the proper domain of the social sciences: but social scientists are ill equipped to study them. Urban born, based and biased social scientists know little about the countryside, less about farming, and less still about grazing livestock. Further, the vast majority of social scientists hail from Europe, where modern livestock technology and related institutions evolved along with capitalism, or from those parts of the New World — North America, Australia and New Zealand — where indigenous societies were obliterated to make way for the new capitalist one, and have therefore little opportunity to observe the conflicts created in traditional societies by the imposition of capitalist pastoral technologies and institutions.

Diversity of resource exploitation

There are profound differences in the ways the world's pastoral resources are exploited. Two primary distinctions can be recognized: first, those countries where capitalist institutions predominate and individual tenure of grazing land is the norm; and second, the countries where noncapitalist institutions continue to dominate, and grazing is communal. The first, capitalist, category of countries can be subdivided, on the one hand into those of capitalism's European heartland and the countries of the New World — America north of the Rio Grande and Oceania — where the indigenous hunter-gatherers were exterminated and transplanted capitalism developed on a *tabula rasa*; and, on the other hand, those countries outside the European mainland where, in the course of a violent 16th century, capitalist colonialism completely possessed the territories but, for the profit of the colonisers, suffered the indigenes to survive. This group consists of Latin America and Ireland.

Exploitation of pastoral resources under capitalist institutions, using capitalist technology, has been conducive to social wellbeing and development in the countries of the European heartland of capitalism, of North America and of Oceania, as indicated in Chapters 6 and 7. Pastoral resource exploitation has been to a high degree incompatible with social wellbeing in the second group of countries where capitalist institutions predominate, Latin America and Ireland; and the incompatibility has heightened with the accelerated development of metropolitan capitalism since the industrial revolution of the early 19th century. It has been characterised in Latin America by an inefficient, unproductive agriculture and by chronic political instability. It has been characterised in Ireland by a stagnating volume of agricultural output, by a long established decline in employment opportunities, and more recently by sectarian strife between Protestants and Catholics competing for fewer jobs.

The impact of capitalist institutions and technology on pastoral resource exploitation in the Old World outside Europe, where noncapitalist cultures have for the most part survived, has differed according to the local culture. Chronic overstocking has been the most important effect on traditional pastoralism, as practised principally in Africa; depletion of cattle/buffalo stocks has occurred in predominantly crop growing South East Asia; and in the special case of India, there has been overstocking of communal grazing and the diversion of crop products for cattlefeed.

Diversity in the manner of pastoral resource exploitation and in the impact of capitalism on indigenous cultures complicates analysis. A model designed to explain the chronic tendency towards understocking in Latin America will not be helpful in explaining overstocking in Africa or India. On the other hand, a theory designed to explain the overstocking of African and Indian communal pastures is unlikely to explain the destocking of communal pastures in South East Asia. Only when the problem is viewed as a whole, as the exploitation of global pastoral resources according to different local circumstances, does it become possible to formulate a theory of rational pastoralist behaviour sufficiently general to encompass the widely divergent and apparently contradictory practices of the world's most ubiquitous and oldest form of production after hunting-and-gatherng.

Common wealth and private profit

Change provides opportunity for profit. Opportunities for profit are probably better in pastoralism than in any other major economic activity. It has been suggested (pp. 25–6), for example, that pastoralist profits gave England the lead it held for two centuries in capitalist colonialism. Equally, in no other major economic activity do private profits accrue so directly at the expense of the common good. An individual in an exchange economy, by excluding others from land in a manner that would be irrelevant with crop growing, can profitably exploit a countryside with grazing livestock while employing little if any labour. The grazier's profits depend on the number excluded and the area they are excluded from. The communal grazier's returns are normally achieved entirely at the cost of fellow graziers. Adam Smith's concept of society benefiting incidentally from the individual entrepreneur pursuing his private interest (cf. Smith 1910 pp. viii-x) is inapplicable in the case of pastoral resource exploitation, where, generally, the individual's profit is society's loss.

Ireland perhaps provides the clearest example of the conflict between the private profit of the pastoralist and the common wealth. Following demand change in the British market after the Battle of Waterloo (pp. 29–30) "the landlords of Ireland are at length deeply convinced that, though a stock of cattle or sheep will afford profit a stock of mere human creatures, unemployed, will afford none" (British Parliamentary Paper 1825). The human population of Ireland during the following century and a half has been reduced, by starvation and emigration, from seven to three millions (Ireland, Central Statistics Office 1936 p. 6, 1977 p. 22); while total agricultural production remained unchanged, cattle stocks increased from some three millions to seven millions (Crotty 1966 p. 354, Ireland, Central Statistics Office 1977 p. 22). The value of land, that measures the private profitability of pastoralism, has meanwhile risen a millionfold in Ireland, from about one penny per acre in 1650 to £4000 an acre now (Bottigheimer 1971 pp. 142-63, *Guardian* 9.1.79).

The possibility of profit on this scale influences the direction of change. Profit makers have an incentive to press for change beneficial to them. Society, which loses, can poorly resist, because of the power and insensitiveness of the modern type state that enforces change; because of the inarticulateness and poverty of the immediate losers; because of the complexity of the issues that obscures them from others; and because of the unprofitableness to the individual of defending what is in everyone's interest to defend. Political decision makers, under the circumstances, benefit by adding to, and sharing in, the profits of the profit makers.

An initial orientation of policy and institutions favourable to the generation of private profit from pastoral resources is reinforced in many ways. The vested interests created are powerful, able to reward those who serve, and to punish those who oppose them. Ancillary interests are created that share the private profits of pastoralism. For example, development banks benefit from cattle projects that are privately profitable but socially harmful (pp. 103–4, 181, 180). The banks, concerned to add to their corporate status, and their officers, concerned to advance their careers, lend for cattle projects to governments, by whom loan repayments are guaranteed regardless of project outcome. Politicians, who win popularity from a loan's disbursement, need not concern themselves unduly about its productiveness: they may not be in office when repayment falls due; and even if they are, they can rely, as is usual with public debt, on repaying one debt by creating another, larger one. Cattle projects financed by development banks appear to be socially unproductive.

It would be surprising if the judgment of technologists and social scientists, that is in any case normally poorly informed on complex, many faceted pastoral issues, were not influenced by considerations of private gain. Research resources are controlled by institutions that, in one way or another, share in the private profit of pastoral resource exploitation. These research resources are more likely to be allocated in ways that increase rather than decrease private profit. The Indian landless cow keeper, for example, working 25 days for a ton of straw for his cow, cannot finance research into the causes of, or remedies for, his impoverishment; but resources are liberally available for research into the benefits of generation and disposal of the European dairy surpluses that contribute to the Indian cow keeper's impoverishment. There are, finally, large immediate private gains and social losses from the application of preventive medicine to grazing livestock in LDCs. The individual livestock owner, for reasons already suggested (pp. 103 and 127–8) cannot resist this application.

Homo sapiens, like his grazing animals, is gregarious. Major departures from established thought patterns occur rarely and are received with difficulty. The intellectual maverick's position, isolated from the herd, is precarious. The weight of current orthodoxy is against recognition if he is right and makes of him a pariah if he is wrong. Most intellectual progress is, therefore, gradual, consisting of minute refinements of, or additions to, current orthodoxy. But it is difficult to identify an intellectually tenable intermediate position between acceptance and rejection of the policies and institutions governing pastoral resource use. Cases of obvious abuse tend to be seen as aberrations, requiring *ad hoc* remedies, from a fundamentally sound system rather than as manifestations of an antisocial system. Understandably, criticism and suggestions by social scientists with, in any case, little direct knowledge of pastoralism, are directed to matters of detail rather than principle; and are couched in "politically realistic" terms that endorse the *status quo*.

More fundamental critics gravitate to an opposite, revolutionary position. Perceived inequities and inefficiencies are attributed to contradictions inherent in, and ultimately fatal to, the capitalist, market-guided system. A gregarious acceptance of dogma precludes rigorous analysis of pastoral situations and leads to such recommendations as the liquidation, rather than the taxation, of the exploiters of pastoral resources. It is possible to agree with the revolutionary view that present irrational, inefficient, inequitable pastoral resource exploitation constitutes a threat to the capitalist, market-guided system, without accepting that the manner of exploitation is inherent in the system. A more rational, socially responsible, market-guided manner of exploitation is held to be the principal condition for efficient, equitable pastoral resource use.

This view is confirmed by the lack of success of the Soviet Union in its revolutionary approach to exploiting its very extensive pastoral resources. The USSR's output of beef per unit area of pasture is only two thirds that of countries classed "developed" by the FAO. Though it has one third more pasture per person than the developed countries, its output of meat per person is one fifth less. The USSR is, along with India, the only major outlet for the EEC's embarrassing dairy produce surplus.[1]

Summary and prognosis

Explosive change is occurring in finely balanced, pastoral resource exploitation systems that are a complex of social, political, cultural, economic and husbandry elements. Powerful, insensitive, western type states are the agents of change that opens unparalleled opportunities for private gain at public expense. The many who lose by change that benefits a few are diffused and, for the most part, poor, weak and inarticulate. Social scientists, who are in any case poorly informed on the topic, have many inducements to reach conclusions that favour the extraction of private profit from pastoral resources at public cost.

A realistic appraisal of the misuse of the world's pastoral resources and of the causes of that misuse does not warrant a sanguine view of the prospects of a more rational, productive future use. Self interest and general incomprehension are likely to continue to outweigh any recognition of the tremendous gains, benefiting principally the world's poorest, to be derived at little cost from a more rational exploitation of the world's pastoral resources that has been the overriding concern of this work. The work would, nevertheless, be incomplete if it did not finally suggest measures of a more general nature than those adumbrated in the regional chapters and that are in line with what is perceived as a more rational exploitation of pastoral resources.

General and Multilateral Action

Controlling change

Explosive change places intolerable strains on ancient institutions and forms of pastoral production that have evolved over millennia. These strains are manifested in declining living standards for the poorest, in political polarisation and dictatorships of the left and right, and in the threat of widespread social collapse. Preventive medicine, applied to man and his grazing livestock, is seen as the most potent, single cause of change. There is an insatiable demand by individuals for medical and veterinary services, which are sufficiently effective to transform the size of populations within decades. The services that are desired by, and benefit, individuals create intractable problems for society; they bring changes more quickly than ancient institutions and modes of production can be adapted to cope with. The medical and veterinary services result in more people having more cattle, and the people and the cattle enduring more hunger.

Reproductive powers can outstrip productive powers under virtually any circumstance. Human or bovine reproductive powers exercised at anywhere near their biological limit, if not matched by equally high mortality rates, must quickly result in populations of people or cattle in excess of what the system can sustain. If collapse is to be avoided, reduction in mortality rates among people must be related to

---

1. The USSR is also a major beef importer (FAO 1977b pp. 53, 96).

reduction in birth rates; and reduction in unplanned mortality rates among grazing livestock must be related to increase in pasture productivity.

Decline in human death rates usually precedes decline in birth rates (Cassen 1978 p. 45–50). A lag between declines in death and birth rates gave rise to rapid population growth in the West in the 18th and 19th centuries. A similar lag now causes population growth in LDCs. There is, however, no assurance that birthrates in LDCs will eventually decline, as they did in DCs, to equal the low death rates brought about by modern preventive medicine. It is at least conceivable that equilibrium will be restored by the return of death rates to their former high levels, with malnutrition replacing disease as the more common and more stressful cause of death among larger populations of poorer people. Something of this nature has happened in the Sahel (Chapter 9), in parts of Malaysia, and elsewhere.[2] If birth rates do not automatically follow death rates downwards, there may be a need on the part of policy makers for concern to achieve an acceptable coincidence between both rates.

Accepted demographic thinking does not encourage unilateral action to reduce birth rates. "Massive, world-wide evidence shows that parents choose family size . . . Targets (by Health Regions) for reduced infant and child mortality should be set and monitored; their achievement will reduce the birthrate" (Lipton 1978 p. 167). The undisputed, widespread, positive association between birth and death rates is ascribed a causative relationship by the hypothesis sometimes referred to as the Value of Children, or VOC, hypothesis. VOC hypothesizes that poor people have children to benefit from their childhood labour, or as an insurance against destitution in old age. Prudence requires them, when death rates are high, to have many children to ensure that some survive. If death rates are reduced, people will in time recognize this and react by having fewer children, because more will survive to provide childhood labour or as an insurance against old age destitution.[3] It follows from the VOC hypothesis that birth rates are only likely to come down after death rates have been reduced.

The VOC hypothesis is here rejected on theoretical and empirical grounds. First, by imputing to the poor the values and standards of permanently, pensionably, lucratively employed and frequently childless social scientists, it conceals the most distressing and distinctive characteristic of poverty, which is that the acuteness of present wants precludes forethought. The conduct of the poor is determined by the wants and passions of the moment, albeit circumscribed as these may be by socio-religious taboos and mores. Only by imputing to the poor implausibly low rates of time discount, or I, could the benefits from childhood labour, or the more problematic and more distant benefits of maintenance in old age, have any substantial present value, or a value exceeding that of the more immediate, inescapable cost of rearing children.[4] Realistic rates of time discount reduce to insignificance any benefits to the poor, other than those accruing now or in the immediate future.[5]

Four demographic phenomena have been discussed or touched on in the present work that contradict the VOC hypothesis. "The European marriage rate" (above pp. 21–2) implied that, at least since the Middle Ages, marriage, and therefore birth rates have been constrained, although survival prospects in cold, bleak, impoverished

2. Crotty 1978a p. 237. L. R. Brown (1976) suggests that death rates have recently commenced to rise in a number of countries.
3. Lipton 1977 p. 15. The insurance and saving aspects of having children are central to Cassen's (1978 pp. 63–76) explanation of high fertility in India.
4. Cassen (1978 p. 64) suggests annual time discount rates of 5–10%; Boxall et al (1978 p. 87) impute an annual time discount rate of 11% to Indian grain growers.
5. Data quoted by Boxall et al (1978) show that in fact the operative rate of time discounting among Indian grain growers exceeds 40% (Crotty 1979b).

northern Europe cannot have been better than elsewhere. The decline in the English marriage and birth rates that occurred from the 15th to the 17th centuries (above, p. 25, note 18) owed nothing to declining death rates. Likewise the rise in the European birth rate in the 18th century was not occasioned by a rise in the death rate; rather, it appears to have accompanied a death rate decline. Finally, the collapse in the marriage rate, and therefore in the birth rate, in Ireland in the 1830s occurred under circumstances of desperate and worsening poverty and of rising death rates that improved only after a 15 year lag (Crotty 1966 p. 40).

The view favoured here is that human procreation is a natural, biological process; and that people, who have normally lived at, or close to, the subsistence level, normally procreate to their biological limit. Particular circumstances may prevent people from so procreating, and this has been especially the case in the difficult northern European environment, where the need for capital prevented young people in medieval Europe, in Tudor and Stuart England and in 19th century Ireland, from marrying and having children. Accelerated capital formation, that marked the industrial revolution, relaxed these constraints on marriage and the birth rate in much of western Europe.

Escape from subsistence standards permits people to contemplate the future, and to weigh, among other matters, the advantages of having children. Europe's property owning peasants were the first large social class to so escape, to contemplate the cost of rearing children, to offset against that the later benefits from the labour these children must provide, and to find on balance a credit. Europe's better paid proletariat in the 19th century next effected escape; and because they could not anticipate a return from their children working on family capital, the net present discounted cost of children (COC) was positive; and they reduced the birth rate by artificial birth control.

The rate of time discount is negatively correlated with income: the person starving can give no thought to the future; the satiated millionaire is indifferent between a present and a future good. As incomes rise and the rate of time discount, I, decreases, the cost of having children, discounted to the point of conception, rises and people have fewer. The death rate simultaneously declines — not because the birth rate has fallen, but because nutrition has improved.

Given the desirability of a lower birth rate, the proceeds of the suggested land tax (Chapter 8) and cattle tax (Chapters 9 and 11) offer a means of achieving it. The disposal of these funds primarily as equal capitation grants to adult citizens, by raising the incomes of poor people, would also reduce their rate of time discount and so raise the present value of the net future cost of having children, COC. This would be conducive to lower birth rates, that would be more or less offset by lower death rates resulting from the better nutrition that higher incomes would permit. Part of the social surplus attributable to the adult citizenry is necessarily preempted for socially provided services for children. It would seem appropriate, under the circumstances of an excessive birth rate, to recover some or all of these costs from the persons responsible — the parents. This could be done by making appropriate deductions from the basic payment due to the childless adult from the land/cattle tax revenue according to the number of children individuals had.[6]

The maximisation of revenue from land/cattle taxes requires, as noted in Chapters 9 and 11, the provision of credit to potentially suitable exploiters of pastoral resources. Normal banking considerations suggest the prudence of excluding from these credit

6. It has been reported since the above was written (*Daily Telegragph* 15.3.79) that the People's Republic of China is to pay a subsidy to couples with fewer than two children. Compulsory crop deliveries, which effectively are a land tax, have for long been a major source of public revenue in the Republic. These two measures – a subsidy not to have children and a land tax – though very unMarxian, are the best possible way to stabilise population and to have land worked efficiently to support that population.

facilities persons with many children, and therefore with little forethought and little prospect of servicing debt.

Downward adjustment in the capitation disbursements of the proceeds of land/cattle taxes to adults *pro rata* to the number of living children they have and restricted access to credit for pastoral resource exploitation could be substantial costs that would be payable as soon as children were born. The value of these costs, discounted to the time of conception (COC), would be further increased by the lowering of time discount rates that would follow from the income increases resulting from the land/cattle tax revenue disbursements.

Given population growth that strains society's capacity to absorb, and given the possibility that birth rates can move independently of death rates, it would appear expedient to shift the weight of social expenditure from death prevention to birth prevention. That would make it easier and less costly for people not to have children. A shift in the emphasis of public expenditure from death to birth prevention, taken together with the measures already suggested for raising the present cost of having children (COC), should achieve some reduction in the birth rate, bringing it closer into line with a declining death rate. The closer the birth rate declines with the death rate, the more rapid and the more sustained will the latter decline be.

There are difficult moral and political issues involved in transferring public resources from death to birth prevention, so as to halt or to slow the population growth that has caused as large an increase during the past 25 years in the number of people depending on grazing livestock as occurred in the preceding 10 or 12 000 years. Similar difficulties do not arise in bringing about a better balance between the use of public resources to save animals from dying and to increase the amount of fodder available. The poor have enough cattle, but their cattle like themselves have too little to eat (p. 6). The heavy emphasis given under these circumstances to veterinary services that stop animals from dying and the inadequate emphasis given to producing more feed for the existing stock of cattle cannot be justified.

Case for a young cattle trade

More efficient use of resources will increase pastoral production. It is envisaged (p. 144) that most of the additional meat, milk and draft services will be consumed in the producing countries. These countries will, however, probably wish to trade internationally some of the additional pastoral products for nonpastoral products, so raising the question of the prospects for international trade in cattle and cattle products.

It is clear from a global view of cattle producing resources, as these are categorized and represented in Fig. 5.1, that they occur in different combinations. Taking the resource "time" to mean the ability to wait, or command over capital, then, broadly speaking, DCs have a relative abundance of "time" and a relative scarcity of land, while LDCs have a relative abundance of land (and in some cases "other") and a scarcity of "time". This different combination of cattle producing resources gives rise to the phenomenon illustrated by Fig. 4.3: per unit weight, the price of young cattle is less in LDCs and greater in DCs than the price of fat cattle. The relationship between the values of young and of fat cattle, derived from Equation 5.16, shows why:

$$\text{VFA} = \text{Pc} \cdot \text{I}^{\theta} + \text{P}_v\text{V}_1 \cdot \text{I}^{\theta/2} \tag{12.1}$$

The cost of variable inputs, PvV_1 being high relative to the value of fat cattle, VFA, in LDCs (pp. 93–4), these must be used sparingly, causing the fattening period, θ to be prolonged. I, θ and PvV_1 relative to VFA, having high values in LDCs and low values in DCs, Pc/VFA must have a low value in LDCs and a high value in DCs.

The benefits from a trade in young cattle from LDCs to DCs have been considered above (Fig. 8.2). It is clear from that analysis that, if a trade in cattle or cattle products is to take place between LDCs and DCs, abstracting from transaction costs, the profitability of the trade will be greater the younger are the traded cattle.

The potential scale as well as profit of a trade in young cattle may be noted. Given the changes in taste and technology noted in Chapter 7, the availability in DCs of young cattle of appropriate quality and cost would be likely to result in a substantial switch in production from pig and poultry meat to beef. Demand for young cattle should therefore be buoyant, in part because of increasing demand for beef associated with rising incomes in DCs, and in part because of the scope for replacing pig and poultry meat with beef.

Replacement of grain fed pig and poultry meat by fodder fed beef would increase the grain surplus of the DCs and, to that extent, reduce its cost to LDCs, that are, as a whole, net grain importers. Increased LDC exports in this case could therefore conceivably, and probably uniquely, result in improved terms of trade for the exporter: the more young cattle LDCs export, the larger will be the DCs' grain surplus, and the lower will be the cost of grain imports to LDCs.

Quality of cattle

Young cattle from LDCs are very different from those now fattened in DCs; as observed in the preceding chapter, none of the 10 million yearling cattle that starve to death in India annually would realise the high prices now paid in DCs. Yet even now, selected LDC young cattle, offered at an appropriately low price, would be attractive to fatteners for DC markets. Though their carcass configuration and feed conversion rates may not be as suitable as those of DC breeds, they do have an advantage, in addition to low cost, that is of increasing importance: their carcasses usually have a lower fat content. The use of appropriate sires on foundation breeding stock to produce crossbred young cattle for export is a quick and inexpensive way of adapting LDC cattle for DC markets.

Transaction costs

Abstracting from transaction costs, the advantages of a trade in young cattle over one in mature cattle are clear cut. Allowing for transaction costs, of which there are many elements, the issue is less clear cut. Brief consideration of the nature and orders of magnitude of transaction costs is indicated in view of the *prima facie* advantages of a trade in young cattle.

Transport is the most obvious transaction cost. The cheapest, most appropriate transport form is a pragmatic issue that depends on circumstances. Driving, or otherwise shipping alive, cattle may be less expensive than shipping chilled or frozen beef to markets, that in any case usually prefer locally slaughtered to imported meat. Ocean shipment of young feeder cattle is feasible in appropriately designed vessels or "floating feedlots" (Stenswick 1972 p. 5).

Movement of large numbers of cattle invariably involves casualties that become a cost of movement. For a given distance, the lower the transport cost incurred, the higher the casualty rate (cost) will be. Young calves shipped long distances by sea are all likely to die in transit; but casualties among 400–500 lb feeder cattle air freighted a similar distance are likely to be insignificant. Differences in prices of cattle at different ages in exporting and importing countries, differences in freight rates for different forms of freighting (droving, trucking, railing, shipping, air freighting) and differences in casualty rates for different forms of freighting and different ages of cattle determine the most profitable age and form of freighting.

A health hazard attaches to any social intercourse, including an international trade in cattle and their products. The risk, actual or perceived, need not, *a priori*, be greater for young cattle than for beef. A trade in young cattle is perceived as supplying a limited number of large cattle fattening units in DCs, with appropriate disease control and isolation measures at all stages, including purchase, assembly, shipment, fattening and slaughter. The risk of infection to cattle or people in importing countries would appear, under these circumstances, to be, at worst, no greater than in the case of carcass or tinned meat shipments that have normally been distributed through numerous, scattered retail sale points before infection is discovered.

Trade restrictions, purportedly to control disease, are a common form of protection. Restrictions reasonably justified to secure the health of local livestock for the long term benefit of consumers cannot always be easily distinguished from restrictions that principally protect local producers from outside competition, or principally provide a *raison d'être* for veterinarians who devise and implement them. The severity of veterinary import restrictions and the stringency of their implementation varies directly with the perceived risk of infection, and the perceived risk of infection commonly varies inversely with the acuteness of the need for the product felt in the importing country. If local consumers have not a firm demand for the product, and/or if local producers oppose its entry, then the perceived risk of infection is likely to be greater and import restrictions correspondingly severe. DC consumers are unconcerned to get LDC beef, but politically powerful DC producers are concerned to exclude it so as to get a better price for their own product. DC beef producers, on the other hand, welcome imports of young cattle, that are a major production cost, with a view to reducing these costs and widening profit margins.

Import restrictions, other than of purportedly veterinary character, are also normally, if not invariably, less stringent on young cattle than on beef for the same reasons (UK 1972). The analysis on pp. 80–4, that points to calf prices in DCs rising towards half the value of slaughter cattle, suggests that DCs will continue, probably to an increasing extent, to minimise veterinary and other restrictions on young cattle imports, and to treat them more favourably than beef imports.

Opposition to an extensive trade in young cattle is likely from persons concerned about the attendant hardship to animals. Traders in their own interest will avoid hardship that reduces stock value needlessly. The trade would be impeded and the interests of producers in LDCs and consumers in DCs would suffer if hardship to animals were reduced at a cost greater than the resultant increase in stock value. The rights of persons who find animal suffering abhorrent could be safeguarded without imposing on the rights of LDC producers to get the highest price for their cattle or the rights of DC consumers to get beef at lowest cost, by inviting animal lovers to subsidise slaughtering facilities in export countries, or improved shipboard conditions.

The principal transaction cost, which is also perceived to be the principal reason for the failure of a trade in young cattle between LDCs and DCs to materialize, is perceived to be opposition within exporting, or potentially exporting, countries. There is, if not populist opposition to, a lack of support for, an export trade in young cattle in those countries where a trade exists or might be developed. Kenya's government, for example, has made no apparent effort to expand exports of young cattle to the Middle East though it has supported efforts to develop beef exports to Europe.[7] Colombia's government looks with disfavour on live cattle exports to neighbouring Venezuela and Ecuador.[8] The Irish government prohibited the export of young cattle until required by conditions of EEC membership in 1973 to liberalize those exports (Crotty 1974 p. 26).

Opposition to, or lack of support for, an export trade in young cattle is usually

---

7. Kenya's cattle exports are less now than they were 25 years ago. Africa was a major net exporters, but is now a net importer, of live cattle (FAO 1955 p. 231, 1978b p. 42).
8. ECLA-FAO 1962 p. 18. Mexico and Argentina also discourage cattle exports (Stenswick 1972 p. 4).

attributable to populist autarkic sentiments expressed in the pseudoeconomics phra
of "maximising value-added". Young cattle exports, it is argued, even at a val
OLAC, Fig. 8.2, remove raw materials that could be worked up to a much great
value, OKFD, or more if the cattle are slaughtered and their meat exported in vacuu
packed retail cuts, or similar highly processed forms. The reality is that, for a varie
of reasons touched upon in earlier chapters, the calves worth OGBC are not worke
up into mature cattle and exported for OKFD or more. Land and labour instea
remain unemployed.

A somewhat more sophisticated argument is that the export of simple, unprocesse
products both manifests and perpetuates economic dependency (e.g. Valenzuela
Valenzuela 1978 pp. 535-57). A self perpetuating relationship is perceived of lo
employment, a small economy, and low productivity that places the exporting countr
in a relationship of perpetual subordination to, and dependence on, importers. Th
Irish case is perhaps the classic illustration of the dependency relationship associate
with the export of unprocessed cattle. A fivefold increase in the price of labou
extensive cattle relative to the price of labour intensive wheat between 1810 and 197(
caused cattle exports, that were unchanged frpm 1665 to 1805, to increase ninefol
by 1875 and to continue to increase thereafter. This was associated with the virtua
cessation of all other exports and with an unbroken decline in the Irish (Republic
workforce from three to one millions between 1841 and 1971 (British Parliamentar
Paper 1843; Ireland, Central Bank 1978, Statistics Appendix p. 80).

The accuracy of the diagnosis of the cause, and the efficacy of the prescription fo
economic dependency are questionable. Taking the latter point first: two consideratio
suggest that an insistence on exporting highly processed (i.e. meat) rather than poor
processed (i.e. young cattle) pastoral products will increase rather than decrease LD
dependency on DCs. Converting young cattle to beef is capital intensive (Equatic
12.1). If attempted by LDCs, it will require them either to forego other investme
or to borrow more capital from DCs, the one course curtailing economic growth ar
the other increasing dependence on capital borrowed from DCs. Capital can only t
borrowed, for converting calves into meat or other purposes, on creditors' terms th
more or less circumscribe the freedom of action, or sovereignty, of the debtor.

Marketing the meat into which calves are processed requires the goodwill
importing countries that normally can choose from many supply sources, includir
domestic ones. Securing this goodwill further circumscribes the sovereignty of expor
ing LDCs.[9] In short, an LDC that borrows to convert its young cattle into beef th
it must sell to its creditors in competition with many other suppliers, including tl
creditors' own, would seem to place itself in a position of extreme dependence.

A trade in land and/or labour intensive young cattle from capital-scarce LDCs
capital-rich and land-scarce DCs is an alternative to the flow of capital from DCs
LDCs that, if it occurs at all, will only occur on terms that are likely to accentua
the dominance of the latter and to perpetuate the dependence of the former. A trac
in young cattle makes minimal demands on the exporter's capital. It involves
commodity for which there is an increasing demand and diminishing supply in DC
The trade, for these reasons, seems less likely to perpetuate a dependency relatic
than a trade in beef.

As to the cause of dependency: rising export prices make possible increased benefi
to society; if these benefits do not occur, the cause is not high export prices, but th
institutional maladjustments that cause high pastoral product prices to harm societ
in the producing countries. The institutional maladjustments can take various form
High prices for wool exports forced peasants in Tudor England from their land, a
high prices for cattle exports caused the eviction and starvation of many peasants i

---

9. Botswana maintains a representative in Brussles for the purpose of securing continued
   preferential access for its beef to the EEC.

19th century Ireland. High prices for pastoral products, through the paradox of property, can result in land being used inefficiently (pp. 92, 114). High prices for the products of communal grazing accentuate the problems that affect this form of grazing under modern circumstances (pp. 127–8 and 173–4). These harmful effects may be mitigated by measures that hold down the value of pastoral products, especially if simultaneously the products then become the raw material of labour intensive industry. The land and cattle taxes suggested above (pp. 114, 139–40, 188–9) more effectively avoid the ill effects of high pastoral product prices. They do so without lowering the value of society's products and without requiring LDCs to increase their dependence on DCs, for their goodwill in permitting imports of unwanted beef and for their capital to finance the conversion of young cattle into beef in LDCs.

A young cattle trade that raises cattle values realizes the increasing value of the LDC's pastoral resources in a world where land is fixed and capital accumulates apace. Appropriate land or cattle taxes would ensure that these realised values, that are now socially harmful, would be socially beneficial. Discouraging a young-cattle trade, or failing to develop one, immobilises pastoral resources or makes their exploitation dependent on an accentuation of dependency. Land or cattle taxes that appropriate for social purposes the profits of a young-cattle trade are the radical escape from dependency.

Joint development of trade

A trade in young cattle readily develops within countries and between neighbouring countries. Cattle can be moved on foot, by truck or by rail, in small or large numbers, at preferred times and over distances that can be extended or shortened at will. A marginal approach is possible. A trade in beef to distant markets can likewise be developed gradually, with little pioneering outlay. Small consignments of chilled, frozen or tinned beef can be shipped abroad, using normal shipping services, and be received and distributed by established meat importers in distant countries. There are, in addition to those discussed, formidable logistical barriers to the spontaneous development of an international trade in young cattle.

The envisaged trade would move young cattle from the regions of chronic surplus (South America, Africa and India) to the capital rich regions of shortage (North America, western Europe and Japan). An export trade in young cattle to a distant market needs to be initiated on a scale sufficient to warrant chartering a well equipped, specialist cattle boat, handling several thousand head of cattle. Farmer clients to buy the cattle must be organised in the importing country before assembling commences. Adequate inducements must be offered to these potential buyers to persuade them to buy store cattle of unknown, untested calibre instead of cattle from traditional sources, of known quality.

Veterinary regulations at import and export points must be researched and provision made for compliance with them. Provision needs to be made for assembling and holding facilities in the exporting country on a scale sufficiently large to hold a shipload of cattle, possibly for several weeks prior to shipment to conform to veterinary regulations.

It will be necessary to identify in the exporting country the type of cattle most suitable for an export trade and to establish that these will in fact fatten satisfactorily in the importing country and will produce a carcass that is acceptable there. It will be necessary to arrange for the buying of the cattle in a way to minimise speculation and to minimise the disruption which is likely to arise when a new, substantial buyer of cattle first appears.

Financing the buying of a shipload of cattle from point of purchase from breeder/rearer in an LDC to delivery to fattener in a DC is a major undertaking. New lines of credit will need to be opened to ensure full, prompt payment on receipt of cattle.

These, though formidable, need not be insurmountable pioneering problems. On the trade is established, subsequent risks and uncertainties will be on a much low level. Many, in importing and exporting countries, will benefit if a trade is establishe But no individual or firm can expect to benefit sufficiently to warrant incurring t heavy, high risk, initial expenditure. A single country might not consider the effe warranted as, apart from populist misconceptions about the potential benefits of young cattle trade, the single state would reason like the single firm: if its pioneeri were successful, other countries would enter the trade and, by their competition, dilu the benefits to the pioneering country.

The situation, where there is a prospect of large but widespread gains in return an absolutely large but relatively insignificant outlay, is preeminently suited to jo international action. The investigative and pioneering work required to develop trade in young cattle between LDCs and DCs seems preeminently appropriate to t United Nations Conference on Trade and Development (UNCTAD).

Refinancing cattle development loans

Development banks benefit from lending for cattle development projects when lo repayment is guaranteed by the governments of recipient countries (p. 197). Sever cattle projects so financed can be identified as conceived on lines that preclude bene to the countries concerned; it is difficult to identify cattle projects so financed that a well conceived. Borrowing countries would appear reasonably entitled to expect fro development banks and associated agencies standards of technical competence a integrity that do not result in decisions and recommendations involving loss borrowers. If systematic assessment of cattle projects financed by internatior development banks establishes that an unreasonably large proportion involve loss the borrower, a political case would seem to exist for refinancing the loans. Countr that borrowed in good faith for cattle projects that were ill conceived by developme banks and associated agencies might be deemed excused from repayment, whi would then become a charge on the bank's reserves. The envisaged assessment cou be performed on behalf of a consortium of debtor countries by a small research tea at low cost.

Countercyclical action

Cycles in the beef industries of DCs are notorious and could hamper LDC attemp to develop exports of beef and cattle. This is partly because LDC supplies to D markets are marginal and tend to be forced to absorb most of the cyclical chang in quantity and price; and partly because protectionist pressures acquire add strength when prices to domestic producers are cyclically depressed. The 1973/ collapse in beef prices in DCs, for example, was followed by the reintroduction severe restrictions on beef imports, including a virtual embargo on imports by t EEC.

It is relatively easy to predict the course of cattle cycles.[10] Monitoring market tren would enable exporting countries to warn importing DCs of the consequences of cyc inducing policies. For example, the EEC's beef intervention system clearly is cyc inducing (Crotty 1974 pp. 21-2). An informed LDC cattle lobby could press f reforms of the system to reduce its destabilising forces.

Credit is a major source of instability in beef markets. Rising beef prices encoura cattle producers to borrow and encourage lenders to lend to cattle producers. Injectic of credit — the same as a temporary reduction in I — make it profitable to div female cattle from slaughter to breeding and to retain fattening cattle for furth fattening. There is a short run reduction in the supply of beef, and its price ri

10. See above, p. 133.

further in a self justifying speculative movement. Eventually the additional cattle are forced on the market, partly through pressure of numbers and partly because of the need of cattle owners to service debts incurred to expand production. Cattle prices break and overstocked, indebted cattle owners hasten to offload their cattle, causing further and sometimes steep declines in cattle prices.

A cattle industry monitoring system could make possible better countercyclical use of credit. High cattle taxes and tight credit for cattle producers in exporting countries would increase disposals, to counter inflationary trends in importing countries; lower cattle tax rates and relaxed credit would encourage retention and help to support sagging prices in importing countries. Countercyclical action of this sort, by stabilising cattle supplies and prices, would reduce protectionist opposition to imports and also the destabilising effect on LDC producers of cattle price fluctuations.

A competent cattle industry monitoring service, as well as guiding export countries in disposing of their cattle in a countercyclical manner, could help to dampen cycles

Table 12.1   IBRD financed projects with cattle content

Fiscal year	Total agricultural projects		Projects with cattle content		Cattle projects as proportion of total agricultural	
	No.	Value $M	No.	Value $M	By No. %	By Value %
1970	32	938.8	6	119.2	19	13
1974	51	1821.9	18	585.0	35	32
1976	68	3685.5	15	611.9	22	17

See IBRD 1970, 1974b, 1976.

in DCs by bringing about a more informed use of credit there also. It is noted in this context that the World Bank's record on cattle investment has been to accentuate rather than to dampen cattle cycles. The Bank, responding to the mood of the moment, increased its involvement in cattle projects from six projects costing $119 million in fiscal year 1970 to 18, costing $585 million in 1974, at the peak of the world cattle boom (Table 12.1). Thereafter, like commercial banks, the World Bank lent more cautiously for cattle projects.

Multilateral Action

Having considered the scope for multilateral action by LDCs to develop pastoral resources, especially in relation to a trade in young cattle, attention is briefly directed to two cases that seem to offer scope for tripartite action of an exceptionally fruitful nature.

Indian calves and Japanese beef

Japan's meat consumption is the 10th largest and the most rapidly expanding in the world.[11] Consumption consists largely of poultry meat produced with imported feed grain, of which Japan is now also the largest importer (FAO 1978b p. 127). Japan could lessen its rapidly increasing dependence on feed grain imports by drawing on India's surplus young cattle (pp. 169, 191–2) in two ways.

One way would be for Japan to establish in neighbouring Sri Lanka fattening facilities on lines suggested in Appendix B. The operation would combine Middle East oil (for urea fertiliser), surplus Indian calves, and a relatively small area of Sri Lanka to grow grass with annual yields of 15 tons of high protein dry matter per acre.

11. Japan is the sixth largest meat producer in the OECD (OECD 1978a p. 20). Only the USSR and China among non-OECD countries produce more meat than Japan (FAO 1978a p. 218–9).

The project would have for Japan the advantage over alternative sources of beef c
overall control of a many faceted enterprise producing beef on factory lines a
constant, or declining, cost according to scale of operation.

Sri Lanka's climate is suitable for the operation; the country is convenient to th
Indian source of young cattle; and it has no religio-cultural objections to cattl
slaughter. Tact will be necessary to minimise offence to Indian religious scruples i
initiating a trade that, it can be pointed out, will remove young cattle to conditior
far superior to those experienced by the cattle remaining in India, half of which ar
bound to starve to death. A trade, once initiated, will generate its own vested intere
in its perpetuation and expansion. Indian prohibitions on cattle slaughter are th
easier to implement because no one loses from them: the overstocking that is cause
on communal grazing damages the community, but not individuals; and cattle are i
any case valueless if slaughtered. A trade in young cattle could pay Indian cattl
owners for young cattle that are now valueless. Once payments were established
India's several million cattle owners would wish to see expanding a trade that coul
pay them for a commodity that they have in abundance, but is now valueless.

The second way in which Indian young cattle could reduce Japan's dependence o
feed grain imports is through a direct trade between India and Japan. The price c
calves, Pc, must tend towards half the value of fat cattle, VFA, in Japan, (a) becaus
the Japanese being lactose intolerant, calves will be unavailable as a byproduct of
substantial dairy industry; and (b) because of Japan's high capital:land ratio (Chapte
7). This seems to preclude a substantial, wholly domestic beef industry. However,
beef industry using surplus Indian young cattle would seem to have better prospec
and to be a possible alternative to poultry meat produced from imported feed grair

Japan's rapid capital accumulation emphasises the comparative advantage c
perennial over annual crops discussed above (pp. 72–4). There may be scope, therefor
to divert some of the country's rice growing resources to fodder production, fc
fattening low cost young cattle. This development, while allowing Japan to reduce i
dependence on feedgrain imports, would increase its imports from Asian countrie
— of young cattle from India, and possibly of rice from other Asian countries.]
would secure employment, probably of a more congenial nature, for Japan's forme
rice growing farmers.

Middle East cattle fattening

There appear to be possibilities of combining the wealth of oil producing Middle Ea
countries with Africa's extensive land resources to produce beef efficiently. Feedlo
in North Africa and the Middle East could fatten young cattle from south of th
Sahara, using locally produced urea, high quality, vitamin rich fodder grown o
irrigated land, and roughage from arid lands. This diet would need to be supplemente
by imported grains to produce high quality beef for local consumption and export t
DCs.

The rising cost of calves in Europe and their embarrassing surplus in Africa an
India open for the Middle East the possibility of playing once more, in modern guis
its historic, pre-16th century role of emporium to Europe for the products of th
South and East. Fattening African and Indian young cattle in the Middle East woul
have major advantages over fattening them in Europe, where much of the beef woul
be consumed. Land for feedlot sites is cheaper, and there would be less difficulty ther
over disposing of feedlot slurry. Climatically the area is probably more suited tha
Europe for feedlotting beef, rainfall being low and seasonal temperature ranges bein
narrower. The risk of infecting local cattle with disease through imported stock woul
be less in the Middle East because of the lower density of the cattle population; an
if local cattle were infected, the consequences would be less serious because of th
unimportance of the indigenous cattle industry. The region is excellently placed t

import grains and other feeds, possibly as backloading on appropriately adapted oil tankers at about half the cost of feedstuffs to European beef producers (EEC 1979 p. 40). Fattening cattle in feedlots, as a technologically advanced agricultural enterprise with considerable local linkages, should be attractive to capital rich oil producing countries, even at lower profit margins than those acceptable in Europe.

Two arguments have been advanced here against LDC attempts to develop beef exports to DCs: one is the capital intensity of beef production; the other is the strength of farm protectionism in DCs, especially the EEC. Capital is not a problem for oil rich countries with embarrassingly large foreign reserves. These countries are also uniquely well placed to smash through European farm protectionist barriers.

A confrontation by Middle East oil producers with European countries, that offered the latter the choice of Middle East oil *and* beef, or neither, would inevitably result in Middle East beef being admitted. Oil rich countries have the resources to secure this position by developing sophisticated production and marketing channels that controlled the entire process, from breeding the cattle in Africa or India to retailing the beef to European consumers. Establishing this position of strategic, permanent dominance would appear to be an attractive alternative to accumulating reserves of depreciating foreign currencies.

A major breach by Middle East beef would effectively end European agricultural protectionism and would have global repercussions. Domestic European prices, not only for beef but for all higher quality foods, would have to be reduced in line with imported beef if they were to be sold. European producer prices, not only for meat but for the grain on which European meat production is based, would have to be reduced, unless governments supported farm prices above the free market level by massive deficiency payments. European beef producers would be under pressure to reduce costs in order to compete with Middle East beef, and this pressure would favour the importation of young cattle from LDCs to Europe. That is to say, the more young cattle from Africa and India the Middle East fattens and ships to Europe, the greater the pressure there will be on European beef producers also to import young cattle from Africa. The argument can be extended to other agricultural inputs from LDCs, including oil seeds, oilcakes and fishmeal.

The potential scale of a trade in young cattle from India and Africa to supply beef producing industries in Sri Lanka, Japan, and the Middle East is great. The supply of young cattle in India and Africa is virtually limitless and the demand for beef in developed countries, as an alternative or supplement to pig or poultry meat is also virtually limitless. Because, as noted above (p. 202), the more beef that is produced from LDC young cattle, the less pig and poultry meat will be consumed in DCs; therefore the less feedgrain will be used in DCs; and therefore the more feedgrain will be available and the lower its cost will be, for cattle fattening in Sri Lanka, Japan and the Middle East.

Research and Development

Agronomists and anthropologists, economists and geographers, sociologists and veterinarians, in their respective ways and institutions, study aspects of mans' exploitation of his grazing livestock as these aspects are manifest in particular locations and circumstances. Their success in finding better ways of exploiting the species has been limited, considered either by the standard of acquiring such elementary tools of analysis as recognition of the difference to the decision making grazier between communal and individual tenure of grazing land; or by the standard of widespread, grave misuse of pastoral resources. Some explanations for this limited success have been offered above (pp. 194—8). Here the point is made that, given explosive change now in man's relations with his grazing livestock that have evolved through aeons as the origin of misuse of pastoral resources, any prospect of influencing change beneficially must depend on understanding the process of change itself and the role of the principal elements involved. That understanding is unlikely to result from the partial approaches that are now characteristic of studies of society's relations to domestic grazing stock. The essence of the object of study being the effects of transfer of technology, culture and institutions, the broader the study base, the better the prospect of success.

There may be scope, under the heading of multilateral action, for an institute of international and interdisciplinary character, to research, to teach and to advise on the exploitation of the world's pastoral resources. The institute ideally would command agronomic, anthropological, economic, geographic, sociological and veterinary expertise. Its approach would be global, concerned to develop a general understanding of the status of pastoral exploitation; and concerned in particular cases to understand how they relate to, and are influenced by, the general. The institute's methods would be historical, insofar as the concern is change over time; and comparative, in so far as the concern is change in different societies. Its members ideally would have had practical involvement, as owners or as the dependants of owners of grazing livestock and would therefore bring to their subject a knowledge and understanding that rarely and with difficulty percolate ivory academic towers or the corridors of administrative power, but are as integral as their bone marrow to the 500 million or so people whose livelihood depends on their grazing livestock.

Cattle and Related Statistics

A.1. Africa

	(1) Population $\times 10^3$	(2) GNP US \$ $\times 10^6$	(3) Arable land ($\times 10^3$ ha)	(4) Grazing land ($\times 10^3$ ha)	(5) Cattle stocks ($\times 10^3$)	(6) Beef and veal meat production ($\times 10^3$tons)	(7) All meat production ($\times 10^3$ tons)	(8) Milk production ($\times 10^3$ tons)	(9) Cereal production ($\times 10^3$ tons)	(10) Pulse production ($\times 10^3$ tons)
Algeria	14 700	8340	6792	37 416	950	30	117	342	1346	68
Angola	5717	2780	900	29 000	2900	46	72	135	570	72
Botswana	641	150	512	41 080	2200	28	39	72	55	15
Burundi	3580	270	1166	435	761	10	17	48	552	280
Cameroon	6206	1530	7300	8300	2500	41	75	54	692	46
Cape Verde Islands	280	90	40	10	18	0	1	1	13	1
Central African Rep.	1710	280	5900	100	460	13	27	28	119	4
Chad	3873	320	7000	45 000	2800	29	41	81	577	70
Comoro Islands	260	40	90	15	72	1	1	0	16	0
Congo	1199	410	630	14 300	45	1	1	0	14	0
Benin	2947	330	1546	442	740	9	28	11	400	28
Egypt	35 619	8820	2852	0	2160	126	389	620	7908	342
Equatorial Guinea	313	80	221	104	4	0	0	0	0	0
Ethiopia	26 550	2290	13 730	65 130	24 663	177	364	532	5545	741
Afars, Issas	101	160	1	244	18	0	3	0	0	0
Gabon	520	680	127	5100	5	0	21	0	3	0
Gambia	493	60	200	400	292	4	5	5	107	1
Ghana	9313	2760	2574	11 237	1100	21	81	9	877	10
Guinea	5243	570	1500	3000	1880	14	25	43	765	26
Guinea-Bissau	510	170	275	1280	253	3	8	8	65	0
Ivory Coast	5887	2250	8887	8000	480	41	93	4	560	11
Kenya	12 480	2150	1670	3944	7400	114	171	721	2118	310
Lesotho	1165	120	355	2495	490	9	17	17	211	11
Liberia	1452	450	366	240	33	2	7	0	208	0
Libya	2160	7620	2521	7000	121	6	53	17	173	6
Malagasy Republic	8301	1260	2856	34 000	9712	110	175	44	2093	68
Malawi	4833	530	2895	1840	596	9	25	19	1347	34
Mali	5370	370	11 600	30 000	4500	26	53	90	891	19
Mauritania	1257	250	263	39 250	1800	9	25	60	34	8
Mauritius	860	360	106	7	51	2	3	22	1	1
Morocco	15 903	5080	7437	12 500	3700	90	231	480	4849	379
Mozambique	8283	3110	3009	44 000	2250	34	53	57	901	70
Niger	4357	450	15 002	3000	2800	20	43	46	847	100
Nigeria	71 262	15 050	21 795	20 720	10 918	187	434	284	7806	880
Reunion	470	570	56	8	18	1	8	4	12	1
Rhodesia	5900	2520	1837	4856	4150	95	116	250	2369	26
Rwanda	3980	290	807	817	740	6	15	26	167	120
Sao Tome & Principe	77	40	30	1	4	0	0	0	0	0
Senegal	4070	1160	5364	5700	2266	29	49	91	635	14
Seychelles	55	20	17	0	5	0	0	0	0	0
Sierra Leone	2787	460	3664	2204	280	5	11	7	556	25
Somalia	3042	250	957	20 568	2972	17	71	82	325	5
S. Africa & Namibia	24 265	25 420	13 742	137 106	13 300	453	816	3290	13 509	98
Sudan	17 051	2260	7134	24 000	14 000	187	312	1320	2527	71
Swaziland	463	150	171	1342	610	13	17	31	103	1
Tanzania	13 974	1830	16 251	40 202	12 098	115	165	620	1031	185
Togo	2119	380	2160	200	225	3	16	3	138	24
Tunisia	5459	2530	4510	3250	690	19	67	130	1137	48
Uganda	10 829	1610	4888	5000	3840	66	99	274	1261	256
Upper Volta	5714	410	5377	13 755	1400	9	23	38	699	95
Zaire	23 438	3200	7200	24 803	1111	17	184	27	858	209
Zambia	4646	2020	4800	33 800	1748	30	43	79	831	79
Total Africa	391 684	114 300	211 283	787 201	148 129	2277	4710	10 127	67 821	4536

See FAO 1975a, IBRD 1975b.

A.2. Asia

	(1) Population × 10³	(2) GNP US $ × 10⁶	(3) Arable land (× 10³ ha)	(4) Grazing stocks (× 10³ ha)	(5) Cattle stocks (× 10³)	(6) Beef and veal/meat production (× 10³ tons)	(7) All meat production (× 10³ tons)	(8) Milk production (× 10³ tons)	(9) Cereal production (× 10³ tons)	(10) Pulse production (× 10³ tons)
Afghanistan	16 634	1420	7980	6020	3550	42	171	310	4702	55
Bahrain	232	210	2	4	4	1	3	6	0	0
Bangladesh	74 000	5910	9112	600	26 698	255	241	713	17 401	230
Bhutan	1124	70	5	20	191	0	1	11	396	2
Brunei	145	240	13	6	3	0	3	0	6	0
Burma	29 509	2360	18 920	371	7800	75	189	330	8613	291
China (including Taiwan)	826 776	227 000	127 000	200 000	63 487	1460	15 268	3457	230 137	8467
Cyprus	635	930	432	93	33	3	31	27	216	11
Hong Kong	4160	5950	12	0	11	30	177	6	7	0
India	581 911	71 590	164 980	13 130	179 900	71	813	8400	108 199	9286
Indonesia	124 415	15 980	18 100	9875	6724	135	363	43	25 560	286
Iran	32 136	27 830	16 153	11 000	5760	75	378	1021	6348	203
Iraq	10 410	8880	4999	39	2059	51	169	257	2175	42
Israel	3210	9660	417	818	280	20	161	530	350	11
Japan	108 350	393 000	5296	389	3750	290	2136	4806	16 480	244
Jordan	2540	870	1300	100	40	2	17	7	261	33
Khmer Republic	7566	550	1836	580	1800	17	67	19	705	17
Korea, Dem. People's Rep. of	15 040	5160	1894	50	767	20	118	19	6533	215
Korea, Rep. of	32 905	13 250	2387	18	1546	45	202	104	8057	31
Kuwait	880	10 610	1	134	7	1	14	8	0	0
Laos	3180	200	950	800	464	4	59	5	930	13
Lebanon	2977	2790	345	10	84	54	56	70	72	18
Macau	260	70	0	0	0	0	8	0	0	0
Malaysia	11 302	6490	3523	52	363	8	147	14	2062	0
Maldives	114	10	3	1	0	0	0	0	0	2
Mongolia	1357	740	789	139 894	2235	57	199	158	358	16
Nepal	12 020	1100	1980	2000	6535	4	63	210	3351	0
Oman	720	610	36	1000	0	0	0	0	0	809
Pakistan	66 230	7740	19 385	5000	13 154	133	314	919	12 315	29
Philippines	40 219	11 170	11 145	846	2200	86	643	15	7883	6
Portuguese Timor	640	90	80	150	85	1	11	0	35	0
Qatar	180	1090	2	50	6	0	0	0	0	5
Saudi Arabia	7745	12 470	878	85 000	310	10	82	32	556	0
Sikkim	216	20	10	20	138	0	1	4	33	0
Singapore	2185	3990	11	0	1	0	61	1	0	0
Sri Lanka	13 180	1560	1979	439	1673	18	35	201	1912	9
Syrian Arab Republic	6948	2800	5874	6497	539	12	83	220	2335	200
Thailand	39 400	10 600	13 927	308	4800	92	406	4	15 855	273
Turkey	37 930	22 600	28 196	26 135	12 408	178	445	2580	17 014	696
United Arab Emirates	320	3720	20	200	0	0	0	0	0	0
Vietnam, Dem. Rep. of	23 220	2600	2018	2000	899	12	387	13	4450	55
Vietnam, Rep. of	19 870	3200	3296	2870	853	24	229	0	7362	43
Yemen Arab Republic	6217	620	1200	7000	1250	15	68	75	1105	60
Yemen, Democratic	1560	170	252	9065	99	1	15	6	95	0
Total Asia	2 170 566	897 920	476 738	532 584	352 506	3263	23 834	24 601	513 869	21 658

See FAO 1975a, IBRD 1975b.

A.3. Europe

	(1) Population $\times 10^3$	(2) GNP US $ $\times 10^6$	(3) Arable land $(\times 10^3$ ha)	(4) Grazing land $(\times 10^3$ ha)	(5) Cattle stocks $(\times 10^3)$	(6) Beef and veal meat production $(\times 10^3$ tons)	(7) All meat production $(\times 10^3$ tons)	(8) Milk production $(\times 10^3$ tons)	(9) Cereal production $(\times 10^3$ tons)	(10) Pulse production $(\times 10^3$ tons)
Albania	2295	1060	556	688	400	19	54	194	607	18
Austria	7530	26 460	1612	2181	2624	197	558	3250	4012	5
Belgium	9760	44 470	835	733	2896	306	1056	3734	2012	12
Bulgaria	8622	13 710	4502	1480	1454	95	472	1410	6797	80
Czechoslovakia	14 572	41 820	5311	1749	4556	410	1284	5491	10 599	57
Denmark	5020	26 140	2668	318	3115	230	1069	4810	7261	11
Faeroe Islands	40	150	3	0	3	0	0	0	0	0
Finland	4660	16 760	2714	52	1905	114	254	3133	2852	10
France	52 160	236 610	18 632	13 883	22 864	1780	4702	29 600	41 070	102
Germany, Federal Republic	61 970	329 670	8081	5347	14 364	1260	3943	21 554	22 663	97
Germany, Dem. Republic	16 980	50 850	4858	1429	5482	389	1564	7804	9400	68
Gibraltar	28	40	0	0	0	0	0	0	0	0
Greece	8930	16 720	3631	5239	1050	96	390	656	3928	122
Hungary	10 430	19 320	5555	1280	1930	131	871	2092	12 855	90
Iceland	210	1060	1	2279	67	2	18	129	0	0
Ireland	3030	6520	1179	3662	7270	348	572	4040	1169	11
Italy	54 890	134 520	12 235	5249	8408	1040	2715	10 200	16 934	425
Luxembourg	350	1730	64	70	216	13	23	255	134	0
Malta	320	340	14	0	8	2	10	20	5	2
Netherlands	13 430	58 180	834	1267	4978	357	1548	9900	1314	38
Norway	3960	18 460	790	114	955	64	171	1803	1127	0
Poland	33 360	69 860	15 107	4219	13 023	619	2720	17 000	22 983	233
Portugal	8994	12 690	3875	530	1150	82	309	490	1533	94
Romania	20 830	18 539	10 426	4478	5679	245	1254	4382	13 232	148
Spain	34 740	59 360	20 979	11 301	4413	416	1824	5084	13 158	539
Sweden	8140	48 070	3018	700	1898	143	458	3083	6651	20
Switzerland	6430	39 220	384	1633	1973	149	416	3319	812	0
United Kingdom	56 000	171 380	7164	11 519	15 227	1078	3042	14 076	16 254	312
Channel Islands	132	320	7	3	12	1	1	23	0	0
Isle of Man	58	100	21	10	35	1	3	13	14	0
Yugoslavia	20 956	21 160	8087	6344	5681	287	848	3349	15 631	218
USSR	249 750	506 490	232 101	375 800	106 266	6400	14 700	91 800	186 620	8720
Total Europe	718 577	1 991 779	375 244	463 557	239 902	16 274	46 849	252 696	421 627	11 432

See FAO 1975a, IBRD 1975b.

A.4. North and Central America

	(1) Population × 10³	(2) GNP US $ × 10⁶	(3) Arable land (× 10³ ha)	(4) Grazing land (× 10³ ha)	(5) Cattle stocks (× 10³)	(6) Beef and veal meat production (× 10³ tons)	(7) All meat production (× 10³ tons)	(8) Milk production (× 10³ tons)	(9) Cereal production (× 10³ tons)	(10) Pulse production (× 10³ tons)
Antigua	69	30	26	3	8	0	0	5	0	0
Bahamas	190	440	15	1	4	0	5	2	0	0
Barbados	239	240	26	4	21	0	3	9	2	0
Belize	132	90	47	17	42	1	1	8	20	0
Bermuda	55	260	0	0	0	0	0	2	0	0
Canada	22 130	120 510	43 767	24 896	13 318	919	2181	7570	31 478	139
Costa Rica	1872	1320	490	1558	1767	58	70	230	178	10
Cuba	8920	4850	3595	2439	7500	190	264	560	540	24
Dominica	74	30	17	2	4	0	1	1	0	0
Dominican Republic	4432	2310	972	1436	1800	39	87	340	270	67
El Salvador	3771	1320	651	665	1009	32	46	174	520	32
Greenland	51	140	0	5	0	0	0	0	0	0
Grenada	106	40	16	1	6	0	1	0	1	0
Guadeloupe	342	360	55	17	76	3	4	10	1	0
Guatemala	5175	2590	1484	1015	1916	62	89	300	723	80
Haiti	4454	570	370	500	737	18	51	39	669	47
Honduras	2781	890	823	3413	1661	47	58	175	319	32
Jamaica	1967	1950	241	247	275	12	43	49	12	5
Martinique	343	460	28	25	47	2	5	11	0	0
Mexico	56 047	49 830	27 469	69 789	27 500	502	1148	3506	14 047	1319
Netherlands Antilles	234	360	5	0	8	1	2	4	6	0
Nicaragua	1973	1060	873	920	2600	52	65	220	335	52
Panama	1570	1450	542	1141	1333	42	54	57	231	5
Panama Canal Zone	67	200	1	11	0	0	0	0	0	0
Puerto Rico	2950	6420	207	330	541	22	52	383	3	5
St. Kitts-Nevis-Anguilla	45	20	14	1	8	0	1	0	0	0
St. Lucia	106	50	21	3	14	0	1	2	0	0
St. Vincent	90	30	18	1	7	0	1	0	0	0
Trinidad and Tobago	1059	1380	139	6	71	2	22	7	16	4
United States	210 400	1 304 530	191 053	244 277	127 670	10 654	23 596	52 352	204 480	1195
Virgin Islands (US)	71	420	6	9	7	0	1	3	0	0
Total North and C. America	331 715	1 504 150	272 971	352 732	189 950	12 658	27 852	66 019	253 850	3016

See FAO 1975a, IBRD 1975b.

A.5. South America and Oceania

	(1) Population × 10³	(2) GNP US $ × 10⁶	(3) Arable land (× 10³ ha)	(4) Grazing land (× 10³ ha)	(5) Cattle stocks (× 10³)	(6) Beef and veal meat production (× 10³ tons)	(7) All meat production (× 10³ tons)	(8) Milk production (× 10³ tons)	(9) Cereal production (× 10³ tons)	(10) Pulse production (× 10³ tons)
Argentina	24 282	39 760	26 028	144 947	58 000	2226	2860	6151	23 160	146
Bolivia	5331	1200	2921	28 365	2326	60	119	34	508	13
Brazil	101 051	76 950	34 082	107 274	88 000	2100	3685	7303	26 404	2257
Chile	10 230	7360	5672	11 538	3050	175	310	1186	1706	145
Colombia	22 500	9900	5054	17 084	23 032	488	620	2600	2676	148
Ecuador	6786	2560	3815	2200	2645	52	122	752	614	66
French Guiana	52	70	2	5	2	0	0	0	1	0
Guyana	772	320	833	2428	254	5	20	17	229	0
Paraguay	2416	1000	1048	15 100	5814	123	169	92	332	42
Peru	14 531	9070	2822	27 465	4500	108	345	940	1139	99
Surinam	398	350	38	9	⁴3	1	7	8	150	0
Uruguay	2995	2850	1851	13 629	10 790	349	450	710	1192	5
Venezuela	11 279	18 340	5214	13 847	8843	266	468	1092	836	42
Total South America	202 623	169 730	89 380	383 891	207 299	5953	9175	20 855	58 947	2963
American Samoa	28	30	3	0	0	0	0	0	0	0
Australia	13 130	57 170	45 189	452 700	30 882	1302	2183	6876	16 822	141
British Solomon Islands	179	50	145	39	17	0	1	1	1	0
Fiji	551	360	146	65	165	4	5	45	23	1
French Polynesia	130	350	64	20	13	0	1	1	0	0
Gilbert and Ellice Islands	58	20	36	0	0	0	0	0	0	0
Guam	100	410	4	8	4	0	0	0	0	0
New Caledonia	126	630	80	400	124	4	5	8	1	0
New Hebrides	92	40	80	25	90	3	5	2	1	0
New Zealand	2960	10 900	834	12 680	9415	401	969	5654	730	64
Pacific Islands (Trust Terr.)	103	50	27	18	16	0	1	0	0	0
Papua New Guinea	2596	1050	431	89	83	2	35	1	5	19
Tonga	95	20	53	2	3	0	1	0	0	0
Western Samoa	153	40	63	6	21	0	2	1	0	0
Total Oceania	20 301	71 120	47 155	466 052	40 833	1716	3208	12 589	17 583	225

See FAO 1975, IBRD 1975b.

The Feasibility of Fattening Cattle on Intensive Grass in the Rainforest Tropics

Description of Project

It is envisaged that 1100 acres of good quality land, either rolling gently or level and well drained, would be used for intensive grass production. One-tenth of this land would be out of production at any time, as the pasture would need to be renewed every five years, a process which immobilizes the land for six months. There would be an effective 1000 acres of grassland. The project is assumed to be located in Malaysia and prices are in Malaysian dollars.

Two tons per acre per annum of a balanced fertilizer would be applied to the producing grassland to get an output of 15 tons per acre per annum of dry matter of fattening quality. The grass would be cut, carted and fed to fattening cattle/buffalo held in slatted floor houses. The equivalent of twelve 300 lb cattle per acre of productive grassland would be bought each year and fattened to 600 lb liveweight.

The indicated costs and returns from the project are as below. The numbered items are discussed in the text.

Cattle/Buffalo Fattening Input/Output Data

		M$
Land and fixed capital	1. 1100 acres of land at $1200/acre	1 320 000
	2. Conversion to grassland, including ring fence, at $300/acre	330 000
	3. Cattle housing at $500/acre	550 000
	Total land and fixed capital	2 200 000
	4. Per effective acre of grassland	2200

		M$/acre/annum
Recurrent costs	5. Fertilizer costs	1000
	6. Management, labour and machinery costs	140
	12 store cattle, 300 lb at 85 cts lb	3060
	Total recurrent costs	4200
	12 fat cattle, 600 lb at $1.00/lb	7200
	Gross margin	3000

Notes

1. It is assumed that land can be acquired for the project at the price of good rubber land under aged trees. This is taken to be $1200/acre. This is the financial cost of land, based on its value to private enterprise. This in turn is determined by the market value of rubber. But the social marginal value of rubber is less than its market value because of the low price elasticity of demand for Malaysian rubber (Crotty 1979c). The social value of land used for rubber production is, for that reason, less than its value to private enterprise. That is to say, the economic cost of land for a cattle project is less than its financial cost as reckoned here.

2. The development cost of $300/acre assumes that rubber trees can be cleared at zero cost; that the value of the timber will cover the cost of cutting and removal. The indicated cost of pasture establishment includes a ring fence, 5.6 miles long, costing $1840 per mile, or $10/acre. These costs exceed the following estimated costs of grassland establishment in Malaysia: (i) Vickers 1969: estimated cost per acre of pasture establishment, including $13 for fertilizers and $6 for application, but excluding fencing: $192. (ii) Groome 1973 p. 77. (iii) FAO/IBRD 1970; Appendix Tables 16 and 17. Fencing costs are estimated at $23/chain, or $1840/mile. Estimated cost per acre of pasture establishment, including $50 for fertilizers, but excluding fencing $166. (iv) Malaysia, Economic Planning Unit 1974: fencing cost: $1009 per mile. Estimated cost per acre of pasture establishment, including seed, fertilizer and lime $205.

3. Cattle housing costs are believed to be in line with those for similar type housing in modern feed lots in the Italian Po valley where spectacular advances in fattening cattle in feedlots have occurred in recent years. Malaysian costs should be substantially lower than Italian costs because of the much narrower temperature ranges in Malaysia and the smaller type of cattle held there. Italian feedlot housing is designed for summer temperatures in excess of those in Malaysia and winter temperatures below freezing point. Cattle in Italian feedlots range in weight from 300 lb to 1200 lb; cattle weights in Malaysian feedlots will range from 300 lb to 600 lb.

4. The capital charge of $2 200 000 is spread over the 1000 acres which will at any time be in production. The remaining 100 acres will be immobilized for pasture renewal. (The cost of staff housing is assumed to be included in the purchase price of land).

5. Assumed annual fertilizer applications per established acre of grassland and the cost are: (Predicted 1985 costs in brackets)

	M$/Cost per acre
N : 914 lb from 2000 lb urea	760 (75)
P_2O_5 290 lb from 806 lb CIRP	32 (21)
K_2O : 806 lb from 1344 lb Muriate of Potash	290 (139)
	1 082 (235)
Less allowances for slurry	82
Net cost of fertilizer	1000

Costs are based on following fertilizer prices: (Predicted prices in brackets)
CIRP 36% P_2O_5 : $250 per ton (29)
Muriate of Potash 60% : $482.50 per ton (116)
Urea 46% : $850 per ton (42)
Source: ICI (Malaysia), quotation, January, 1975. "Predicted prices" are the world fertilizer prices predicted in 1975 by the IBRD for 1985, at the exchange rate US$1 = M$2.

6. The principal cost will be cutting and carting grass. This is estimated at $64 per acre per annum on the basis of 15 tons of dry matter per acre, based on costs reported by Tan Hong Tong & Pillai 1974. All other management and labour costs are assumed to total $76 per acre per annum. It is assumed that costs will be held to a minimum so as to generate a maximum surplus to pay higher prices for young cattle.

It may be possible to increase liveweight gain above, and to reduce fertilizer expenditure per acre below, the levels assumed above. Tan Hong Tong & Pillai have shown that latex sludge can be used as a fertilizer for grassland to produce high quality grass. Uniroyal Estate, Kedah, has been carrying cattle for several years on land fertilized solely with latex sludge. Dalzell has shown that unprocessed palm-oil sludge can be fed to cattle to give acceptable performance.

Latex sludge and palm-oil sludge are pollutants and an embarrassment to processors. Both sludges are available in Malaysia in quantity at cost of handling and transport.

Characteristics of Project

The cattle project outlined above has three distinctive characteristics:

  (i) high output of grass per acre;
  (ii) specialist fattening;
  (iii) cut and carry, or zero grazing.

These characteristics and their justification are considered in the following subsections.

Intensive grass

The cattle/buffalo project outlined above incorporates advanced, intensive grassland husbandry. The project will get its young store stock from a breeding/rearing industry operating on primitive, scavenging lines. A less stark contrast between the two technologies which it is proposed to marry to produce beef in the rainforest tropics may appear intuitively preferable. A less radical change from the present system of beef production might seem more appropriate. Specifically, grazing lightly fertilized grass/legume pastures, with imported stock and their progeny, might appear preferable. The point merits examination.

The technical feasibility of producing large quantities per acre of good quality grass, of cutting and carting this, and of fattening local K-K cattle and buffalo has been established in Malaysia beyond reasonable doubt. Labu Estate, Seremban, has been growing heavy crops of good quality grass on an extensive acreage for a number of years. It has been cutting and carting this grass at reasonable cost. It is established that K-K heifers can gain about 1 lb liveweight daily at a conversion rate of 9 lb dry matter per 1 lb weight gain, on an all grass diet. Universal experience suggests that noncastrated males of the same breed will perform 20–25% better. Buffalo are also likely to perform better than the K-K cattle. Malaysia has already adapted successfully and inexpensively poultry houses used for intensive production in temperate countries; there is every reason to expect that the modern, intensive, slatted floor houses used for intensive cattle fattening in Europe can be likewise adapted to Malaysian conditions.

The technology of extensive grass production, grazed by imported cattle or their progeny, is, however, still at the experimental stage in Malaysia. It has not been possible to locate in Malaysia an extensive area of lightly fertilized grass/legume pasture that has survived a number of years of commercial grazing conditions. Probably a technique will be developed of establishing and maintaining at reasonable cost for a reasonable time mixed grass/legume pastures of reasonable productivity;

but such a technique does not appear to exist at present. Or if it does, it involves pasture and stock management skills of an order which has so far precluded, and seems likely to continue to preclude, its extensive use under commercial or quasicommercial conditions.

Many questions likewise remain unanswered about the performance in Malaysia of cattle even from so contiguous an area as North Queensland, and about the performance of the progeny of these cattle. Their fertility, longevity and feed conversion efficiency under commercial conditions in Malaysia have all to be established. Meanwhile, the record with imported cattle has not been encouraging.

The evidence suggests that in Malaysia the cost per unit of nutrition from grassland declines through a wider range of output per acre and reaches a minimum at a much higher output per acre than in temperate countries. Land is costly in Malaysia. It is costly in terms of resources required to clear jungle land. Accessible jungle land of agricultural quality and the resources to bring this into cultivation are limited. Cleared land has valuable alternate uses in a country with a large, rapidly growing and, in many instances, underemployed population. Fixed, or overhead, costs of grassland are therefore high in Malaysia, probably as high as in most developed, temperate countries.

The variable costs of grass production are high in Malaysia. It is much more difficult to establish pastures on cleared land in Malaysia than in temperate countries. Such pastures, once established, unless intensively and expertly managed, have a low output of poor quality grass; they quickly revert to scrubland. Confirmation of these characteristics of extensively managed pasture in Malaysia can be got by visiting the country's grazing reserves.

Research, especially at Chemara, has established two important economic characteristics of Malaysian grassland:

(a) as output per acre increases, the quality of the grass also improves;
(b) output per acre increases in response to fertilizer application far above the levels that are customary for grassland in temperate countries.

Two important economic considerations follow from this experimental work:

(a) while the variable cost per unit of nutrition from grassland is high in Malaysia, this cost may decline initially as, with fertilizing, the quality as well as the quantity of grass produced increases; and
(b) because of the continued volume and quality response to fertilizer applications up to very high levels per acre, the variable cost per unit of nutrition produced remains more or less constant over a wide range of outputs per acre and does not rise as soon as with temperate grasslands.

Given the low output and poor quality of extensive grass in Malaysia, the variable cost per unit of nutrition produced will be high. Added to that is the high fixed cost per unit of output at low output levels. The combination of high variable and high fixed costs results in a very high level of total costs per unit of output from extensive grassland.

Given that the variable costs per unit of nutrition from grassland at first decline and then do not increase over a wide range of output, and given that fixed costs approach asymptotically towards zero as output per acre increases, it follows that total (i.e. variable + fixed) costs per unit of nutrition from Malaysian grassland, while being higher generally than in temperate countries, will at first decline more rapidly than in temperate countries as output per acre increases and will then continue to decline over a wider range of output than in temperate countries. Total cost per unit of nutrition from grassland in Malaysia is, however, unlikely ever to fall as low as in temperate countries. These countries have a comparative advantage over Malaysia in grassland, just as Malaysia has a comparative advantage over them in tropical crop production.

Fig. B.1   Cost per unit of grass

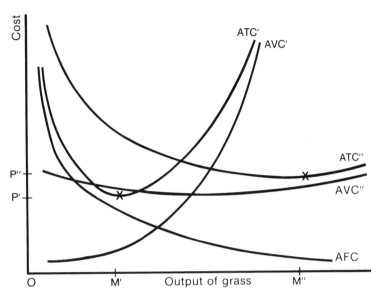

The foregoing analysis is presented in standard diagrammatic form (Figure B.1). While the slopes and respective heights of the curves are believed to be consistent with what is known of the costs of grass production in temperate countries and Malaysia, the curves do not purport to represent actual cost levels or cost relationships, within either temperate countries or Malaysia, or between these countries and Malaysia.

Two sets of grass production costs are envisaged: a temperate country set and a Malaysian set. For each set there are two separate cost curves:

(a) an average variable cost curve, AVC′ for the temperate country and AVC″ for Malaysia;
(b) an average total cost curve: ATC′ for the temperate country, and ATC″ for Malaysia.

An average fixed cost curve, AFC, is presumed common to both countries.

AVC′ is shown as being much lower than AVC″ originally, but rising rapidly at a lower level of output per acre. This depicts the situation in temperate countries where relatively low outputs of grass are attainable at low cost; but once output per acre is increased beyond a moderate level, the cost of further production rises rapidly.

AVC″, on the other hand, while initially much higher than AVC′, is represented as declining initially under the twin influences of higher outputs of better quality grass in response to initial fertilizing. AVC″ remains fairly level over a wide range of output per acre, depicting the point established at Chemara and elsewhere: that tropical grassland responses to increments of fertilizer remain fairly constant up to a total output some five times as great as in temperate countries. Only then does AVC″ rise sharply.

Average fixed costs, AFC, are assumed, for convenience and in line with the statement on fixed costs above, to be the same in the temperate country and in Malaysia. It approaches the horizontal axis asymptotically.

ATC′ and ATC″ are composites of AFC and AVC′ and AVC″. At any point on ATC′, its height from the horizontal axis is equal to the sum of the heights of AVC′

and AFC at the same point. Likewise, any point on ATC″ is the sum of the corresponding heights of AVC″ and AFC.

OP′, corresponding to where ATC′ reaches a nadir, is the lowest price at which grass can be produced in the temperate country. OP″, corresponding to where ATC reaches a nadir, is the lowest price at which grass can be produced in Malaysia. Over the price range, P′P″ grass can be produced profitably in the temperate country but at a loss in Malaysia. Grass is produced at minimum cost, OP′, in the temperate country at an output of OM′ per acre. It is produced at minimum cost, OP″, in Malaysia at an output OM″.

The fact that the total cost per unit of nutrition from grassland in Malaysia is likely to be at a minimum at a much higher yield than is customary in temperate countries does not ensure that this cost will be less than the value of the nutrition produced. (As already noted, the minimum cost of commercial grass produced in Malaysia is likely to be substantially higher than its minimum cost in temperate countries). But it does follow that the chances of producing grass in Malaysia at a cost less than its value will be greater with intensive than with extensive production that is, with high yields rather than with low yields. It also follows that if in Malaysia low yielding grassland can show a profit, high yielding grassland, with lower costs per unit of output and more units produced per acre, will be more profitable.

It is conceivable that the cost of grass produced at lowest cost — i.e. at high yield levels – will exceed its value and therefore incur a loss on each unit produced. The loss per unit of higher cost grass on low output grassland will, in that case be greater. It is impossible to say, a priori, whether the loss per acre on high output grassland will be greater or less than the loss per acre on low output grassland. The high output grassland will incur a smaller loss per unit produced but will incur this loss on more units per acre; the low output grassland will incur a greater loss per unit produced but will incur this loss on fewer units per acre.

The policy conclusion, on the basis of present knowledge of grassland response in Malaysia, is that commercial grass production is more likely to be successful with high yields than with low or moderate yields.

Specialist fattening

Given the high cost of producing quality grass in Malaysia, specialist cattle/buffalo fattening is more likely to be successful than integrated breeding-rearing-fattening. The argument in support of this proposition is the same as that which causes almost universal specialization in commercial cattle production (see, for example, above pp. 106–7).

A specialized fattening operation is in accordance with the normal cattle husbandry practice of reserving the better quality, more expensive feed for fattening. The operation relies on buying young stock from the scavenging section of the industry where these can be bred and reared at low cost but where they cannot be easily fattened.

The envisaged fattening project would carry 12 000 yearling cattle, or the equivalent of 6000 livestock units. An integrated breeding-rearing-fattening operation, with the same stocking density and having a reared calf percentage of 80, could carry 375 breeding/suckling cows, fattening their progeny, 3000 calves, to two years of age when they would weigh 600 lb. The annual value of cattle added by the integrated project would be 3000×$600=$1 800 000. The annual value of cattle added by the specialist operation, using the same resources, would be:

12 000 (600 lb at $1 − 300 lb at 85 cts) =$4 140 000

Only if the price per unit weight of 300lb young cattle increased from the present 85% to 150% of the price per unit weight of fat cattle would an integrated operation be as profitable as a specialist fattening operation on intensively produced grass.

Two criticisms in particular are likely to be expressed about a specialist cattle/buffalo fattening project. One is that the project will alter the existing demand for young stock, raise their price and cause profits to be transitory. The other is that a fattening project will be parasitical, living off the existing cattle/buffalo industry but contributing nothing either to improving the quality of the stock or increasing numbers. It is desirable to consider both criticisms.

The likelihood of a rise in the price of young stock is a valid criticism. It makes the project commercially, though not economically, unattractive. Even if the project were undertaken so as not to disrupt the market for young cattle, the pioneering firm could not expect to continue to get high profits. Others, learning from the pioneer and attracted by the profits, would enter the business, which requires little capital relative to turnover and little expertise. These newcomers, by bidding up the price of young cattle, would quickly eliminate all abnormal profits. This consideration appears to rule out the project being pioneered by private enterprise. Prospective pioneers will appreciate that if the project fails, as any pioneer project is liable to, the firm would bear the costs; if it succeeds, imitators will quickly reduce profits to a low level which allows no reward for the risks of pioneering.[1]

The state, under the circumstances, would appear to be justified in pioneering cattle fattening, or in paying private enterprise to incur the inevitable risks involved. If the operation is a success and is followed by expansion of the original project or by other similar projects, so that demand for young cattle is increased and their price rises, this, though making the enterprise commercially unattractive, would enhance rather than reduce its economic benefits.

It appears at present prices of young cattle ($255) and fat cattle ($600), that an abnormal profit of about $150 per head could be made by an efficient fattening operation. It is possible that establishing the project would cause an immediate rise in young cattle prices of $100, which would reduce abnormal profits, from the start, to $50/head. But the corollary of the decline in fattening profits is that breeding/rearing profits will rise by a similar amount.

If others enter the fattening business and force the price of young cattle up to $400, abnormal fattening profits will disappear (unless, that is, the efficiency of the fattening operation is increased). But this will increase rather than reduce the economic benefits of the project. The object is to stimulate beef production at a cost consumers are prepared to pay — not to generate abnormal profits.

It is desirable first that an effective fattening operation be established which, because it is needed and if it is efficient, will be initially profitable. It is desirable after that that these profits be dissipated in higher prices for young cattle/buffalo to provide the incentive, which is now missing, to increase breeding stocks. This point is treated diagrammatically in Figure B.2.

SS is the long term supply curve for young cattle. The short term supply curve is SBH. The existing supply of young cattle is perfectly inelastic in the short term. D^1D^1 is the present demand curve for young cattle. Intersecting SS at B, it results in a quantity OC young cattle being produced and their price being OA.

A cattle fattening project is established that causes the demand for young cattle to expand to D^2D^2. This raises the price of young cattle to OE. As a result of the price rise, fattening profits are reduced by AEFB, but breeding/rearing profits are increased by the same amount.

Normal profits are obtained from efficient fattening at a price OG for young cattle. At a price OE, for young cattle, abnormal profits of EG per head continue to be made

---

1. The problem is similar to that of developing young cattle exports (Chapter 12).

Fig. B.2   Increasing the demand for young cattle

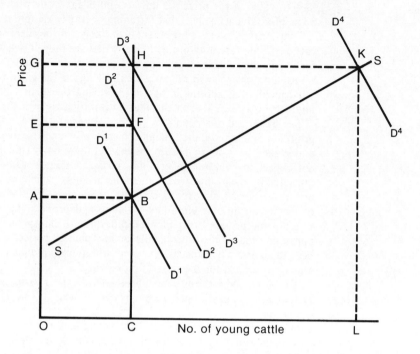

by fatteners. These abnormal profits will attract new fatteners, once the technology
has been established, and over the long term the demand for young cattle will increase
to D³D³ and so on.

If young cattle numbers did not increase, the new equilibrium position, following
the introduction of the new fattening technology, would be at H, with a price OG for
young cattle; output OC; total breeders'-rearers' incomes OGHC and normal profit
being earned by fatteners.

But over time the supply of young cattle will increase, in response to higher prices
as indicated by the SS curve. The long term equilibrium position will be K, with an
output OL young cattle at a price OG and a demand D⁴D⁴. Cattle breeders'-rearers
incomes will have been increased from OABC to OGKL. No abnormal fattening
profits will be earned.

It is because no abnormal profits can be earned from fattening in the long run —
and very few can be earned in the short run, because of the short run inelasticity of
supply of young cattle and the ease with which new fatteners can enter the industry
— profit motivated firms are unlikely to undertake the cost and risk of pioneering
cattle fattening in Malaysia.

The principal microeconomic benefits of establishing cattle fattening in Malaysia
will accrue to breeders-rearers. The net benefit to them will be AGKB. Their total
income will increase from OABC to OGKL, but their additional costs will only
increase by CBKL. The area AGKB also represents the economic returns to Malaysia
from a pioneer cattle fattening project.

The second criticism noted above of specialist fattening is that it will not improve
stock quality or increase numbers. Fattening, unlike an integrated breeding-rearing
and-fattening operation, will not directly affect the quantity and quality of
cattle/buffalo in the country. Indirectly, however, its effects may be greater and more
beneficial. There is no reason to think that Malaysian cattle/buffalo producers respond
to economic stimuli differently from other cattle/buffalo producers. The history of

cattle breeding throughout the world is of animals being bred to suit prevailing conditions. The important conditions Malaysian breeders respond to at present are a difficult climate for cattle and low prices for young stock. If prices for young male stock are raised relative to the cost of cows, by creating a firm demand for young males for fattening, then it would be surprising — and probably unique in livestock breeding history — if Malaysian stockowners did not respond quickly by increasing the supply and improving the quality of young stock.

The view that cattle/buffalo numbers in Malaysia have declined to such a low level that they cannot any longer reproduce themselves and that the breeding herd must be augmented by imports needs to be challenged. There are at present reported to be some 530 000 cattle/buffalo in Peninsular Malaysia. Half of these, at least, or 265 000 are females, capable of producing 200 000 reared calves annually. 100 000 of these calves would be heifers, available for adding to the national breeding herd. Allowing for culling to remove 30 000 breeding animals annually, there would be sufficient young breeding stock available to increase the breeding herd by 70 000 or 25% annually.

The evidence suggests that Malaysia's cattle/buffalo breeding herd is declining because of low prices for young stock. This situation can best be rectified by increasing the demand for young stock through the establishment of cattle/buffalo fattening facilities. There is a danger, in importing breeding stock, of adding to the supply of young stock while leaving the demand for these unaffected, and so forcing their price down further. This could result in the indigenous cattle/buffalo industry reducing its breeding stocks as rapidly as, or more rapidly than, new breeding stock is imported.

Feeding trials indicate that the fattening capabilities of Malaysian cattle/buffalo at present are adequate to make a fattening project profitable at present prices. These capabilities fall short of the performance of cattle in other countries where conditions for cattle are more favourable. Nevertheless, it should be appreciated that the country has a valuable pool of foundation K-K cattle and padi buffaloes, which have been evolved to meet difficult local conditions and which, with skilled selection and well considered breeding programmes, could almost certainly be quickly adapted to exploit a more favourable demand for young cattle. An adequate incentive, in the form of better prices for young stock of good quality, is a prerequisite for any successful programme of upgrading the local cattle/buffalo.

Meanwhile, concern must be felt over large scale importations of breeding cattle to Malaysia. These imported cattle, of a remarkably heterogenous character, may fulfil their purpose of improving the quality of local stock. They may, on the other hand, cause irrevocable harm to a valuable national asset by adulterating the genetic pool of the indigenous K-K cattle.

Cut and carry

Cutting and carrying grass to livestock, or zero grazing, involves expenses not incurred by the more orthodox system of grazing the grass in situ. Additional expenses are those of cutting and carting the grass to the animals; housing the animals, which would otherwise be held on the grazed land; and spreading the droppings from the cattle/buffalo which grazing animals deposit in situ. Cut and carry, because of these additional costs, is rarely practised.

The special circumstances of a cattle/buffalo fattening project in Malaysia suggest that in this case the costs of cut and carry would be substantially less than the additional benefits from the system.

The estimated cost of cut and carry for a fattening project are as follows:

(a) Cutting and carrying (above p. 217) $64/acre/annum

(b) Housing: capital cost per acre: $500 (above p. 216). Less saving on internal fencing, per acre: $50. Net additional capital cost per acre: $450. Annual charge: $45/acre/annum

(c) Slurry disposal, assumed equal to 25% of cutting and carrying costs, $16/acre/annum. Thus making a total of $125/acre/annum.

The total of $125/acre/annum is equivalent to 11% of the estimated annual costs per acre, or to 4% of the estimated gross output per acre (above p. 215).

The following benefits accrue from cut and carry:

(i) Animals gain weight more rapidly with less feed because they do not expend energy grazing. (ii) Animals are under close control for medication, weighing and other purposes. (iii) Grass is not lost by trampling or fouling during grazing. (iv) Land is not puddled and made unproductive during wet weather. (v) Slurry can be applied evenly if, where and when required. (vi) Slurry can be dried and sold at a premium over its fertiliser value. (vii) It is the only practical way of feeding large numbers of young bulls.

The advantages of bull-beef production have been noted above. The only practical safe way of handling bulls of the required age — i.e. 9 to 18 months old — is in suitably designed houses. Large herds of young bulls grazing would constitute an unacceptably serious danger to those tending them. It would be virtually impossible to provide internal fencing that would be proof against these herds.

These considerations indicate that, under the circumstances envisaged, cut and carry, or zero grazing, has advantages that substantially outweigh its costs.

Other Issues Briefly Considered

Brief reference is made below to some other issues which would require detailed consideration before proceeding in the rainforest tropics with a cattle/buffalo fattening project.

Procuring store cattle buffalo

The cattle/buffalo trade in Malaysia is small and poorly organized, as is to be expected in a country where stock numbers are so few. Great difficulties are to be expected initially in getting adequate supplies of store stock for a fattening project. Where it will be possible to get 100 cattle when the trade is established, it will be difficult to get 10 initially, because there are no established cattle dealers and because people are unaccustomed to selling young stock.

A functioning fattening project will be able to pay good prices for young stock. Once such a project and a developed trade in young cattle/buffalo exist, it will be possible readily to procure adequate and increasing supplies of young stock at prices remunerative to breeders and fatteners.

Meanwhile, an internal trading system in young cattle hardly exists. It will be necessary for the project virtually to set up such a system, appointing local buyers throughout the country to buy small numbers of cattle/buffalo at villages for forwarding to the fattening project.

Consideration ought to be given in this connection to buying young stock from Thailand, where store cattle are understood to be available at 65 cents/lb liveweight. Imports initially would expedite the development of a cattle/buffalo fattening industry in Malaysia, that would, in time, provide a ready market at good prices for local store stock.

Importing store cattle/buffalo from Thailand under appropriate veterinary supervision for fattening would involve minimal risk of infection with foot-and-mouth and other diseases. The stock would be confined in large units where they could be readily inspected. Incubating diseases would become manifest long before the animals left the feedlots fat, and any necessary counter measures, including the slaughter of infected stock, could be easily and quickly implemented.

The use of waste and semi-waste products

There are interesting possibilities of using such products as latex sludge, palm oil sludge, tapioca waste and molasses in the project. Latex sludge is an embarrassing polluting byproduct of rubber production, and has been successfully used as a grassland manure. Palm oil sludge is also an embarrassing, polluting byproduct of the palm oil industry, and has been used successfully for feeding cattle. Large quantities of both products should be available at the cost of handling and transporting them. It would probably be possible, using bulk transport, to use both products economically, the one to reduce fertiliser costs and the other to increase cattle/buffalo weight gains.

Sale of Dried Slurry

The faeces and urine from livestock drop through the slats in a slatted floor shed, leaving the surface clean and dry. The droppings accumulate in a pit in a semiliquid form underneath and, as slurry, move by gravity to an open tank or lagoon. The slurry can then be pumped into a liquid bulk container for distribution on the grassland.

It may be more profitable to dry and sell the slurry. A market exists in Malaysia for sun dried cow dung at a price well in excess of its fertiliser value, and reflecting the high opinion vegetable growers have of its soil improving qualities. The estimated sale value of the droppings of an animal over a year is $30; the cost of supplying the equivalent nutrients from artificial fertilisers is $6.

Seasonal fluctuations in grass growth

Malaysia's climate makes possible grass growth virtually throughout the year, in contrast with the highly seasonal pattern in temperate countries. Production, nevertheless, does vary seasonally according to rainfall. Output declines during the two brief dry seasons which normally occur annually in Malaysia (Tan & Pillai 1973 p. 23). There are a number of ways, at least conceptually, of dealing with these fluctuations in grass output. Some of these, which are practised more or less widely by cattle owners elsehwere, are listed below.

(i)   The amount of grass fed can be reduced during the dry season. "Feast and famine" conditions are an established pattern in countries with variable feed supplies. Cattle are allowed to lose weight when fodder is scarce. The practice is unlikely to be economic in Malaysia because the high cost per unit of fodder there makes it necessary to achieve good feed conversion rates.

(ii) Cattle stocks can be adjusted to meet feed supplies, which is especially easy with a fattening project. As many cattle as possible are sold off fat at the approach of the dry season and no store cattle are bought.

(iii) Grass that is surplus during the wet season can be conserved in situ. The grass-cutting sequence is arranged so as to ensure a good cover of grass on all land at the onset of the dry season. This accumulated grass is then used to carry stock through the dry season until growth recommences.

(iv) Grass that is surplus during the wet season can be conserved as hay or silage. Haymaking in the Malaysian wet season would probably be impractical, but silage making would be simple, especially with grass cutting and carrying equipment available on the farm.

(v) Supplemental feeding with tapioca waste, palm oil sludge, molasses and other low cost feeds. Tapioca waste can be ensiled and accumulated to meet seasonal peak requirements.

(vi) Portions of the land could be inundated and as much of the remaining land as is necessary irrigated with water drawn from the reservoirs by tractor driven pumps. The irrigation reservoir(s) could be used as fish ponds during the wet seasons, the fish being fed with cattle slurry and grass from the farm. Irrigation would probably make possible yields much above 15 tons of dry matter per acre per annum.

Rotation grass

There is no reason in principle why a cattle/buffalo fattening project should not be integrated with other enterprises into a mixed farming system. Mixed farming frequently results in valuable complementary relationships, with the various enterprises on the farm contributing to each other's profitability. For example, it might be considered desirable to integrate the fattening project with tapioca production. This would make possible the introduction of a grass ley as a break in tapioca growing that would leave the land in better condition to grow further crops of tapioca. The slurry would be a valuable manure for the tapioca. The fattening enterprise, for its part, would stand to benefit from the availability of tapioca tops, chips and waste.

Nomenclature and Solution of Simultaneous Equations

Nomenclature in Alphabetical Order

Lower case letters (English)	First occurrence in text. Page no.	Upper case (single letters)	First occurrence in text. Page no.
a	44	C	42
b	44	D	153
c	81	F	42
ch	182	I	48
g	45	K	42
h	45	M	42
n	42	N	125
s (1)	16	S	16
s_r	16	S_r	16
s_e	16	S_e	16
s (2)	45	V_1	40
t	40	V_2	40
u	45	V_3	40
v	45	W	153
w	45	Y (1)	16
		Y_r	16
		Y_e	16
		Y (2)	99

Lower case letters (Greek)		Upper case (double letters)	
α	44	CC	52
β	44	NR	47
γ	44	Pc	49
δ	44	Pd	153
ϵ	44	Pf	52
ζ	44	Pm	50
η	44	Pv	50
θ	40	Tt	58
λ	44	WG	45

Upper case (triple letters)	
ACC	176
AMC	124
NMC	124
NR (C)	51
NR (R)	51
Pcf	124
Pcm	125
TWG	58
VBH	98
VDA	153
VFA	51
VFH	98

Solution of Simultaneous Equations

Net benefit from cattle (NR) is maximised when the following conditions are met:

$$\frac{\delta NR}{\delta K} = \frac{\delta NR}{\delta \theta} = \frac{\delta NR}{\delta V_1} = \frac{\delta NR}{\delta V_2} = \frac{\delta NR}{\delta V_3} = 0 \tag{5.25}$$

Equation 5.7 gives the value of V_2 in terms of t, for which it is more convenient to solve.

$$NR = PmM + PcC - (Pc \cdot I^t + PvV_2 \cdot I^{t/2})K/n - PvV_3 \tag{5.24}$$

The term $(PcI^t + PvV_2 \cdot I^{t/2})K/n$ is the annual cost of herd replacement or depreciation. It is denoted here as ADH, giving

$$NR = PmM + PcC - ADH - PvV_3 \tag{C.1}$$

$$\frac{\delta NR}{\delta K} = \frac{Pm}{}\frac{\delta M}{\delta K} + \frac{Pc}{}\frac{\delta C}{\delta K} + \frac{C}{}\frac{\delta Pc}{\delta K} - \frac{\delta ADH}{\delta K} - PvV_3^{\cdot} \tag{C.2}$$

(where $PvV_3^{\cdot}$ is annual expenditure on V_3 per cow)

$$\frac{\delta NR}{\delta \theta} = \frac{Pm}{}\frac{\delta M}{\delta \theta} + \frac{Pc}{}\frac{\delta C}{\delta \theta} + \frac{C}{}\frac{\delta Pc}{\delta \theta} - \frac{\delta ADH}{\delta \theta} \tag{C.3}$$

$$\frac{\delta NR}{\delta t} = \frac{Pm}{}\frac{\delta M}{\delta t} + \frac{Pc}{}\frac{\delta C}{\delta t} + \frac{C}{}\frac{\delta Pc}{\delta t} - \frac{\delta ADH}{\delta t} \tag{C.4}$$

$$\frac{\delta NR}{\delta V_1} = \frac{Pm}{}\frac{\delta M}{\delta V_1} + \frac{Pc}{}\frac{\delta C}{\delta V_1} + \frac{C}{}\frac{\delta Pc}{\delta V_1} - \frac{\delta ADH}{\delta V_1} \tag{C.5}$$

$$\frac{\delta NR}{\delta V_3} = \frac{Pm}{}\frac{\delta M}{\delta V_3} + \frac{Pc}{}\frac{\delta C}{\delta V_3} + \frac{C}{}\frac{\delta Pc}{\delta V_3} - \frac{\delta ADH}{\delta V_3} - KPv \tag{C.6}$$

Denote $Q1 = ab^{-\delta} V_3^{\beta-\delta\zeta} F^{-\gamma+\delta\lambda} \cdot K^{\alpha-\delta\epsilon}$ (C.7)
$P1 = (1 - \delta\mu)C^{-\delta\mu} - Q1 \cdot \theta(\delta\lambda - \gamma)/2F$ (C.8)

$$\frac{\delta M}{\delta K} = [(\alpha - \delta\epsilon)/K + (\delta\lambda - \gamma)(t - \theta)/2nF] Q1/P_1 \tag{C.9}$$

$$\frac{\delta M}{\delta \theta} = [(\delta\lambda - \gamma)(C/2 - K/2n)/F] Q1/P_1 \tag{C.10}$$

$$\frac{\delta M}{\delta t} = [(\delta\lambda - \gamma) \cdot K/F \cdot 2n)] Q1/P_1 \tag{C.11}$$

$$\frac{\delta M}{\delta V_1} = 0 \tag{C.12}$$

$$\frac{\delta M}{\delta V_3} = [(\beta - \delta\zeta)/V_3] Q1/P_1 \tag{C.13}$$

Denote $Q2 = a^{-\mu}bV_3^{\zeta-\beta\mu} \cdot K^{\epsilon-\alpha\mu} \cdot F^{\gamma\mu-\lambda}$ (C.14)
$P_2 = (1 - \delta\mu)C^{-\delta\mu} - Q2 \cdot \theta(\gamma\mu - \lambda)/2F$ (C.15)

$$\frac{\delta C}{\delta K} = [(\epsilon - \alpha\mu)/K + (\gamma\mu - \lambda)(t - \theta)/2nF)]Q2/P_2 \tag{C.16}$$

$$\frac{\delta C}{\delta \theta} = [(\gamma\mu - \lambda)(C/2 - K/2n)/F] Q2 \cdot /P_2 \tag{C.17}$$

$$\frac{\delta C}{\delta t} = [K(\gamma\mu - \lambda)/2nF]\, Q2/P2 \tag{C.18}$$

$$\frac{\delta C}{\delta V_1} = 0 \tag{C.19}$$

$$\frac{\delta C}{\delta V_3} = [(\zeta - \beta\mu)/V_3]\, Q2\,./P_2 \tag{C.20}$$

Denote $Q3 = -\theta\,.\,I^{-\theta}Pfh\,.\,V_1{}^{w}\,.\,v(K + F)^{-(v+1)}$ $\qquad$ C.21

$$\frac{\delta Pc}{\delta K} = Q3 \left[1 + (t - \theta)/2n + \frac{\delta C}{\delta K}\,.\,\theta/2 \right] \tag{C.22}$$

$$\frac{\delta Pc}{\delta \theta} = Pc/\theta - Pc\,.\,\text{Log I} - P_v\,.\,V_1\,.\,\text{Log I}/2\,.\,I^{\theta/2}$$

$$+ Q_3 \left(c + \theta \frac{\delta C}{\delta \theta} - K/n \right)\Big/2 \tag{C.23}$$

$$\frac{\delta Pc}{\delta t} = Q3 \left[K/2n + \frac{\delta C}{\delta t}\,.\,\theta/2 \right] \tag{C.24}$$

$$\frac{\delta Pc}{\delta V_1} = -Q3[w(K + F)/V_1.v] - \theta\,.\,P_v/I^{\theta/2} \tag{C.25}$$

$$\frac{\delta Pc}{\delta V_3} = Q3 \left[\frac{\delta C}{\delta V_3}\,.\,\theta/2 \right] \tag{C.26}$$

Denote $Q4 = Pv(g/t)^{1/u}\,.\,(K + F)^{s/u-1}\,.\,s/u\,.\,I^{t/2}$ $\qquad$ C.27

$$\frac{\delta ADH}{\delta K} = ADH/K + \left\{ \frac{\delta Pc}{\delta K} + Q4 \left[1 + (t - \theta)/2n + \frac{\delta C}{\delta K}\,.\,\theta2 \right] \right\} K\,.\,I^t/n \tag{C.28}$$

$$\frac{\delta ADH}{\delta \theta} = \left[\frac{\delta Pc}{\delta \theta} + Q4(C/2 + \frac{\delta C}{\delta \theta}\,.\,\theta/2 - K/2n) \right] K\,.\,I^t/n \tag{C.29}$$

$$\frac{\delta ADH}{\delta t} = \text{Log I}\,.\,ADH + \left\{ \frac{\delta Pc}{\delta t} - Q4 \left[g(K + F)/st + \text{Log I}(K + F)u/2s \right.\right.$$

$$\left.\left. - \frac{\delta C}{\delta t}\,.\,\theta/2 - K/2n \right] \right\} K\,.\,I^t/n \tag{C.30}$$

$$\frac{\delta ADH}{\delta V_1} = \frac{\delta Pc}{\delta V_1}\,.\,K\,.\,I^t/n \tag{C.31}$$

$$\frac{\delta ADH}{\delta V_3} = \left(\frac{\delta Pc}{\delta V_3} + Q4\,.\,\frac{\delta C}{\delta V_3}\,.\,\theta/2 \right) K\,.\,I^t/n \tag{C.32}$$

Values for the 20 partial derivations, $\dfrac{\delta M}{\delta K} \ldots \dfrac{\delta ADH}{\delta V_3}$ as given in Equations C.9 to C.32, are substituted in Equations C.2 to C.6. The set of five simultaneous, nonlinear equations can then be solved by iteration for values of K, θ, t, V_1 and V_3 that maximize NR.

References

Adams, M. E.; Hales, J. (1977) Sudan, the eternal desert. *Geographical Magazine* 49, 760–763.

Allen, R. G. D. (1938) Mathematical analysis for economists. London; Macmillan.

Anon (1972) No meat for half the year. *Andean Air Mail and Peruvian Times* (Lima) 25 February.

Applebaum, S. (1972) Roman Britain. In: Finberg, H. P. R. (*Ed*) The agrarian history of England and Wales Vol.1.2, AD 43–1042. London; Cambridge University Press, pp.3–27.

Atkinson, K. M. T. (1965) Reflections on the Roman rule of law; an inaugural lecture delivered before the Queen's University of Belfast on 27 January 1965. Belfast; Queen's University.

Australian National University, Department of Demography (1974a) African drought bibliography, 1973. Canberra.

Australian National University, Department of Demography (1974b) African drought bibliography, first supplement, 1974. Canberra.

Barlow, C. (1978) The natural rubber industry: its development, technology and economy in Malaysia. Kuala Lumpur; Oxford University Press.

Barraclough, S.; Collarte, J. C. (*Eds*) (1973) Agrarian structure in Latin America: a resumé of the CIDA land tenure studies of Argentina, Brazil, Chile, Colombia, Ecuador, Guatemala and Peru. Lexington; Lexington Books. Tables reprinted by permission of the publisher.

Barth, F. (1964) Nomads of South Persia: the Basseri tribe of the Khamseh confederacy. Oslo; University Press.

Bird, R. (1974) Taxing agricultural land in developing countries. Cambridge, Mass.; Harvard University Press.

Birnie, A. (1955) An economic history of the British Isles, 8th edn. London; Methuen.

Bloch, M. (1966) French rural history: an essay on its basic characteristics. Translated by J. Sondheimer. London; Routledge.

Bolton, G. (1966) The passing of the Irish Act of Union: a study in parliamentary politics. London; Oxford University Press.

Botswana, Central Statistics Office (1975) *Government Paper* No. 2 of 1975. Gaborone.

Botswana, Central Statistics Office (1976) The rural income distribution survey in Botswana, 1974/75. Gaborone.

Botswana, Central Statistics Office (1977) Statistical Abstract, 1976. Gaborone.

Bottigheimer, K. S. (1971) English money and Irish land. Oxford; University Press.

Boulding, K. E. (1955) Economic analysis, 3rd edn. New York; Harper & Bros.

Bowman, I. (1916) The Andes of Southern Peru. Geographical reconnaissance along the seventy-third meridian. New York; Holt.

Boxall, R. A.; Greeley, M.; Tyagi, D. S.; Lipton, M.; Neelakanta, J. (1978) The prevention of farm-level food grain storage losses in India; a social cost-benefit analysis. Brighton; Institute of Development Studies.

Brabb, G. J. (1970) Introduction to quantitative management. London; Holt, Linehart and Winston.

Braudel, F. (1973) Capitalism and material life 1400–1800. Translated by M. Kocham. London; Weidenfeld & Nicolson.

British Broadcasting Corporation Channel 1. News 10.1.78.

British Parliamentary Paper (1825) IX (181). Minutes of evidence taken before the Select Committee of the House of Lords appointed to enquire into the state of Ireland, more particularly with reference to the circumstances which may have led to disturbances in that part of the United Kingdom.

British Parliamentary Paper (1843) XXIV. (433). Census of Ireland 1841.

Brown, E. H. P.; Hopkins, S. V. (1962) Seven centuries of the price of consumables compared with builders' wage rates. In: Carus Wilson, E. M. (*Ed*) Essays in economic history Vol. 2. London; Arnold.

Brown, L. R. (1976) World population trends: signs of hope, signs of stress. *Worldwatch Paper* No. 8. Washington D.C.

Butzer, K. W. (1970) Physical conditions in eastern Europe and western Asia and Egypt before the period of agricultural and urban settlement. In: The Cambridge ancient history, 3rd edn, Vol. 1 Part 1. Prolegomena and prehistory. London; Cambridge University Press, pp. 35–70.

Caesar, C. J. (1951) The conquest of Gaul. Translated by S. A. Handford. Harmondsworth; Penguin.

Camoens, J. K. (1976) The buffalo in Malaysia. *Malaysia Ministry of Agriculture Bulletin* No. 145. Kuala Lumpur; Ministry of Agriculture.

Carson, R. A. G. (1970) Coins ancient, medieval and modern, 2nd edn. London; Hutchinson.

Cassen, R. H. (1978) India: population, economy, society. London; Macmillan.

Chambers, R.; Feldman, D. (1973) Report on rural development. Gaborone; Ministry of Finance and Development Planning.

Clark, C. (1977) Population growth and land use, 2nd edn. London; Macmillan.

Claveran, R. (1975) Applying technology at the level of the farmer and the cattleman. In: Proceedings of seminar on potential to increase beef production in tropical America. Cali; Centro Internacional de Agricultura Tropical.

Coale, A. J. (1969) The decline of fertility in Europe from the French Revolution to World War Two. In: Behrman, S. J.; Corsa, L. Jr.; Freedman, R. (*Eds*) Fertility and family planning: a world view. Ann Arbor; University of Michigan Press, pp. 3–24.

Columbus, C. (1969) The four voyages of Christopher Columbus: being his own log book, letters and dispatches, with connecting narrative drawn from the Life of the Admiral by his son Hernando Colon and other contemporary historians. Translated by J. M. Cohen. Harmondsworth; Penguin.

Conrad, A. H.; Meyer, J. R. (1964). The economics of slavery and other studies in econometric history. Chicago; Aldine Publishing Company.

Conway, A. G. (1974) A production function for grazing cattle. *Irish Journal of Agricultural Economics and Rural Sociology* 5 (1), 1–108.

Crotty, R. (1966) Irish agricultural production: its volume and structure. Cork; Cork University Press.

Crotty, R. (1973a) Letter. *Economist* (London) 28 April.

Crotty, R. (1973b) Letter. *Irish Farmers' Journal* (Dublin) 29 April

Crotty, R. (1973c) Will the next six months see a sharp slump in cattle prices. *Business and Finance* (Dublin) 16 May.

Crotty, R. (1974) The cattle crisis and the small farmer. Mullingar; National Land League.

Crotty, R. (1978a) Constraints on smallholder treecropping in Malaysia. *Internationales Asienforum* 9, 229–241.

Crotty, R. (1978b) Economies and diseconomies of scale in Malaysian agriculture. *Agricultural Mechanization in Asia* 9 (3), 24–32.

Crotty, R. (1979a) Capitalist colonialism and peripheralisation: the Irish case. In: Seers, D.; Schaffer, B.; Kiljunen, M. L. (*Eds*) Underdeveloped Europe: studies in core periphery relations. Hassocks; Harvester.

Crotty, R. (1979b) Better or more storage? *Food Policy* 4(3).

Crotty, R. (1979c) Review of Colin Barlow's "The natural rubber industry: its development, technology and economy in Malaysia" *Journal of Development Studies* 16(1).

Dahl, G.; Hjort, A. (1976) Having herds: pastoral herd growth and household economy. Stockholm; Dept. of Social Anthropology University of Stockholm.

Daily Telegraph (London) 15.3.79

Davidson, B. (1974) Africa in history: themes and outlines. St. Albans; Paladin.

Deane, P.; Cole, W. A. (1967) British economic growth 1688–1959: trends and structure, 2nd edn. Cambridge; Cambridge University Press.

De Carvalho, E. C. (1974) 'Traditional' and 'modern' patterns of cattle raising in southwestern Angola. *Journal of Development Areas* 8, 199–225.

De Miranda, R. M. (1975) The role of beef cattle in the development of Latin America. In: Proceedings of seminar on potential to increase beef production in tropical America. Cali; Centro Internacional de Agricultura Tropical.

Devlin, R. M.; Barker, A. V. (1971) Photosynthesis. New York; Van Nostrand Rheinhold.

Dodwell, H. H. (*Ed*) (1934) Cambridge shorter history of India. Cambridge; University Press.

Duby, G. (1974) The early growth of the European economy: warriors and peasants from the 7th to the 12th century. Translated by H. B. Clarke. London; Weidenfeld.

Due, J. F. (1963) Taxation and economic development in tropical Africa. Cambridge, Mass.; Massachusetts Institute of Technology Press.

Dyson-Hudson, N. (1966) Karimojong politics. Oxford; Clarendon Press.

Economic Commission for Europe; Food and Agriculture Organisation (1960) Prices of agricultural products and fertiliser 1958/59. New York; United Nations.

Economic Commission for Europe; Food and Agriculture Organisation (1976) Prices of agricultural products and selected inputs in Europe and North America 1974/75. *Annual ECE/FAO Price Review* No. 25. New York; United Nations.

Economic Commission for Europe; Food and Agriculture Organisation (1978) Prices of agricultural products and selected inputs in Europe and North America 1976/77. *Annual ECE/FAO Price Review* No. 27. New York; United Nations.

Economic Commission for Europe; Food and Agriculture Organisation (1979) Prices of agricultural products and selected inputs in Europe and North America 1977/78. *Annual ECE/FAO Price Review* No. 28. New York; United Nations.

Economic Commission for Latin America; Food and Agriculture Organisation (1962) Livestock in Latin America: status problems and prospects; Vol. 1 Colombia, Mexico, Uruguay and Venezuela. New York; United Nations.

Economist (London) 5.4.75 p. 99

Epstein, T.S. (1973) South India: yesterday, today and tomorrow. Mysore villages revisited. London; Macmillan.

European Communities, Commission (1968) Memorandum on the reform of agriculture in the European Economic Community. Brussels, 85 pp.

European Communities, Commission, Statistical Office (1974) Foreign trade analytical tables, Vol. A, Chapter 1.24, 1972 Brussels.

European Communities, Commission, Statistical Office (1976) Foreign trade analytical tables, Vol. A, Chapter 1.24, 1975 Brussels.

European Communities, Commission (1977) The agricultural situation in the Community. 1976 report. Brussels.

European Communities, Commission (1978a) The agricultural situation in the Community. 1977 report. Brussels.

European Communities, Commission (1978b) Eleventh general report on the activities of the European Communities 1977. Brussels.

European Communities, Commission, Statistical Office (1979) Agricultural markets: vegetable products, prices, April 1979. Brussels.

Evans, R. V. (1977) An analysis of UK bilateral aid in the livestock sector. London; Ministry of Overseas Development.

Evans-Pritchard, E. A. (1940) The Nuer: a description of the modes of livelihood and the political institutions of a Nilotic people. Oxford; Clarendon Press.

Everard, J. E.; Fourt, D. F. (1971) Forest drainage in Wales. In: *Welsh Soils Discussion Group Report* No. 12: Drainage. Aberystwyth.

Fielder, R. J. (1973) The role of cattle in the Ila economy. *African Social Research* 15, 327–361.

Financial Times (London) 12.4.78.

Finberg, H. P. R. (1972) Anglo-Saxon England to 1042. In: Finberg, H. P. R. (*Ed*) The agrarian history of England and Wales, Vol. 1.2, A.D. 43–1042. London; Cambridge University Press, pp. 385–566.

Finley, M. I. (1960) Was Greek civilization based on slavery. In: Slavery in classical antiquity: views and controversies. Cambridge; Heffer.

Finley, M. I. (1975) The ancient economy. London; Chatto & Windus.

Fogel, R. W.; Engerman S. L. (1974) Time on the cross: the economics of American negro slavery. Boston; Little.

Food and Agriculture Organisation (1955) Trade yearbook 1954. Rome.

Food and Agriculture Organisation (1966) Production yearbook 1965. Rome.

Food and Agriculture Organisation (1967) Agricultural commodity projections for 1975 and 1985. Vol. 2. Rome.

Food and Agriculture Organisation (1969) Trade yearbook 1968. Rome. Vol. 22.

Food and Agriculture Organisation (1970) Production yearbook 1969. Rome. Vol. 23

Food and Agriculture Organisation (1971a) Kenya: beef industry development project, ad hoc report part II. Rome.

Food and Agriculture Organisation (1971b) Agricultural commodity projections, 1970–1980. Vol. 2. Rome.

Food and Agriculture Organisation (1972a) Beef industry development, Kenya. Interim report. Rome.

Food and Agriculture Organisation (1972b) Production yearbook 1971. Rome. Vol. 25.

Food and Agriculture Organisation (1973a) Kenya: beef industry development project working paper: feeding trials using molasses based rations for intensive beef production. Rome.

Food and Agriculture Organisation (1973b) Kenya: beef industry development project: a social cost benefit analysis of intensive beef fattening at Lanet, Kenya. Rome.

Food and Agriculture Organisation (1973c) *World Animal Review* No. 8 1973. Rome.

Food and Agriculture Organisation (1974) Production yearbook 1973. Rome. Vol.28.2.

Food and Agriculture Organisation (1975a) Production yearbook 1974. Rome. Vol.29.

Food and Agriculture Organisation (1975b) Trade yearbook 1974. Rome.Vol. 28.

Food and Agriculture Organisation (1976a) Interim evaluation report, World Programme WFP/CFA: 1/10 Add. C7. Rome.

Food and Agriculture Organisation (1976b) Production yearbook 1975. Rome.

Food and Agriculture Organisation (1977a) Production yearbook 1976. Rome.

Food and Agriculture Organisation (1977b) Marketing livestock and meat. *Animal Production and Health Series* No. 1. Rome.

Food and Agriculture Organisation (1978a) Production yearbook 1977. Rome.

Food and Agriculture Organisation (1978b) Trade yearbook 1977. Rome. Vol. 31.

Food and Agriculture Organisation; International Bank for Reconstruction and Development (1970) Livestock project identification mission to Malaysia, draft report. Rome.

Forde, C. D. (1934) Habitat, economy and society: a geographical introduction to ethnology. London; Methuen.

Frank, T. (1962) An economic history of Rome. New York; Cooper Square Publishers.

Fussell, G. E. (1972) The classical tradition in West European farming. Newton Abbot; David and Charles.

Galeano, E. (1973) Open veins of Latin America: five centuries of the pillage of a continent. Translated by C. Belfrage. *Monthly Review* V.24 (New York).

Garg, J. S.; Azad, M. P. (1975) Economics of a cross-bred cow: a case study. *Indian Journal of Agricultural Economics* 30 (3), 149–150.

Glamann, K. (1977) The changing patterns of trade. In: The Cambridge Economic History of Europe, Vol. 5. London; Cambridge University Press.

Gluckman, M. (1968) Economy of the Central Borotse Plain. Manchester; Manchester University Press.

Groome, J. St. J. (1973) Some management practices in commercial beef production. In: Proceedings of the symposium towards more beef. *Veterinary Services Bulletin* 133. Kuala Lumpur; Ministry of Agriculture.

Guardian (London) 9.1.79

Gulliver, P. H. (1955) The family herds: a study of two pastoral tribes in East Africa: the Jie and Turkana. London; Routledge.

Gupta, S. C. (1964) The village community and its disintegration in Uttar Pradesh in the early nineteenth century. In: Ganguli, B. M. (*Ed*) Readings in Indian economic history. London; Asia Publishing House, pp. 102–113.

Gwyer, G. (1977) Herd simulation in relation to domestic requirements for beef. *MEDA-UNDP/IBRD regional planning assistance project, Technical Paper* No. 8. Manila.

Habib, I. (1963) The agrarian system of Mughal India, 1556–1707. London; Asia Publishing House.

Hajnal, J. (1965) European marriage patterns in perspective. In: Glass, D. V.; Eversley, D. E. C. (*Eds*) Population in History: essays in historical denography. London; Arnold, pp.101–143.

Harris, M. (1975) Cows, pigs, wars and witches: the riddles of culture. London; Hutchinson.

Hatcher, J. (1970) Rural economy and society in the Duchy of Cornwall, 1300–1500. London; Cambridge University Press.

Haywood, R. M. (1959) Roman Africa. In: Frank, T. (*Ed*) An economic survey of Ancient Rome. Paterson, N. J.: Pageant Books.

Huang, Y. (1971) The economics of padi production in Malaya: an economy in transition. Ph.D. thesis, Princeton University.

Huntingford, G. W. B. (1950) Nandi work and culture. London; HMSO.

India, Fertilizer Association of India (1972) Statistics 1971–72. New Delhi.

India, Ministry of Agriculture, Directorate of Economica & Statistics (1967) Estimate of area and production of principal crops in India 1963–64 and 1964–65. Delhi.

India, Ministry of Agriculture, Directorate of Economics & Statistics (1969) Indian livestock census 1961 Vol. 1. Delhi.

India, Ministry of Agriculture, Directorate of Economics and Statistics (1971a) Studies in the economics of farm management in Kerala, 1962–63. Delhi.

India, Ministry of Agriculture, Directorate of Economics and Statistics (1971b) Indian livestock census 1966 Vol. 1. Delhi.

India, Ministry of Agriculture, Directorate of Economics and Statistics (1972) Agricultural situation in India, July 1972. Delhi.

India, Ministry of Agriculture, Directorate of Economics and Statistics (1973a) Studies in the economics of farm management in Deoria district (Uttar Pradesh) 1968–69. Delhi.

India, Ministry of Agriculture, Directorate of Economics and Statistics (1973b) Studies in the economics of farm management in Ferozeper District (Punjab) 1968–69. Delhi.

India, Ministry of Agriculture, Directorate of Economics and Statistics (1975) Agricultural situation in India, July 1975. Delhi.

India, National Commission on Agriculture (1971) Interim report on milk production through small and marginal farms and agricultural labourers. New Delhi; Ministry of Agriculture.

Indian Dairy Corporation (1976) Detailed report of the second UN/FAO World Food Programme evaluation mission on Operation Flood. Delhi.

India, Planning Commission (1974) Draft five year plan 1974–1979 Vol. 2. New Delhi.

India, Planning Commission, Statistics and Surveys Division (1975) Basic statistics relating to the Indian economy 1950–51 to 1972–73. New Delhi.

India, Register General and Census Commissioners of India (1972) Pocket book of population statistics. New Delhi.

International Bank for Reconstruction and Development (1970) Annual report 1970. Washington D.C.

Internation Bank for Reconstruction and Development, Computing activities department (1972) A users' guide to BL 1Voo herd development simulation with cash flow and rate of return. Washington D.C.

International Bank for Reconstruction and Development (1974a) Sector policy paper: agricultural credit. Washington D.C.

International Bank for Reconstruction and Development (1974b) Annual report 1974. Washington D.C.

International Bank for Reconstruction and Development (1975a) Annual report 1975. Washington D.C.

International Bank for Reconstruction and Development (1975b) World Bank Atlas Population, per capita product and growth rates 1974. Washington D.C.

International Bank for Reconstruction and Development (1976) Annual report 1976. Washington D.C.

International Livestock Centre for Africa (1975) Animal production and health in tropical Africa. Addis Ababa.

Ireland, Agricultural Institute (1975) Animal Production Research Report 1974. Dublin.

Ireland, Central Bank (1978) Annual report 1977. Dublin.

Ireland, Central Statistics Office *Irish Statistical Bulletin* (various issues). Dublin.

Ireland, Central Statistics Office (1936) Statistical Abstract of Ireland 1936. Dublin.

Ireland, Central Statistics Office (1973) Statistical Abstract of Ireland 1970–71. Dublin.

Ireland, Central Statistics Office (1977) Statistical Abstract of Ireland 1974–75. Dublin.

Ireland, Department of Agriculture *Farm Bulletin*. Dublin.

Irish Farmers' Journal (Dublin) 28.10.78.

Jensen, E. (1937) Danish agriculture: its economic development. A description and economic analysis centering on the Free Trade epoch, 1870–1930. Copenhagen; J. H. Schultz.

Jones, A. H. M. (1956) Slavery in the ancient world. *Economic History Review*, 2nd series 9, 1, 185–199.

Jones, A. H. M. (1966) The decline of the ancient world. In: Longman's general history of Europe, Vol. 1. London; Longmans.

Jones, A. H. M. (1974) The Roman economy. In: Brunt, P. A. (*Ed*) Studies in ancient economic and administrative history. Oxford; Blackwell.

Journal of the Royal Statistical Society, Series A, Vol. 92 (1929) and 130 (1967).

Kearney, B. (1975) Economics of dairying as a farm enterprise. *Farm and Food Research* 6, 126–128. Agricultural Institute, Dublin.

Kennedy, J. (1962) A history of Malaya, A.D. 1400–1959. London; Macmillan.

Kenya (1974) Development plan 1974–1978. Nairobi; Government printers.

Klein, J. (1964) The Mesta: a study in Spanish economic history, 1273–1836. Port Washington; Kennikat.

Konczacki, Z. A. (1978) The economics of pastoralism: a case study of sub-Sahara Africa. London; Cass.

Kottak, C. P. (1972) Ecological variables in the origins and evolution of African states: the Buganda example. *Comparative Studies in Society and History* 14, 351–384.

Kuznets, S. S. (1966) Modern economic growth: rate, structure and spread. New Haven; Yale University Press.

Lal, M. (1967) Cow cult in India. In: Shah, A. B. (*Ed*) Cow slaughter: horns of a dilemma. Bombay; Lalvani Publishing House.

Latouche, R. (1961) The birth of the western economy: economic aspects of the Dark Ages. Translated by E. M. Wilkinson. London; Methuen.

Lattimore, O. (1951) Inner Asian frontiers of China, 2nd edn. Irvington-on-Hudson; Capital Publishing Co.

Lattimore, O (1962) Nomads and commissars: Mongolia revisited. New York; Oxford University Press.

Le Duc, T. (1966) History and application of US land policy to 1862. In: Cochran, T. C., Brewer, T. B. (*Eds*) Views of American economic growth, Vol. 1 The agricultural era. New York; McGraw Hill.

Lewis, W. A. (1966) Development planning. London; Allen and Unwin.

Lipson, E. (1959) The economic history of England: Vol. 1 The Middle Ages, 12th edn. London; Black.

Lipton, M. (1974) Towards a theory of land reform. In: Lehmann, D. (*Ed*) Agrarian reform and agrarian reformism: studies of Peru, Chile, China and India. London; Faber, pp.269–315.

Lipton, M. (1977) Why poor people stay poor: a study of urban bias in world development. London; Temple Smith.

Lipton, M. (1978) Botswana: employment and labour use in Botswana. Final report, Vol. 1. Gaborone; Government printer.

Livingstone, I. (1976) Cowboys in Africa: the socio-economics of ranching. *Occasion Paper* No. 17, Institute of Development Studies, University College, Nairobi.

Lloyd, T. H. (1973) The movement of wool prices in medieval England. London; Cambridge University Press for *Economic History Review* supplement 6, 75 pp.

Maguire, W. A. (1972) The Downshire estates in Ireland: the management of Irish landed estates in the early nineteenth century. Oxford; Clarendon Press.

Malaya, Federation of, Department of Statistics (1960) Population census of the Federation of Malaya, report no. 14: final report — summary tables. Kuala Lumpur; Government Press.

Malaysia, Department of Statistics (1973) Foreign trade statistics, 1973, Vol. 2 imports. Kuala Lumpur; Government Press.

Malaysia, Department of Statistics (1977) Census of population and housing, 1970, general report Vol. 1. Kuala Lumpur.

Malaysia, Economic Planning Unit (1971) Second Malaysia Plan, 1971–1975. Kuala Lumpur; Government Press.

Malaysia, Economic Planning Unit (1973) Mid-term review of Second Malaysia Plan, 1971–1975. Kuala Lumpur; Government Press.

Malaysia, Economic Planning Unit (1974) The Pahang Tenggara beef project feasibility study. Kuala Lumpur.

Malaysia, Federal Agricultural Marketing Authority (1975) *Quarterly commodity statistics* 6 (4).

Malaysia, Federal Land Development Authority (1974) Representative costs as recorded in Penang complex. Memorandum, 24 June.

Mattingly, H. (1961) The imperial recovery. In: The Cambridge ancient history, Vol. 12. The Imperial crisis and recovery A.D. 193–324. London; Cambridge University Press. pp. 297–351.

Maxwell, S.; Singer, H. (1979) Food aid to developing countries: a survey. *World Development* 7, 225–246.

McIlroy, R. J. (1972) An introduction to tropical grassland husbandry, 2nd edn. Oxford; Oxford University Press.

Mellart, J. (1970) The earliest settlements in western Asia from the ninth to the end of the fifth millennium B.C. In: The Cambridge ancient history, 3rd edn., Vol. 1 Part 1, Prolegomena and prehistory. Cambridge; Cambridge University Press, pp. 248–327.

Mitchell, B. R. (1975) European historical statistics 1750–1970. London; Macmillan.

Mitchell, B. R.; Deane, P. (1962) Abstract of British historical statistics. London; Cambridge University Press.

Monod, T. (*Ed*) (1975) Pastoralism in tropical Africa: studies presented and discussed at the 13th International African Seminar, Niamey, December 1972. London; Oxford University Press.

Morse, R. M. (1964) The heritage of Latin America. In: Hartz, L. (*Ed*) The founding of new societies; studies in history of the United States, Latin America, South Africa, Canada and Australia. New York; Harcourt, Brace and World, pp. 123–177.

Muellar, E. (1977) The economic value of children in peasant agriculture. In: Ridker, R. (*Ed*) Population and development: the search for selective interventions. Baltimore; John Hopkins, pp. 98–153.

Nag, M.; Peet, R. C.; White, B. (1977) Economic value of children in two peasant societies. In: Proceedings of the International Population Conference, Mexico 1977. Liege; International Union for the Scientific Study of Population.

Newberry, D. M. G. (1976) A feasibility study of intensive cattle feeding. In: Scott, M. F. G.; MacArthur, J. D.; Newberry, D. M. G. Project appraisal in practice. London; Heinemann.

Nisbet, C. T. (1967) The informal credit market in Chile. Ph.D. thesis, University of Oregon.

Oertel, F. (1961) The economic life of the empire. In: The Cambridge ancient history, Vol. 12. The Imperial crisis and recovery A.D. 193–324. London; Cambridge University Press, pp. 232–280.

Oppenheim, A. L. (1964) Ancient Mesopotamia: portrait of a dead civilisation. Chicago; University of Chicago Press.

Organisation for Economic Cooperation and Development (1971) Meat balances in OECD member countries, 1955–1969. Paris.

Organisation for Economic Cooperation and Development (1972) Milk and milk product balances in OECD member countries, 1955–1970. Paris.

Organisation for Economic Cooperation and Development (1978a) Meat balances in OECD member countries, 1963–1976. Paris.

Organisation for Economic Cooperation and Development (1978b) Milk, milk product and egg balances in OECD member countries, 1963–1976. Paris.

Osborne, H. (1954) Bolivia: a land divided. London; Royal Institute of International Affairs.

Pant, S. P.; Karanjkar, S. V. (1965) Economics of dairy enterprises in Jabalpur, with special reference to the scale of enterprise. *Indian Journal of Agricultural Economics* 20 (1), 116–121.

Pares, R. (1956) Yankees and Creoles: the trade between North America and the West Indies before the American revolution. London; Longmans.

Pares, R. (1960) Merchants and planters. London; Cambridge University Press. for *Economic History Review*, supplement 4.

Patel, S. M.; Pandey, M. K. (1976) Economic impacts of Kaira district cooperative milk producers' union (Amul dairy) in rural areas of Kaira district (Gujarat State). Ahmedabad; Institute of Cooperative Management.

Pendle, G. (1963) Argentina, 3rd edn., London; Oxford University Press.

Perham, M. (1937) Native administration in Nigeria. London; Oxford University Press.

Pettifer, J. (1978) The Chinese way: a report by Julian Pettifer. BBC 2, 7 February.

Picardi, A. C. (1974) A framework for evaluating long term strategies for the development of the Sahel-Sudan region. Annex 5. A systems analysis of pastoralism in the West African Sahel. Massachusetts; Massachusetts Institute of Technology.

Power, E. E. (1975) Medieval women. Cambridge; University Press.

Rabb, T. K. (1967) Enterprise and empire: merchant and gentry investment in the expansion of England, 1573–1630. Cambridge, Mass.; Harvard University Press.

Rajapurohit, A. J. R. (1975) Bovine feed availability and requirements in Karnataka, with reference to dairy development programmes. *Indian Journal of Agricultural Economics* 30 (3), 111–120.

Rheinstein, M. (*Ed*) (1954) Max Weber on law in economy and society. Cambridge, Mass.; Harvard University Press.

Rigby, P. (1969) Cattle and kinship among the Gogo: a semi-pastoral society of Central Tanzania. Ithaca; Cornell University Press.

Rostovtzeff, M. I. (1953) The social and economic history of the Hellenistic world, Revised edn. Oxford; Clarendon Press.

Rostovtzeff, M. I. (1957) The social and economic history of the Roman Empire, 2nd edn. Revised by P. M. Fraser, 2 Vol Oxford; Clarendon Press.

Russell, J. C. (1972) Population in Europe 500–1500. In: Cipolla, C. M. (*Ed*) The Fontana economic history of Europe: the Middle Ages. London; Collins.

St. Croix, F. W., de (1944) The Fulani of northern Nigeria. Lagos; Government printer.

Schneider, H. K. (1957) The subsistence role of cattle among the Pakot in East Africa. *American Anthropologist* 59, 278–300.

Schumacher, A. (1975) Government policy and the Latin American beef producer. In: Proceedings of seminar on potential to increase beef production in tropical America. Cali.

Sheridan, R. (1974) Sugar and slavery: an economic history of the British West Indies 1623–1775. Barbados; Caribbean Universities Press.

Sills, D. L. (*Ed*) (1968) International encyclopedia of the social sciences. London; Macmillan. 16 vols.

Simoons, F. J. (1973) New light on ethnic differences in adult lactose intolerance. *American Journal of Digestive Diseases* 18, 595–611.

Simoons, F. J. (1978) The geographic hypothesis and lactose malabsorption: a weighing of the evidence. *American Journal of Digestive Diseases* 23, 963–980.

Simpson, M. C. (1973) Alternative strategies for rangeland development in Kenya. *Rural Development Study* No. 2, Department of Agricultural Economics, University of Leeds.

Slicher van Bath, B. H. (1963) The agrarian history of western Europe, A.D. 500–1850. Translated by O. Ordish. London; Arnold.

Smith, A. (1910) The wealth of nations. London; Dent. 2 vols.

Spufford, M. (1965) A Cambridge community: Chippenham from settlement to enclosure. Leicester; University Press.

Sri Lanka, Department of Census and Statistics (1977) Sri Lanka year book 1977. Colombo.

Srivastava, R. K. (1970) Impact of cattle development programme on rural economy in the Kaira district. In: Symposium on Livestock Statistics. New Delhi; Institute of Agricultural Research Statistics.

Stenswick, L. E. (1972) World shortage of calves and feeder cattle. *Foreign Agriculture* (USA), 22 and 29 May.

Stubbings, F. H. (1975) The expansion of the Mycenaean civilisation. In: The Cambridge ancient history, 3rd edn. Vol. II, Part 2. London; Cambridge University Press, pp. 165–188.

Tan Hong Tong; Pillai, K. R. (1973) Response of Napier and Guinea grass to fertilizers and harvesting intervals. Research Station Report, Chemara, Malaysia.

Tan Hong Tong; Pillai, K. R. (1974) Cattle feeding trial with mixed effluent treated Napier grass. Research Station Report, Chemara, Malaysia.

Thailand, Ministry of Commerce (1978) Consumer price index for Bangkok metropolis (June).

Thirsk, J. (1967) Enclosing and engrossing. In: Thirsk, J. (*Ed*) The agrarian history of England and Wales, Vol. 4, 1500–1640. London; Cambridge University Press, pp. 200–255.

Thomas, Saint, Aquinas (1948) Selected political writings. Edited by A. Passerin d'Entraves. Translated by J. G. Dawson. Oxford; Blackwell.

The Times (London) 11.1.78, p. 6.

The Times (London) 22.11.78, p 7.

Times Atlas of the World (1967) Comprehensive edition. London; Times Newspapers.

United Kingdom (1972) European Communities secondary legislation. Part 20. Beef and veal.

United Kingdom, Department of Trade (1974) Annual statement of overseas trade, 1973, Vol. 1. London; HMSO.

United Kingdom, Department of Trade (1969a) Annual statement of overseas trade, 1968, Vol. 1. London; HMSO.

United Kingdom, Ministry of Agriculture, Fisheries and Food (1969b) Annual review and determination of guarantees, 1969, Cmnd. 3965.

United Nations (1977) Year book of national accounts statistics, 1976. New York.

USA, Agency for International Development (1973) Spring review of small farmer credit. Country surveys. Vol. 17. Washington D.C.

USA, Bureau of the Census (1903) Statical atlas, twelfth census of the United States taken in the year 1900. Washington D.C.

USA, Bureau of the Census (1960) Historical statistics of the United States, colonial times to 1957. Washington, D.C.

USA, Bureau of the Census (1976) The statistical history of the United States from colonial times to the present. New York; Basic Books.

USA, Department of Agriculture (1940) Agricultural statistics.

USA, Department of Agriculture (1957) Agricultural statistics.

USA, Department of Agriculture (1960) Agricultural statistics.

USA, Department of Agriculture (1966) Agricultural statistics.

USA, Department of Agriculture (1967) Agricultural statistics.

USA, Department of Agriculture (1972) Agricultural statistics.

USA, Department of Agriculture (1974) Agricultural statistics.

USA, Department of Agriculture (1976) Agricultural statistics.

USA, Department of Agriculture, Economic Research Service (1958) Livestock and meat statistics: *Statistical Bulletin* No. 230.

USA, Department of Agriculture, Economic Research Service (1968) Livestock and meat statistics: *Statistical Bulletin* No. 333.

USA, Department of Agriculture, Economic Research Service (1969) Major uses of land in the USA: *Agricultural Economic Report* No. 247.

USA, Department of Agriculture, Economic Research Service (1976) Livestock and meat statistics, August.

USA, Department of.Agriculture, Economic Research Service (1977) Livestock and meat statistics, August.

USA, Department of Agriculture, Economic Research Service (1978) Livestock and meat statistics, August.

USA, Department of Agriculture, Economics, Statistics and Cooperative Services (1978) Livestock and meat situation, June.

USDA, Statistical Reporting Service (1973) Livestock and meat statistics: *Statistical Bulletin* No. 522.

USA, Massachusetts Institute of Technology (1974) A framework for evaluating long term strategies for the development of the Sahel-Sudan region. Vol. 1. Summary report. Massachusetts.

Valenzuela, J. S.; Valenzuela, A. (1978) Modernization and dependency: alternative perspectives in the study of Latin American underdevelopment. *Comparative Politics* 10, 535–557.

Vickers, M. E. H. (1969) Growing and grazing good grass in West Malaysia. *The Planter* 45 (5) and (6).

Vincent, J. (1971) African elite: the big men of a small town. London; Columbia University Press.

Walters, A. A. (1968) An introduction to econometrics. London; Macmillan.

White, J. M. (1971) Cortes and the downfall of the Aztec empire: a study in the conflict of cultures. London; Hamish Hamilton.

Wittfogel, K. (1959) Oriental despotism: a comparative study of total power. New Haven; Yale University Press.

Worcester, D. E.; Schaeffer, W. G. (1970) The growth and culture of Latin America Vol. 1, 2nd edn. From conquest to independence. New York; Oxford University Press.

Yates, P. L. (1940) Food production in western Europe: an economic survey of agriculture in six countries. London; Longmans.

Zarate, A. de (1968) The discovery and conquest of Peru; a translation of books I to IV of Agustin de Zarate's history of these events. Translated by J. M. Cohen. Harmondsworth; Penguin.

Zeuner, F. E. (1963) The history of the domestication of cattle. In: Mourant, A. E.; Zeuner, F. E. (*Eds*) Man and cattle. Proceedings of symposium on domestication at the Royal Anthropological Institute, 24–26 May 1960. London.

Prepositions, with the exception of "in", have been ignored in determining alphabetical sequence.

cultivation, diffusion of in India 165–6
culture 2, 210
  African 117, 118–21
  Indian 164–5
  S. American 87–8, 89–91
customs 1, 18
cut-and-carry 75, 215, 217, 223–4
cycles, beef and cattle 204–7

DCs 27, 108, 178, 204
Dahl, G. 118 n.2
dairy farmers in S. America 97
dairy farming see dairying
dairy
  policy 186–7
  processing in India 179–81
  products see milk products
  projects 155, 181
  surplus 80, 187, 195, 197
dairying
  calves a by-product 158
  in India 177, 180, 184
  in Malaysia 155
  in W. Europe 67, 69
Dalzell, R. 160, 217, 223
Dark Ages 17, 18, 21, 89, 91, 93, 166
Davidson, B. 118 n.2
Deane, P. 25 n.18, 30
death prevention 201
death rate see mortality
debt 142
  public and cattle projects 197
debtor countries, consortium of 204
Decca plateau 166
decision making 39, 61, 121
deficiency payments, UK 76 n.3
demand (see also beef, calves, milk, young cattle—demand)
    for livestock products 27–37
  changes 23, 27, 30–1, 75–8, 196
dependency, economic 90, 204–5
despotism 165, 168, 173
developed countries 27, 108, 179, 204
development agencies (see also banks, development; livestock
    development) 105–6, 180, 193
Devendra C. 160, 217, 223
Devlin, R. M. 17
Devonshire estates, rents 91 n.6
digestive disorders and lactose intolerance 193
disease
  cattle 120–1, 126, 149
    and trade 107, 202–3
  livestock 2
  people 23
domestication 1, 9, 194
  Doomsday Book 15, 27, 71
double cropping 150–2, 154, 195
Dougall, H. W. 73 n.2
draft animals 49–51, 63
  in Europe 17, 20, 25
  in India 164–5
  in S.E. Asia 145–6, 150–1
    value declining 152–3

draft services 1, 45, 161, 201
  and calf production 159
  and cattle value 49
  in India 164-5, 169, 172, 188
  value
    and double cropping 150, 154
    and "pawah" system 156
drugs replace labour 103
Duc, T. le 89
Due, J. F. 140 n.17
Duby, G. 17, 19-21
dung 1, 119, 121, 169
dynamics of slavery 14-15
Dyson-Hudson, N. 118 n.2

ECE/FAO (see also Economic Commission for
    Europe) 77 n.4, 174
ECLA/FAO (see also Economic Commission for Latin
    America) 170, 203
EEC (see also European Communities Commission) 24,
    113, 152, 164, 209
  beef trade 204
  common agricultural policy (CAP) 79
  cattle owners 79
  dairy surplus 104 n.19, 181, 193, 198
    and food aid 185-8, 191
  market for beef 133
Economic Commission for Europe (see also
    ECE/FAO) 76
Economic Commission for Latin America (see also
    ECLA/FAO) 96
economic development (see also growth, economic) 79, 179
  in S. America 105, 109-11, 116
economic efficiency 28, 143
economic equilibrium and disequilibrium 101, 125-7,
    154-5, 173-4
  models 3, 39-61, 102, 130, 150, 153-4, 196
  progress 79, 179
  surplus 26, 71
  union 79
economics 2-3, 15 n.12, 42, 97, 109, 118
economies, advanced 27, 108, 179, 204
economies of scale 24, 89, 141
Economist 148
economists 2, 210
economy
  cattle (see also cattle economics) 138, 145-7, 150
  riverine 167, 173
  S. American 90, 100
Ecuador 86
Egypt 9, 12, 13 n.9, 14, 165
elasticity of production 68, 77
emigration from Ireland 26, 113
employment opportunities 138, 150
enclosures, Tudor 23, 26, 91, 146
encomienda system 90
Engerman, S. L. 90
England 15, 23-4, 26, 91, 196, 204
epizootics 129
equations, simultaneous, solution 228-9
equator 9, 16, 67, 72, 120, 145-7
equatorial rainforest see tropical rainforest

DATE DUE

DEMCO 38-297